WORDSCAPE 7

WORDSCAPE 7

MYSTERY & SUSPENSE
STORIES AND POEMS

An anthology by Members of the
Metropolitan Toronto Branch of the

CANADIAN AUTHORS
ASSOCIATION

also serving Central and Northern Ontario

Edited by Jennifer Footman

MTB
PRESS

Copyright©2001 MTB Press
Stories and poems used by permission of the respective authors.

Published in Canada by MTB Press
33 Springbank Avenue
Toronto, Ontario M1N 1G2
Telephone and Fax: (416) 698-8687

MTB President: Bill Belfontaine
Editor: Jennifer Footman
Cover and interior design: Karen Petherick, Markham, Ontario
Cover photo: Digital Imagery® copyright 1999 PhotoDisc, Inc.
Printed in Canada by TTP Tradeworx, Mississauga, Ontario

Canadian Cataloguing in Publication Data

Wordscape (Scarborough, Ont.)
    Wordscape

Annual.
[No. 1]
An Anthology by members of the Canadian Authors Association,
Metropolitan Toronto and Ontario regions.

ISSN 1485-063X
ISBN 1-894544-00-7 (7th ed.)

1. Canadian literature (English) — Ontario — Toronto
Metropolitan Area.* 2. Canadian literature (English) —
20th century.* 1. Canadian Authors Association.
Metropolitan Toronto Branch.

PS8257.T67W67   C810.8'0054   C98-300931-7
PR9198.3.T67W67

Table of Contents

Table of Contents

Commentary • Bill Belfontaine

"Reading maketh a full man;
conference a ready man;
writing an exact man."

Francis Bacon 1561-1626

This English philosopher is being quoted knowing full well that ardent feminists may slam this book down because it is not gender neutral— or using that most fearsome of terms—not politically correct (pc). What nonsense!

It was pc at the time of writing because of social conditions and this is not the time to become a critic of that flourishing period that included Shakespeare and Marlow. Surely if Bacon was alive today, and teaching at a university in Toronto, or Alberta or New Brunswick, the gender would be inclusive of all who write. But how could he (or we) improve on the presentation of this wonderful thought?

"Writing an exact man" applies very well today, and to this book, since all WORDSCAPE writers who have provided their art of the written word dwell within the meaning of Bacon's revelation. Writers read to discover, discuss to sharpen their wit and wisdom, and write to express themselves so we may enjoy and learn from their words, too.

Members of the Canadian Authors Association, who perform at a higher level of writing short stories and poetry, have had their work approved for inclusion in this seventh in a series of yearly anthologies. Some are being published for the first time after years of hard work.

This yearly publication, of the best of short stories and poetry gleaned from the writing of almost 300 writers, is produced by MTB press, which is wholly-owned and funded by the members of the Toronto and Central Ontario Branch of The Canadian Authors Association. The cover design and text formatting is by a CAA member.

We join with Jennifer Footman, in thanking and congratulating all on a job well done.

Bill Belfontaine, President
Toronto and Central Ontario Branch*
Canadian Authors Association

*formerly Metropolitan Toronto Branch

Introduction • Jennifer Footman

Why an anthology?

Well ... it seems to me that sometimes I want a bite of entertainment which lasts for a few minutes; sometimes just long enough for a bus ride, subway trip, or for those lovely times in the bath with a glass of wine and a good book. Not the place for War and Peace.

All the items here are below three thousand words--just the right length for a short fix of entertainment.

Why else? Well, it has to entertain. That, above all. In order for it to entertain it has to be varied in material and rhythm. I hope I have done this.

Through reading newspapers, listening to the radio and watching television, I have found that sometimes truth can be stranger than fiction, so this time we have enclosed creative non fiction. A bit of a strange genre but one totally suited to this anthology and one gaining in popularity. To make it simpler for the reader to know what they are getting into, I have labelled the pieces of non fiction as such. Some of our true stories, indeed have been stranger than out fictional ones. I think, that because a piece of writing claims to be the truth, my inquisitiveness leads me naturally into it.

This is a showcase for the members of Canadian Authors Association, Metro Toronto Branch, and I feel they do the reader justice. The material is varied and each piece is very different to its neighbour.

We travel from the Caribbean today, to Canada in Queen Victoria's time, to Florida today and meet murderers, ghosts, man-eating monsters and nurses on would not want nursing one's mother.

In common with most anthologies the reader may not like all the material here but I am sure that they will find something to justify the purchase of the book. The styles of writing are from the very formal to the totally casual. There is material here a reader could find in one of the best literary magazines to material which would not be out of place in a whodunit zene.

I truly hope you enjoy this selection.

Jennifer Footman

WORDSCAPE 7

PATRICIA SNIDER ARMSTRONG was born in Toronto and lived there until the 60's when she moved to Winnipeg with her husband and eight children. She worked for Statistics Canada, was a member of the Canadian Authors Association Manitoba Branch, the Manitoba Writer's Guild, and published articles in the *Prairie Messenger* and other local papers and magazines.

After nearly thirty years in Winnipeg, Patricia moved back to Ontario and lives in Mississauga with her daughter and son-in-law. Now retired, she has had stories or poems published in *Winners' Circle 5*, four *Wordscape* anthologies and *Legacy*. She is working on a book of pioneer stories inspired by tales of her Loyalist ancestors, pioneers in Pennsylvania, New Brunswick and York. She is also writing a young adult novel.

The Investors • Patricia Snider Armstrong

She stared at the blank screen with red-rimmed eyes, willing it to give her an answer. It was the first time she'd turned the computer on since Gerry disappeared, and she wasn't sure why she was doing it now. Maybe just getting back into her old routine would shake her out of the deadly lethargy that gripped her.

It was the not knowing that tore her apart; the hours she'd spent re-examining every conversation, every nuance of voice and gesture— anything to explain why he had removed himself from her life. They'd been engaged, after all. He was going to get her a ring as soon as he'd saved enough money. Sales were picking up in his distribution business, and he'd even hired an office girl to take care of things while he was on the road.

Then nothing. The police found his car in a secluded area of Caledon, with the keys still in the ignition. There were no signs of a struggle, no bloodstains and only his fingerprints on the steering wheel and doors. It was as though he had been whisked away into another world. Vaporized.

The shrill ring of the telephone jolted her out of her trance.

"Oh, hi Marge. No I'm not doing anything important. It's a rotten day so I've stayed home. Yeah, the sky's as black as pitch here and it's sleeting."

Hilary picked up a pencil from its slot on top of the keyboard, and rolled it between her fingers, then threw it onto the desk.

"What? No, I'm not going to the party. Don't feel up to it. Well, you know—I don't want to have to talk to anyone yet. It's too soon."

The line between her brows deepened as Hilary listened to her caller's next words.

"What do you mean? It's not as if he's dead."

"How do you know he's not? How the hell do you know?" Hilary slammed down the handset and slumped into her chair. The dogwood outside the window scraped at the grungy casements and ice pellets sprayed the glass with pea-sized shot. The room was dark, its corners looming with forbidding shapes that danced in a ghostly frenzy, lit by moving images from the screen saver.

She pushed her untidy yellow hair away from her eyes and leaned towards the computer, her hand absently reaching for the mouse on its small grey pad.

Double click. 'Outlook Express.' Click. 'Inbox.' The hard drive mumbled and grumbled as it reached into cyberspace for a message, any message. Hilary closed her eyes and rested back while the electronic box completed its task.

She was locked in a frightful daydream—chasing Gerry down a long, dismal tunnel—when a soft beep signaled the presence of new mail.

She read the 'From:' line and jerked upright.

From: Gerald Cassidy To: Hilary Houston.

The message was dated October 27—two days after Gerry disappeared. Skipping the subject line, she read on: "Dear Hilary. I'm sorry I couldn't tell you before that I would be leaving for a while. Something strange has happened, but I can't talk about it now. Trust me and I'll be back soon. Always remember I love you, baby. Gerry."

Hilary jabbed at the printer button. The machine rattled into life and she clicked the 'print' icon on the computer screen. Better leave the message there and call the police, she thought. She yanked the copy from the machine and re-read the letter.

"Always remember I love you, baby. Gerry."

"My God, he's alive, he's alive," she cried, tears spilling down her cheeks. She snatched a tissue from the desk and patted her eyes, then wiped her nose. Picking up the phone, she dialled the number on the detective's card.

"Hello. This is Hilary Houston. I need to talk to Detective Kobel right away. It's urgent."

The voice on the other end of the line rumbled, "Kobel here."

"I'm glad I caught you. It's Hilary Houston. I've just got an e-mail from Gerry. Gerry Cassidy. You know—he's been missing for over three weeks. My fiancé. Yes, I got it this morning. It's dated October 27—just after he disappeared. Two days."

"Exactly what did he say?" asked Kobel.

Hilary read the message to him, her throat tight, her breath coming in small spurts. "What do you think it means?" she asked.

"Hard to say, at this stage. Sounds as though he left on his own. I'll send someone around in the morning to get a copy. You could try sending an answer to the e-mail address he used. If he's all right, there'll be nothing else for us to do, anyway."

"Yes, yes, of course," said Hilary. "I was so excited I didn't even think of that. Bye."

She smacked the handset into its place and checked the computer screen. There it was: 'g@seeker.net.' She clicked on 'Reply to Author' and began her message. "Dear Gerry, I was so glad to get your e-mail. I've been frantic about you and even called the police when you didn't come home. They found your car with the keys in the ignition on some Caledon side road. Where are you? What's happened? When are you coming back? Please tell me, I can't stand not knowing. All my love, Hilary." She sent it off, not even bothering to check for typos. Get it out. The sooner the better.

What now? Hilary watched the slow, hypnotic dance of the coloured fish on the screen saver, and thought about letting someone else know that she'd heard from Gerry. Ralph Meghan—his partner—better tell him. Although she'd only met Ralph once or twice, he seemed like a good guy. He'd invested considerable money in the business and, according to Gerry, had lots of connections. He certainly looked the part, with his Versace suits and stylish shirts and ties. He fitted the image of a successful tycoon as he selected imported wine for their first dinner at Henri's, and slipped easily into French when ordering the entrée.

Gerry hadn't told her much about the business, but he'd hinted that the 'family members' Ralph talked about were more than ordinary relatives. They had a lot of clout in town, Gerry said, and could throw piles of investment money their way.

"Dollars," he said. "Get those bucks rollin' in and there'll be no stopping us. We'll be on top of the world in no time flat."

Hilary leaned back in her chair; a faint thrill of anticipation washing over her as it always did when Gerry described how their life would unfold.

"A mansion in Vegas. A villa in Monaco, tax-free. No more office work for you, m'dear. It'll be parties all year round, plenty o' booze and all the gorgeous clothes you'll ever want."

She opened her eyes and clicked on the address book for Ralph Meghan's e-mail address. There it was: 'R.Meghan@compo.ca.' "Wonder what I should say," she thought, tapping her index finger idly on the J key.

"Dear Mr. Meghan: I felt I should tell you that I've heard from Gerry. He sent me an e-mail, saying he'll be away for a short while. Just thought you would want to know. Sincerely, Hilary J. Houston."

She clicked 'Send and Receive' and the computer whirred in its metal casing, coughing slightly as the moving blue arrow indicated incoming mail. She peered at the screen in dismay as it rolled out a new message.

"X-From_: MAILER-DAEMON Fri Nov 26 5:24:24 1999 X-Failed-Recipients: g@seeker.net From: hhouston@icall.com. Subject: Mail delivery failed: returning message to sender."

"Damn! My letter to Gerry's come back." Hilary groaned as the blue arrow switched direction, and the program transmitted her message to Ralph Meghan.

She opened the desk drawer and riffled through it for a squashed cigarette pack. She had used nicotine patches to stop smoking months before, but since Gerry's disappearance, she had begun again. She pulled out a cigarette, thrust it between her lips and flicked on her lighter.

She blew smoke at the computer screen, as though it alone was responsible for the failed message. She moved to the love-seat and tucked a scruffy quilt around her shoulders. Might as well lie here for a while. I'm not hungry and I'm too upset to sleep.

The wind had picked up, and now it moaned around the dormers like a disembodied spirit. Fine sleet had turned to hail and battered at the windows relentlessly. On the computer screen, the fish had resumed their languid dance, and cast strange patterns of light into the shadows. Hilary stubbed out her cigarette and closed her eyes.

At exactly three a.m. Hilary woke up. She blinked as the two-note e-mail signal announced the arrival of a new message.

Shit! I never closed the connection. She climbed out from under the quilt, moved to the computer and placed her icy hand on the mouse. The screen saver disappeared, and in its place, she saw a highlighted incoming message.

It's Gerry! She focused her eyes on the screen and gasped.

"Don't tell Ralph Meghan you've heard from me. He's dangerous and he'll come after you if he thinks you know where I am. Sorry, honey. Didn't want to get you into this." Hilary shivered and glanced behind her into the shadowy room. She reached for the desk lamp and pressed the button. Nothing. Must be unplugged. She walked to the wall switch and turned it on. No lights. Had to be the storm. Then why was the computer working?

She went back to the desk and looked again at Gerry's message. 'g@terror.net'. What a strange name for an e-mail address, she thought. Wonder if this one will work for me. Hilary clicked on 'reply' and banged out a message.

"Darling. Got your e-mail but I've already told Meghan that I've heard from you. What now? Are you in trouble? Should I call the police? Love, Hilary." She watched as the small print disappeared from the outbox screen. Better stay on-line so I'll know as soon as he answers.

Need some coffee and another smoke. She stumbled into the kitchen, filled a pot with water and turned on the gas stove. Instant will do. She took a small jar of coffee out of the cupboard and set it on the counter; she took the flattened cigarette package and matches from her pocket, and lit up. She glanced out the kitchen window at the murky street. Too early for working slobs to be leaving. A black van hugged the far curb, its lights out. Two figures huddled in the front seat. Lovers, maybe. Rotten night for making out in a car, though. And if they run the engine, they could die from carbon monoxide poisoning. She was stirring her coffee when the incoming mail signal beeped.

"X-From_: MAILER-DAEMON ..."

"Damn it all to hell!" she snarled. "My letter's come back again."

She paced about the room, taking short, erratic puffs on her cigarette. She plucked another from the pack on the counter and dragged hard, lighting the new one from the smouldering butt.

Now what'll I do? Call Detective Kobel? But what if Gerry's partner is a crook? Does that mean Gerry's a crook too? And why is Meghan after Gerry? What's he done to make Meghan angry? God, it's a whole month since Gerry disappeared. You'd think somebody would know where he is!

Hilary checked her watch. Five o'clock. It's not too early to call the police. Maybe Kobel's on night duty or something.

A voice rasped, "Yeah? Frank Kobel."

"It's Hilary Houston. You know ... "

"Yeah, Ms. Houston. I remember you. Your boyfriend's gone missing. I thought you said he'd turned up."

Hilary took a deep breath and tried to speak calmly. "I told you I got an e-mail from him. Now I've got two. But my messages to him keep coming back. They had two different addresses, and when I tried to send one to him ... " Her voice dwindled to a whisper.

"But Ms. Houston, if you're getting e-mail from him, then he's not missing, don't ya see?"

"I know." Hilary tried to decide what she could safely say without putting Gerry in a bad light.

"There's this fellow he knows. He doesn't know him well but he's done some business with the guy. Name's Meghan—Ralph Meghan."

Silence on the other end of the line.

"Detective Kobel—are you there?"

"Ah, yeah, Ms. Houston. I'm here. Just thinking. What kind of business is your boyfriend in?"

"Sales and distribution," Hilary answered.

"What does he sell and distribute?"

"I never asked. I think Meghan is in for a lot of money."

"I see. Well, I should tell you that Ralph Oswald Meghan heads up one of the biggest crime organizations in this part of the country. We've been trying to put him away for years. Trouble is, he always weasels out whenever we think we've got him nailed. I don't want to scare you, Ms. Houston, but I'd be careful if I were you. It sounds as if your buddy has gotten into trouble with Meghan and is hiding out."

"So what should I do?"

"Just take care about where you go and who you talk to. And watch your back. That's all I can tell you."

Hilary put the phone down slowly. A ripple of fear ran through her thin body. God!

Out on the street, a few cars crept along the slick pavement. Black ice—that's what they called it. A grim sound. Black for mourning. She rubbed her bloodless hands together and tried to think. The black van was still there.

She went over to the filing cabinet, opened the upper drawer and slid her hands along the folders until she came to M. Nothing. "What was the name of that investment company?" she muttered. "Continental? Consolidated? Capital? Something with a C.

"Creative. That's it. Creative Investments." She plunged her hand into the cabinet and removed a folder marked 'Creative Investments—Confidential.' She tossed it onto the desk and stopped. Do I really want to do this? she thought. Do I want to know?

She opened the beige folder and examined the thin, pastel sheets. Invoices. Bills of lading. But no merchandise was listed, only code numbers. She skipped to the dollar value on the bottom line of the first sheet. Fifty thousand dollars! Whatever could've been worth that much?

Baffled, Hilary turned back to the computer just as it beeped. Another message? She watched the little electronic arrow diving into the little in-basket.

"From: g@light.net, To: hhouston@icall.com. I love y I love y I love y I love y I love y I love y I love y I love y … " On and on it ran, down the length of a full page and onto a second. Finally, the message stuttered to a close.

The doorbell's chime seemed to come from far away. Hilary struggled back to reality and opened the door to Detective Kobel's solemn face.

"Ah, good morning, ma'am."

Hilary nodded.

"Sorry to disturb you so early, ma'am, but I'm afraid I have bad news. Can I come in?"

Hilary motioned him inside and sat down. Kobel perched on the edge of a straight-backed chair, then stood up.

"It's just … we've found a body that we have reason to believe is your missing fiancé." He reached out as Hilary doubled over, and patted her shoulder awkwardly.

"His I.D. was in his jacket pocket—wallet, driver's license, social insurance, medical card. All in the name of Gerald Cassidy."

"Where?" Hilary whispered.

"In a landfill north of where we found the car. He ... he had a bullet hole in his forehead. Looks like a contract job."

"How long ... when did he die?" Hilary could barely speak now; her lips were dry, and tears trickled down her wan cheeks, drawing streaks of eyeliner across the waxy skin.

"It's too early to know for sure, until the coroner finishes his examination, but we think, from the condition of the body, that he died when he first disappeared, almost a month ago."

"But the e-mail ... " She closed her lips firmly and held out her hand. "Thank you, Detective Kobel, for all your help."

"Yep. Welcome." He moved toward the door. "We'll need you to identify the body, of course. Later today, say three o'clock?" .

"Yes. Fine. Goodbye, Detective."

She walked to the window, past the blinking computer screen with its silly fish slowly devouring each other. Hilary ran her tongue along her parched lower lip and watched impassively as Detective Kobel's car pulled away from the curb, leaving the black van behind.

The van doors opened and two well-dressed men emerged, one carrying a rather large briefcase. They made their way leisurely across the street, and strolled up Hilary's front walk.

CAROLE LIDGOLD is a church secretary who likes to publish her own books. She had published seven books and will soon publish a historical book. She has been a member of the Canadian Authors Association for about ten years. Fiction is her favourite subject but she seems to find interesting non-fiction historical stories that capture her attention and have to be written. Carole looks forward to all writing challenges and never knows where her writing will take her.

Paradise Vacation • Carole M. Lidgold

I saw the boy early one morning as I strolled beside the misty lake. He was sitting on top of a large boulder on the beach, his knees tight against his chest. His thin arms were folded around his knees, his chin resting on them. His dark hair was untidy, his clothes dirty. I hesitated, then walked closer to him. The boy didn't move or turn his head to watch my approach across the pebbly beach.

"Hello," I called out, "I see that you're an early riser too!"

The boy did not move or acknowledge my presence. He continued staring at the thick mist on the lake. I sensed he was sad and moved closer. As I stood below him, I glanced up and saw raw bruises on his knees, and dirty scuff marks on his sneakers. Then he turned his head and looked at me. His dark eyes stared down at me from a face with more bruises and numerous scratches.

"Oh my God!" I said, suddenly angry, "who did this to you?"

The boy did not reply, just continued staring at me. But I felt his mood soften and welcome me, as if taking comfort from my presence.

"Can I do anything to help?" I asked, reaching out to him. He moved beyond my touch.

"No one can help now," he whispered softly, still looking at me.

"But I can try," I urged. "Tell me what happened and who you are."

The boy smiled and shook his head.

"Thanks," he said then climbed down onto the beach. "I have to go. Be careful." He disappeared into the encroaching fog and I never saw him again. But his last words puzzled me. What did he mean—be careful?

The morning mood was spoiled. I loved to wander in the mist, recording the distorted images on film. Later I painted these scenes on canvas. The name, Marcie Durham, my name shortened from Marcellis, was well-known in the art world. My paintings sold for high prices. But today, meeting that boy had disturbed me. I couldn't concentrate on the watery vistas. Instead an image of the boy on the boulder stayed with me. I hurried back to the rented house where my husband was still sleeping.

I tiptoed into the kitchen through the back door. The old floor creaked beneath my feet. I dried the moisture from my camera and set it on the table. My sketch pad was within easy reach and I drew an accurate image of the boy. It came easily beneath my skilled fingers. Once again troubled, dark eyes stared out at me, the mist behind him obscuring everything but the top of the boulder. Again I thought about his words—be careful—and wondered what they meant.

Several weeks ago I was recovering from pneumonia. I had been very ill and the doctors were very worried about me. They told my husband, Graham, that I needed a rest in the country. He was not to let me wander in the early mornings before the sun was up. Graham couldn't prevent me from doing what I loved, although he tried hard. My health improved but I still needed a rest from illustrating books.

Graham is an accountant and June is a quiet month for him. He took time off to spend with me on a holiday. We were driving around looking for a house by the beach and found this place.

It's a very old house, old-fashioned, but comfortable looking. The high roof is peaked, shingled with slate tiles. White wood siding and gingerbread trim edges along the eaves, making the house an artist's paradise. A wide, roofed porch wraps around three sides of the house where wicker chairs invite visitors to stop and relax. I loved the house immediately.

"Shall we rent it?" Graham asked reading the realtor's sign on the lawn. "You can sit on the porch and paint forever."

"Oh yes," I answered, smiling happily, "but first, let's go up on the porch. I want to see what the lake looks like from there."

Standing on the porch we viewed the sparkling scene of lake and trees. Cottages clung to the shore and boats bobbed at docks. Seagulls squealed and sailed through the air on gentle breezes. As I stood there enjoying the beauty and tranquility, I suddenly felt cold fear. Where did that come from? Shrugging it off I immersed myself in the warmth of the sunlight that was shining on this section of the porch.

"Well, yes or no?"

"Yes, of course yes!"

The road ran in front of the house, with the beach on the other side. We climbed back into the car and followed the road into the small town of Copper Hills. The real estate office was easy to find on the main street, as it was the only one. There was a bakery, a hardware store, a pharmacy, a grocery store and a restaurant. Everything a town needs.

As we opened the real estate office door, an elderly secretary was pounding a typewriter. A silent computer sat nearby on an unused table.

"Can I help you?" the secretary enquired.

"Yes," Graham answered. "We'd like to rent that house on the beach, the white one with the porch."

"Oh that one," the lady replied smiling broadly. "Have a seat and I'll get Mr. Wilbur."

She walked slowly down the short hallway and rapped on a closed door. "Yes, what do you want now?" a male voice growled.

"There's a couple here to rent the Piper house," the woman said calmly. "Do you want to see them or shall I send them away?"

"Of course I want to see them," the voice said eagerly as the door was hastily pulled open. "Send them in."

A beaming Mr. Wilbur sat behind a small desk littered with papers. He tidied the papers into a sloppy pile. "Sit down, sit down," he said without getting up.

I didn't like Mr. Wilbur. His dark, slanty eyes peered out of a pudgy face, below greased hair. He didn't offer to shake hands and I was glad. I didn't want to touch his grubby hand. He wore a white shirt, splattered with egg spots and his tie was crooked. He adjusted the tie and brushed out the wrinkles along the arms of his shirt.

"So you want to rent the Piper house?"

"If that's the white one by the beach, then yes we'd like to rent it."

"It's a great house with lots of privacy. How long do you want it for?"

"Is it available for a month?" Graham asked.

Greed glowed from Mr. Wilbur's eyes and he rubbed his hands together. "Yes, yes, it's available. What month would you like it for?"

"Would June be OK? I know that's next week but we're here for my wife's health."

Mr. Wilbur stared at me and his smile grew even wider while his eyes sparkled ominously. I suddenly felt afraid of him.

"You're in luck. It's not booked until mid July. Shall we sign the papers?"

"How much?"

"Oh, silly me, of course. Because it's June, I'll give it to you for the reduced price of $1,000.00 a week."

"That's four thousand dollars!" I gasped. "Can we afford that, Graham?"

"Well, it's more than we wanted to pay. What's the regular price?"

"Summer months we charge $1,500.00 per week. Look, because of your wife's delicate health," Mr. Wilbur purred, "I can make an exception this time. How about $800.00 a week?"

"Marcie, do you really want this place?" Graham asked me.

Mr. Wilbur's face showed a worried tension as I thought about renting the Piper house. His face radiated with a glowing smile as I said, "Yes, let's take it."

I have never seen so much paperwork involved in renting. We signed sheet after sheet until our hands were tired. "You need to sign this insurance policy," Mr. Wilbur said. "If anything gets broken you'll be covered. It's an old house and things cost more to repair. Just sign here and my secretary will fill in the details later. It's just a standard policy."

Much later, I wished we had never seen the Piper house. The plumbing was antique, the water rusty. The toilet constantly plugged up and gurgled like a waterfall when it did flush. The stairs were shaky and creaked violently as we went up and down to the second storey. The kitchen stove was gas and flared up when lit. There was a basement, creepy and damp, where fireplace wood was stored.

"That needs to be put outside," Graham said, "before we can use the fireplace."

"I hope the chimney is clean," I said, "and the damper works properly."

Graham carried several armloads of wood out into the sun to dry. The basement stairs groaned beneath his weight. The moisture was soon dried off the wood and we used it in the cool evenings. The fireplace worked well.

"Guess I'd better get some more wood," Graham said one morning when there was no more wood to burn. It was the same morning that I'd seen the boy at the lake.

Graham reached to turn on the basement light-switch. There was a loud crack as the step collapsed beneath his feet. He fell against the banister, which splintered, under his weight and he crashed to the basement floor.

In high-school and college, Graham had been an athlete. He landed on his shoulder instead of on his head. However, the floor was solid cement and not cushioned by grass or gymnastic pads.

"Graham!" I screamed, from the top of the stairs, "are you all right?"

"Don't come down," he warned. "I'm fine but I think I've dislocated my shoulder."

Painfully he inched his way carefully up the stairs, testing each step, staying close to the wall. The stairs shook dangerously but held together. Holding on to his uninjured arm, I guided him across the open space where the step had been.

"I hope there's a doctor in this town," Graham said, through clenched teeth.

"At least the phone works well," I said, dialling the operator.

There was a doctor and I drove Graham to a small hospital. The doctor reset Graham's shoulder and put a plaster cast on his wrist. "So much for paradise," I muttered while waiting in the hospital lounge.

"Mr. Wilbur," I said angrily, standing in his office, "you'd better use that insurance policy to repair the basement steps."

"Oh, my dear," Mr. Wilbur gushed, "has there been an accident?"

"My husband fell when one of the basement steps collapsed and the banister broke."

"Was he badly hurt?" Mr. Wilbur asked, his greedy eyes alight with excitement.

"Fortunately not," I replied scornfully, "only a broken wrist and shoulder separation."

Mr. Wilbur's face suddenly looked disappointed. Why? I thought he would be relieved that the injuries were only minor.

"I'll send the repairman out immediately. I'm so glad your husband wasn't badly hurt."

Jake, the repairman, came the next day. Graham was sitting comfortably in a wicker chair on the porch, making the most of his pain.

"Get me another drink, please," he cooed. "I'm so sick!"

"Oh, Graham. You're not dead, get it yourself."

"This place makes a good living for me," Jake, the repairman said. "Seems I'm here every week repairing something. You're a lucky one. The last family here lost their only son in an accident."

"You mean a child died here?" I asked.

"Yup. The kid fell down these very stairs, the same ones you did."

"The basement steps!"

"Yup. One of the middle steps cracked and he hit his head hard on the floor and was killed. Mr. Wilbur had accident insurance and picked up a bundle when the kid died."

"Accident insurance?"

"Yup. Mr. Wilbur knows how to protect himself. This is an old house."

"But I thought the insurance was only for repairs," Graham said.

"That too, but also in case of death."

"You mean if I had died he'd collect on my death!"

"Yup. Really disappointed you lived. You're a nice young couple. Git out of here before something else happens. See!"

Jake held out the broken step, which he had replaced with a sturdy plank. "See here, this is a fresh cut. Somebody wanted you to fall. Been waiting to git some evidence on Wilbur. Now I've got it. Shouldn't have let that kid die. No money's worth that. Guess my income will go down, but I can't take it anymore."

"Have there been others who died here?" I asked glad that Graham wasn't one of them.

"Twelve. Your husband would'a been number thirteen."

"Who are you taking that step to?" Graham asked.

"Down to the city where the cops aren't in on it. Just can't do this anymore."

We quickly packed up and left the Piper house. We would write later and request a refund. Before we left I returned alone to the beach and stared up at the empty boulder. I wondered if it was possible that the boy had been the one who died. Do troubled spirits come back to warn the living?

RICHARD I. THORMAN lives in downtown Toronto, close to cultural, educational, library and recreational facilities, which he frequents for inspiration. His nonfiction credits include works in the U.S. Library of Congress and Onteris. Current writing is focused on speculative fiction and poetry. He has read and been interviewed on the CBC and Rogers Cable. His latest book of poetry and prose entitled *From Cynwyd Castle on Jackson's Point* was released in the Spring of 1997

Things Below • Richard I Thorman

The sunshine state was delivering every promise made in the vacation brochures this March day of the school break. Cloudless skies looked down on white sand beaches shimmering in the noonday sun. Gentle Gulf breezes caressed the tanned and near naked bodies strewn haphazardly as far as the eye could see. No one noticed that all birds avoided a small stretch of Treasure Land waterfront.

The three year old girl in a broad-brimmed, orange sun hat and matching swim-suit was concentrating on the sand castle she had under construction. Her shapely young mother lay face down on a Disney patterned beach towel with crossed arms supporting her head and shoulders. Her skin glistened from protective lotion. She was in that semi-dream-state the fresh air and midday heat induces in Northern Snow-Birds, as Canadian visitors are known.

Her reverie was shattered by a shrill, penetrating scream followed by loud, panic-edged crying. The mother barely had time to turn over before her daughter had hurled herself upon her, arms clutching for her protective and comforting embrace.

"What's wrong darling?" asked the startled mother.

"It bit me," sobbed the small one.

"What bit you?"

"The thing in the pail," she said, pointing a chubby finger toward the castle.

"Where did it bite you?" asked the mother, trying to extricate herself sufficiently from her daughter's stranglehold to make an examination.

"On my ankle."

The mother was becoming more apprehensive as the youngster's level of anxiety and upset showed no signs of abating. With some difficulty, she was able to grasp the child's left ankle and raise it to view. There was a dark dot from which an angry, bluish-maroon circle radiated. One look at the injury brought the mother awkwardly to her feet. She raced to the hotel about nine hundred feet away to summon medical assistance.

Sam, as his father before him, operated Browning's Beach Service. Their portable yellow cabanas and lounges stretched for five miles along the waterfront. He patrolled the beach during daylight hours in a battered old Ford pickup, managing rentals and checking tags for expires and freeloaders.

This day was special because his ten-year-old grandson, Zachary, was helping him. Someday the business would be his and already he exhibited considerable know-how and interest.

"Gramps. Here comes Mr. Garrison," said Zack, pointing to the black and white cruiser hastening down the beach trail. The patrol car braked in a cloud of sand beside the waiting duo.

"Hi Zack. Sam, I need your help. We've been getting complaints of something biting sunbathers when they dig in the sand. Some have had serious reactions. One little girl almost died. It started about a month ago."

"Maybe I can help. Let me show you something." Sam retrieved a glass jar from under the front seat of the pickup. He handed it over to the officer. "I found it in a kid's pail. She must have dug it up. Sure is weird. Never seen anything like it."

The officer slowly twirled the jar. The thing inside was the colour of speckled coral, about an inch long, with appendages resembling those of a crab, with an armoured articulated shell covering the back and a lighter coloured one on its underbelly. Apart from the octagonal black eyes glazed in death, the most unusual feature was the tail, which was about the same length as the body and ended in a hollow, needle-like point.

"I gave it to a friend who works at the Florida Institute for Marine Studies. A week later he brought it a back and reported they didn't know what it was. It resembled a burrowing crab, but there the resemblance ended. They tested the tail for venom and found it highly toxic, saying that in large dosages it could be fatal. They asked me to keep an eye open for more samples."

"Did you find any?"

"Not yet. Too busy to go digging for them."

"Most reports we've had suggest the infestation is presently confined to about a half mile stretch along the beach. So far, they haven't encroached to the east beyond the retaining wall and sidewalk in front of the waterfront properties. We're tracking the incidents on computer, and they're increasing. The city council has said no to any suggestion of a beach closure, at least for the moment. Bad for business. Sam, if you've got any ideas, we'd sure like to have them."

"Let's go for a ride. I want to show you something," Sam said, motioning toward the pickup.

The three climbed into the front seat. The old pickup roared into life and took off along the rutted track of the service route. About a mile to the south, Sam wheeled the truck about and stopped. The trio got out.

"Notice anything strange about the beach here?" asked Sam, scuffing the surface with the toe of his boot.

"No. It looks the way it always does," replied the policeman, looking puzzled.

"You're right. But notice, even though the Works Department tractor rakes the beach regularly, it stays pretty compressed. Sure, there are drifts where the lighter stuff piles up, but most of the beach is like this. No trouble driving on it. Let's get back in the truck."

The pickup headed back in a northerly direction. In about three-quarters of a mile it stopped and the three disembarked. Again, Sam scuffed the beach with his boot.

"This is just about where the infestation starts. See? The surface here is still compressed, but if we walk ahead five or six feet the texture of the beach changes."

Sam led George and Zack north up the tire tracks.

"Notice the beach material is darker here and less bleached by the sun. Also the ruts made by the truck are at least six inches deep compared with one inch where the Ford is parked now." Sam stepped off the track and his boots sank into soft sand. "See" (pointing to his feet)? "Also, it's strange that birds avoid this area. Won't even fly over it."

"Are you saying these things are burrowing around under the surface and loosening up the sand?" asked George, his face furrowed in disbelief.

"I'm not sure what I'm saying exactly, but the whole area of the infestation is like this," replied Sam, noticing that Zack had headed back to the pickup.

"If what you are saying is true, there must be millions of those creatures down there. They've got to be multiplying like crazy .... My gawd, the three hundred complaints in our office could only be the tip of the iceberg."

Meanwhile, Zack had returned from the Ford with a shovel and had commenced to dig about twenty feet away in the direction of the Gulf.

"Sam, we can't let this theory get any publicity. If the newspapers or TV picked this up, we'd have a full blown panic on our hands."

At that instant, Zack shouted and jumped back from the hole he had been digging. "Come here! Quick!"

The two adults ran to his side and stared into the excavation. Their faces blanched. At the bottom of the two-foot hole sat a thing about eight inches in length. Its eyes stared balefully at the three humans peering down at it. The tail waved threateningly.

"Watch," said Zack as he lowered the shovel to about six inches above the creature. The tail struck repeatedly at the face of the shovel with a series of loud dings, each thrust depositing a wet spot of venom.

Then, apparently the thing decided to retreat. In an instant it had disappeared into the wall of the excavation leaving only a drift of sand sliding slowly down the side of the hole.

"That thing is about eight times the size of the one in the jar. Could they all be growing that fast?" asked the startled policeman.

"It could partially explain the expansion of the infested area."

"None of our reports mention anything that big. The ones we've heard about must be babies. My gawd, we could have a slaughter on our hands if the ones that size get aggressive. Did you see the amount of venom it pumped out? Lethal for sure."

"Yah, and what if the things are nocturnal? If they rest during the day and surface after dark to move about and feed, no one would see them because the beach is closed from one to five a.m. every night by City ordinance."

"That's not a very comforting idea. If they are secretly growing in numbers and decide to move beyond the beach where there is no curfew, the whole built-up area becomes especially vulnerable after dark. We've got to get a handle on this situation before it gets out of hand, if it hasn't already done so." The police officer became silent and the furrows on his brow deepened.

Zack shovelled sand into the hole and tamped it down. Then, leaning on his shovel, he examined the faces of the two adults who were still staring at the site of the discovery. He felt his pulse racing with excitement. It was scary, but it was a real life adventure, far more thrilling than the TV horror movies he loved to watch. He was in at the beginning of something that he sensed was going to get much larger. Already he had heard things discussed which could set the City on its ear. He knew he should keep quiet while the two men contemplated their next move, but finally he could constrain himself no longer.

"Why don't we camp out on the beach tonight and see what happens? If they come out after dark, we could capture some like the Marine Centre wants, or maybe we could kill some. Get them mounted to sell to tourists. The kids would love them."

"Slow down, Zack," said his grandfather softly, putting his arm around the thin shoulders.

"It's not a bad idea. Likely the only way we'll test the theory. If I went back to headquarters with a wild story based on speculation, they'd question my sanity. Zack is right. We've got to spend the night here."

The night sky was overcast with heavy black clouds and occasional breaks, through which moonlight filtered dimly. They moved slowly west in response to some vagary of the jet stream, but at ground level the air was still.

Sam and Zack sat in the pickup snacking on diet cola and sour cream potato chips. They hadn't spoken for some time but there was no sign of sleepiness. Their eyes and ears strained to penetrate the darkness. The vague shape of the police cruiser was about two hundred feet in front. It was comforting to know that the big man was armed and inside even though he could not be seen. Thirty feet to their left, the outline of stored cabanas and lounges disappeared into the gloom in front and behind. During the infrequent breaks in the clouds, the dim moonlight revealed a Gulf, flat like a pane of black glass. About a hundred feet to the right the humps of two beach vegetation projects cordoned off and signed PLEASE STAY OFF were dimly silhouetted against the security lights of the commercial strip of hotels and Gulf Drive shops. The vegetation on the humps stood motionless in the still air.

The hour was approaching one p.m. when the cruiser door could be heard opening and the interior light illuminating the husky officer as he slid out. He stretched and pushed the door shut. His flashlight could be seen weaving back and forth as he approached the truck.

Sam rolled down the window, "Pretty quiet so far. Care to join us in a junk food snack? Zack brought enough for a party of ten."

"No thanks. The wife packed a Thermos of coffee and I've just finished off two bologna sandwiches. You know, maybe we've been letting our imagination get the better of us; maybe the ground beneath us isn't crawling with weird creatures; maybe the large one was a solitary adult and the ones giving us the trouble are babies; maybe the soft sand has to do with some quirk in the water table. Anyway, nothing seems to be happening tonight. Nothing but the sound of a quickening breeze." Having said that, the policeman went silent, realizing the air was dead still.

"What the hell is that?" The policeman commenced to wave his flashlight toward the cabanas and lounges. Between them and the truck, the ground seemed to be in motion. He squinted to improve his focus. "My God, those things are coming out of the ground."

Before Sam and Zack could say anything, George started back to the cruiser on the run. He was about half way there when he seemed to stumble. He struck at his left side with the flashlight. In its erratically moving beam, things could be seen attached to his leg. He yelled some profanity and started running. Sam turned on the high-beams of the Ford and then switched them quickly off. The second or two they were on was enough to see the stocky man's legs covered with creatures viciously striking through his flapping uniform trousers. Blood could be seen spurting over the attackers as they crawled up his lower body. The flashlight flailed about for a few moments longer and then fell to the ground.

"Is Mr. Garrison dead?" asked the stunned boy.

"I don't know, son. Make sure the window is up tight on your side and the door is locked. We're getting off this beach right now." Sam reached for the ignition key and turned it. The usual noisy response of the old engine firing wasn't there. Instead, there was a sick whine from the starter as it tried to spin the fan clear of solidly packed things which had climbed unnoticed up under the hood. The battery died as Sam continued to turn the key on and off

"It's no use, Gramps. The battery's dead. We'll be safe in here until morning. Won't we?" The boy moved tightly up to Sam and pulled the old man's arm away from the key and draped it around his shoulders. He clasped both of his slender hands to his grandfather's gnarled one and pressed it to his chest. Sam could feel the young boy's heart pounding wildly.

In the beam of light from George's flashlight could be seen hundreds of things moving about, many larger than the one dug up by Zack. As they crossed the beam, they could be seen dragging lumps of bloodstained meat, some still in scraps of clothing. The flashlight moved and disappeared into the sand.

Sam was saying a silent prayer for his friend when he felt a sharp sting to his leg. He jumped and looked down. Some of the smaller things had crawled up beside the openings for brake and clutch pedals. The old man picked the thing off and stamped his foot down solidly. However, the hard shell resisted his effort to kill, and it turned to renew its attack.

"Get the screwdrivers out of the glove compartment," yelled Sam.

The boy leaped to obey.

Armed with the screwdrivers, they stabbed at the dozen or so intruders scuttling around their feet. The makeshift weapons worked if thrust between the two large plates atop the creatures. Soon the floor was littered with dead bodies oozing a thick green liquid.

"Zack, we've got to keep these things from getting in here. Take off your clothes and rip them into rags we can jam into the openings in the floor and under the dashboard. I'll do the same on my side."

The boy hesitated and looked at his grandfather, "These are brand new jeans and T-shirt."

"Don't worry, I'll buy you a dozen more when we get out of here. Now hurry."

Soon the two were perspiring freely in the enclosed safety of the pickup cab. The things could be heard clattering about the outside of the truck and under the hood.

The two huddled together, their senses straining for any indication the truck cab had been breached. Outside, the dark clouds thickened and what little moonlight had managed to filter through before disappeared. Only the dim lights from Gulf Drive provided any ray of illumination ... and hope.

Sam was silent, staring out the front window at the horror he knew was out there but couldn't be seen. Zack had his head turned toward Gulf Drive and the silhouettes of the commercial buildings.

Suddenly he stiffened and whispered from a throat unnaturally dry, "Gramps, there are now three humps where there should be only two."

Sam tensed and turned to where the boy beckoned. There were indeed three rounded silhouettes raised above the level sand where previously there had been only two mounds of beach vegetation projects. As they stared, their naked bodies frozen in fear, the mound in the centre began to grow. Soon, it dwarfed the ones on either side.

"It's coming this way, Gramps," whispered Zack as a shudder vibrated his meagre frame.

"I know. Stay quiet and maybe it'll pass us by"

The shape grew larger by the second, and the reverberations from its claws hitting and sinking into the sand to firm footing could be felt through the chassis of the old Ford. The vibrations grew stronger until the creature straddled the silent truck. The thick scaly trunks of its legs could be seen as black shapes against the distant lights of the commercial strip. The shadows seemed to rise without end, towering over the vehicle. The monster stood motionless and silent. In the truck, the boy and the old man held their breath and hoped their pounding hearts wouldn't give them away.

The deathly quiet was shattered by a crashing noise on the hood of the truck as the tail of the creature struck, punching through the metal as if warm cheese. The first strike was followed by a second one to the cargo area. The heavier metal punctured almost as easily, but the added resistance caused all four tires to explode like the simultaneous firing of as many shotguns. The noise was deafening in the cab but didn't phase the thing standing high above.

The final strike of the monster's tail penetrated the roof of the cab, flooding it with caustic, life-erasing venom. The gigantic thing moved to the side and with a few movements of its powerful claws scraped a hole large enough to hold the remains of the truck and its lifeless occupants. With a flick of its tail, it rolled the battered hulk into the excavation, pushing in sand and smoothing it. The police car was given the same treatment.

With the intruders to their territory out of the way, the things headed to the water and foraged until just before daybreak when they returned to the beach, each burrowing in to sleep until the next night. The queen-mother returned to the beach vegetation projects and buried herself.

A state-wide search for Zack, his grandfather and officer Garrison failed to provide any clues to their mysterious disappearance. They remain open cases in police files.

The white sand beach of Treasure Land continues to record complaints of things biting sun bathers. In addition, incidents are occurring in increasing numbers to the east as the infestation spreads in the direction of undeveloped wetlands in the centre of the Florida land mass. News media continue to carry stories speculating as to the origins of the hazardous crustaceans. Some writers suggest that there might be a classified government laboratory specializing in genetic engineering on creatures of the land and sea, and one of the more lethal varieties has escaped. Others blame it on a possible leakage of radioactive materials or toxic waste from industrial operations resulting in monstrous mutations in native crab species. Meanwhile, government authorities and research facilities seem unable to agree either on the scope of the problem or appropriate solutions.

Only the dead seem fully aware of the growing danger of the things below.

ALVIN ABRAM has won international awards in the graphic industry. He began his writing career in 1994. Since then he has had short stories published in several anthologies, books, newspapers, tabloids and magazines in Canada and the United States. In January 1998, he sold world rights to Key Porter Books for his non-fiction manuscript, *The Light After the Dark*. A children's illustrated storybook entitled, *Why, Zaida?* was published in April 2000. He has completed a love/mystery manuscript entitled In Search of Justice Denied and is working on a sequel entitled The Minyan. He is also working on a non-fiction manuscript about The (Dirty) Bagel Restaurant on College near Spadina as well as a series of mystery short stories.

Jealous Bullet • Alvin Abram

Donny sat in the kitchen with Suzie, his wife, and his best friend, Charlie Talbot, celebrating his recent promotion with a large bottle of Canadian Club, now a quarter empty.

"A toast," he said.

"To what?" Charlie's words were slurred. "To what?" he repeated.

"To us," Donny answered. "To the three of us. To friendship! To love! And above all, to a charmed life."

"How's that?" Charlie asked.

"'Cos we're indestructible. Nothing can hurt us."

"You wish," Charlie said, flapping his hand disdainfully.

"I *know*," Donny returned. "We've been friends for most of our lives. We fell in love with the same woman and when I married her, our friendship survived. We've been involved in accidents where we should have wound up crippled or dead. No, we're charmed."

"Lucky," Charlie said. "Plain lucky."

Suzie nodded, her glazed eyes blinking hard to focus on what was being said.

"We're indestructible." Donny's voice had risen, his words slurred from alcohol and enthusiasm.

Charlie shook his head. "Lucky," he said again, "and maybe stoopid."

"I'll prove it." Donny staggered to his feet and left the kitchen, thumping down the hall. When he returned he had a revolver in his hand, which he pointed at Charlie. "I'll prove it," he said as he circled the table.

Charlie turned white and his mouth fell open as he stared into the muzzle. Suzie followed the erratic movement of the revolver.

Donny took his seat and rested the weapon on the table. "There's six bullets in this gun. Six. Did you know that? I'll show you," Donny said. He ejected the bullets onto the table. "See? Six." He picked one and with much giggling and clumsiness inserted it into the chamber. He rolled the chamber three times, gripped the revolver in his left hand and staggered to his feet, his right hand on the table to steady his balance. He licked his lips, then grinned at Charlie and Suzie, placing the gun against his temple and pulled the trigger.

His wife and friend gasped at the resounding click.

Donny roared with laughter. "I *told* you we're charmed. Nutting will happen to us. Nutting. He pushed the revolver to Charlie. "Shoot me," he said as he weaved unsteadily.

"You're nuts," Charlie whispered. "You were just lucky."

"No! None of us can be hurt. I proved it. Shoot me. Nutting will happen."

"Forget it." Charlie rose unsteadily to his feet, staring at the gun. "This is stupid."

Donny grabbed the gun, placed it against his temple again and pulled the trigger. Click. He laughed so hard he lost his balance and fell behind the table. He staggered to his feet, a ridiculous grin on his face and shoved the gun towards Suzie. "Go ahead, shoot Charlie. Nutting'll happen."

Suzie stared at the gun, a silly look on her face. Hesitantly, she raised it, and unexpectedly swung it at Donny, and shouted, "Pow!" Then, laughing at her antics, she swung the gun toward Charlie.

Charlie giggled. "You going to shoot me?" He pulled himself up to his full height.

Suzie closed one eye, swayed to one side and aimed. Donny meanwhile, his glazed eyes closing, slumped against the table just as the gun went off and a red stain erupted across Charlie's shirt. With a look of incredulous surprise, Charlie opened his mouth, but all that came out was a strange gurgling sound as he slid to the floor. Suzie looked dumbfounded at the gun in her hand, than screamed in horror. Donny, his head on the table had passed out.

Viewing life from a homicide detective's perspective has a tendency to leave you with an impression that humanity sucks. I know because that's what I've been doing for the past thirty years. Psychologists offer lots of reasons for what makes a person a killer. I have only one— desperation; desperation to prove something, desperation to get back at someone, desperation to get or keep something—just desperation.

After thirty years on the force, twenty on homicide, I've been considering retiring. I'm sixty, a widower, overweight and getting bald. In my younger days, being five ten and trim with coal black hair would have singled me out. Today, I look like someone's grandfather and not a cop. My Superintendent, Greg Holloway, partnered me up with a recruit—his niece, wanting I should take her under my wing and teach her the grisly and the gross about working in homicide before I leave. I've only had a couple of partners over the twenty years on homicide and Greg was with me for sixteen of them. Iris Forester is thirty-six, attractive, divorced and shoots from the lip and to tell the truth, I'm getting to like her.

Iris and I had been working on a couple of knifings that took place at an after-hours club. Two victims showed up at a hospital with several stab wounds; one died. When we found the knifer, he was outside his girl friend's apartment, stoned. She had called the police. By the time we finished the paperwork, it was past nine in the evening. I was hungry. "Let's eat." I said.

The phone rang. I watched Iris as she scrawled on her pad, the expression on her face a blank. When she hung up, I asked, "What?"

"Would you believe Russian Roulette?"

"No shit!"

"There were three. Now there's two."

I stood slowly. My legs were killing me today. "You drive. You know where to go."

Iris shook her head in mock sympathy as I hobbled by. "You sure you can make it? Shall I get your walker?"

"Nice. You're learning. The next stage of your education is how to twist the knife after it's imbedded to the hilt."

She laughed.

The house was in the north part of Toronto on a large property with manicured gardened lawn on a street that reeked of money or big mortgages. Patrol cars blocked the intersections and the yellow caution tape was strung around the property.

"Nice house," Iris said.

It was old home week. Stella Morgan headed the forensic unit, and Constable Howard Claremont guarded the door.

"OK, Howard, what've you got?"

"Good to see you again, Gabe." He looked appreciatively at my partner.

"Meet Iris Forester. Keep your eyes in your head, Howard, she won't marry a cop." Iris jabbed me in the ribs.

"Hello, Iris. I'm Howard Claremont. The old fart making your life miserable?"

Iris smiled. "Only on good days. The rest of the time, it's pure hell."

"He's a pussycat. He grows on you. I know."

"So does fungus."

"Talk to me, Howard, what's inside?"

Howard fished out his memo book. "Three adults—two men, one woman, apparently intoxicated. Celebrating. As near as the woman, Suzie Worth, can recall, there was some talk about being indestructible. Donny Worth, her husband, brought out a gun. She thinks he placed the gun to his head twice and pulled the trigger. She took the gun and pointed it at their friend, Charlie Talbot, but doesn't remember pulling the trigger. He got a bullet in the heart. Her husband passed out." Howard flipped the book shut. "End of story."

"For you." I waved at Stella Morgan to come to the door. "Hi, sweetie."

"I cringe every time you call me that, Gabe."

"That's why he calls us that," Iris said.

"Everyone's touchy tonight. It's been a long day, Stella, and I'm hungry."

"This is an easy one. Open and shut. Three idiots—one's the shooter, one's the victim and one's the instigator. Coroner's on the way, the body's in the kitchen, the booze is on the table and the husband and wife are in drunken shock."

"Aren't we the lucky ones, Gabe?" Iris said. "More paperwork."

Donny and Suzie Worth were sitting on the couch, coffee cups on the small table before them. Mrs. Worth clenched a handkerchief but was no longer shedding tears. Her face was ashen, pasty actually, her eyes red-rimmed. The tears were apparently real. Mr. Worth stared down at his feet, his mouth gaping.

"Good evening," I began. "My name is Detective Gabriel Garshowitz and this is my partner, Detective Iris Forester." And that was how the case started.

This appeared to be an open-and-shut case. A married couple and friend celebrating, with the alcohol taking the celebration from joy to horror. Case over—or so I thought. Iris thought otherwise.

"What's bothering you?" I asked when we had returned to headquarters to write up the report.

"I don't know. I have a feeling there's more to this than what we know. Let's keep it going."

"Why?"

"If I told you I don't like the husband, would that satisfy you?"

"Come again."

"I don't like the husband, and I don't understand the gun."

"They were drunk."

"But why bring out a gun?" she repeated more loudly. "It doesn't make sense to me. If the conversation went the way they remembered, what's the gun got to do with being indestructible?"

"A gesture. A symbol. Hey! The evidence says this was a stupid act. Why are you complicating matters?"

"I want a few more days to satisfy myself that everything is as stated."

"To do what?"

"C'mon, Gabe. What's the hurry? A couple of days to check them out."

"You think he concocted this whole scheme?"

"Maybe. I'm not sure. Look. Mrs. Worth is in jail until she gets a bail hearing. I want to talk to her again. I just want to get rid of this itch I have that something is not right."

"Well, an itch I can understand." I started to laugh. "Maybe you would like me to scratch it?" I said not expecting an answer.

"If I'm on a wild-goose chase, yes, I'll let you scratch it."

"No shit!"

Iris headed for the door. "But I won't tell you where the itch is unless I lose, though."

Her laughter echoed down the hall. Smart kid. Let's see where she takes her itch.

I had no bad feelings about this case. When I worked in Traffic before I became a detective, a drunk driver hit a pedestrian. When asked was he aware that he was speeding, he said that he noticed his gas meter was showing empty and he needed to hurry to the next gas station before he ran out. His answer was perfectly logical to him when he was drunk. After he sobered, he cried when his answer was played back, especially knowing that the pedestrian had died. So I was satisfied with this accidental shooting and knew the Worths, now sober, regretted their actions. Iris was not. I let her have her way. If she was wrong, and I was sure she was, learning that hunches were not always right was a good lesson.

The next day we sat in the interrogation room and advised Suzie Worth that she didn't have to talk to us without her lawyer.

"I know," she said. "I have nothing to hide. What I did was stupid. I was too stewed to be aware of what I was doing." Her faced screwed up as if in pain. "I never would have harmed Charlie. Never." There was a softness in her tone and tears began to run down her cheeks.

Iris took charge, staring intently at Suzie Worth and asked, "Do you and your husband have a good marriage?"

Suzie hesitated before answering. She dried her eyes on her handkerchief as if she needed the time to compose herself for the answer. "Why, uh, why would you say that?"

"The way you said you would never hurt Charlie. It was in the tone of your voice and the expression on your face. I sense more than regret. Did you and Charlie Talbot have a relation-ship, Mrs. Worth?"

Suzie lowered her eyes.

"Did your husband know?"

Suzie shook her head.

"How long?" I asked.

"Awhile," she whispered. "It just happened," she added desperately. It wasn't planned. I was lonely. Donny was always away. We never met when he was home unless Donny was with me. No, he couldn't have known."

"What if he did? How would he react?" Iris asked.

"I don't know. Angry, I suppose. Hurt."

"Could he have planned this?" Iris asked.

"How? He was drunk. I remember him falling down, because he couldn't stand. No!"

"Were you going to tell him?" I asked.

We spoke of breaking it off many times, but we couldn't. We fell in love. You have to understand, Charlie always loved me. It wasn't his fault, it was mine. I made the wrong choice. I should have married Charlie."

"Did Charlie want to break it up?" I asked. "You said you spoke of breaking it up. Who wanted to break it up?"

"I did. But Charlie convinced me that I shouldn't have to deny my feelings. He wanted me to tell Donny. I couldn't."

"Weren't you frightened about being caught, Mrs. Worth?"

"Yes. There was always that possibility. Not from Donny, but from the neighbours."

"You're sure your husband never knew?" I asked.

"How could he?"

"Maybe you wanted out and Charlie wouldn't cooperate," I said. "Maybe you used this as the perfect set-up to get rid of him. Drunk, a foggy mind, an accidental shooting. That's a good cover for getting rid of a problem. You were trapped and became desperate."

"No, not true!" There was a look of desperation in her eyes and panic in her voice.

Knowing she was off guard, I pushed harder. "You said neighbours might catch you. Where did you and Charlie Talbot meet? Not in motels and hotels?"

"No, at my house. Donny called every night. He liked to speak with me before he went to bed. He said talking with me made the empty hotel room bearable. I never knew when he would call. Charlie would park around the corner and enter the house by the back door. I kept the house dark so he couldn't be seen through the window. He was gone by three in the morning."

"I noticed there's a chain lock on your front door. Did you use it?" Iris asked.

"Who'd come in? Donny was a thousand miles away. No one else had the key."

"Could you have heard anyone entering if they did?"

Suzie shook her head. "We always closed the bedroom door. And besides, we ... you know ... were preoccupied."

"Then he could have entered, been aware of what was happening and left without you ever being aware," Iris said.

"But he was out West. We were perfectly safe."

"What you're saying is that you were safe from your husband, but Charlie wasn't safe from you," I added.

There were no charges that could be laid against Donny Worth except owning a gun without a permit. He bought it from a friend who moved to the States before he was married. He said he was sorry for what happened and I believed him. Iris still wasn't convinced. We were on the way to see Donny at his home.

"Somehow he set everything up. He found out about his wife and Charlie Talbot and set it up. I feel it." Iris said.

"We've got no evidence against him. There's more against her. Charlie was his best friend. The evening was a celebration. They were drunk. People do stupid things when they're drunk."

"There's drunk and there's the perception of being drunk by someone who is drunk. We tested her, but not him."

"He wasn't the shooter and he had no motive."

"There would be if he knew about his wife and friend."

"How about the fact he placed the gun against his head and pulled the trigger? Not once but twice?"

"I don't have all the answers—yet."

Donny Worth answered the door, unshaven and bleary-eyed. His clothes looked slept in. He waved us into the house. It had the smell of neglect, partly eaten food was strewn on the corner table by the couch and a blanket lay on the floor. Donny sat on the couch and ran his fingers through his hair, trying to make himself more presentable. He looked at us for a while before asking, "What else can I tell you?"

"How often are you on the road, Mr. Worth and when do you leave?" Iris asked.

He licked his lips before he replied. His words came out slowly, as if forced. "Every second week for four days," he mumbled. "I always go on Tuesday and return on Friday. I have two different routes. One, I fly, the other one is by car."

"Where do you drive?" Iris asked.

"To Hamilton, North Bay, Ottawa and Montreal. I sell electronic accessories for computers." His voice got stronger as he spoke. "When I fly, I go to Winnipeg, Regina, Calgary and Edmonton. I need four days each to cover both routes."

"Ever come back early?" I asked.

"Am I a suspect? What motive do I have?"

"How's your relationship with your wife?" Iris asked.

"My relationship!" There was a look of anger that followed the outburst. "I don't have a relationship with my wife—I love my wife. I blame myself for what happened. As far as your question—no, not possible, my appointment in Edmonton is always in the late afternoon on Thursday. My flight ticket is purchased with air miles, and those tickets are not exchangeable."

"Can you give us your travel vouchers for the last six months?" I asked.

He stood. "No problem. Give me a few minutes and I'll get them." He left the room.

While we waited, I said to Iris, "He looks like he's taking this hard, but you don't buy it, do you?"

"No."

"Are you being stubborn? He's cooperating. Listen, I've had hunches, too, and I've been wrong many times."

Iris stood when Donny Worth returned. He carried an accordion file and handed it to her. "That's everything. It goes beyond six months. Please return it intact, I need them for my income tax at the end of the year."

"Thank you for your cooperation, Mr. Worth. We'll take care of them and make sure they're returned as quickly as possible." I nodded to him and we left.

I drove. Not that I wanted to, but there was fire in Iris's eyes that told me she was about to explode, and the last thing I wanted was her behind the wheel of a moving vehicle when she did.

"There was no bullet in the gun," she said. Her words were thrown out with so much energy I knew she had been mulling that over for a while.

"Come again?" I said.

"There was no bullet in the gun the two times he pulled the trigger.

He palmed it, made like he'd put it in the gun. They were too drunk to know what he really did. There was no bullet in the gun when he pulled the trigger."

Ahead was a strip plaza and I drove into the lot and parked. I faced her and asked, "How did the bullet get back in the gun?"

"He put it in."

"When?"

"You're my partner, can't you think of a way?"

"It's your itch, remember?"

"You're a big help," she said indignantly.

"Sorry. What's next?"

"Follow up on his trips out of town. If we can prove he knew about his wife's adultery, then that's all we need to give him a motive."

"And if you can't?"

Iris stared out the window of the car before answering. "Then I'll back off."

"OK. Let's check him out."

It took two more weeks of checking until Iris finally threw in the towel. She kept her word and gave up. Suzie Worth pleaded guilty and was sentenced to three years in a minimum-security prison for involuntary manslaughter. Donny stood by her right to the bitter end. He changed jobs to one that kept him home. He's waiting for her release, which should be in about a year.

The car angle proved a no-brainer. He had chits, gas vouchers, food bills and hotel receipts that made it impossible to get from one destination to another more quickly than he did. The flights were even more conclusive. His seat on every one of his flights was occupied, his ticket was always used, and his order book showed orders at every call.

A few months later, we sat at a table at Old Nick's on the Danforth. The place was noisy. The Worth case was an on-going subject with Iris. She still felt he had masterminded the shooting deliberately. There were several patrons at the next table telling jokes and it was impossible not to eavesdrop. One man told a story.

"At the beginning of summer a border guard at the San Diego-Mexican border stopped a young boy crossing on his red bicycle with a burlap sack tied over his rear fender. "What's inside?" he asked. "Sand," he was told. "Sand?" He examined the contents and discovered that it was sand. Every week for the entire summer, the same boy crossed the border on his red bicycle with a bag of sand. The guard knew the kid was smuggling, but what? All he ever found was sand. At the end of the summer, the boy never returned. Many years later, the guard was vacationing in the Canary Islands when he saw a young man, whom he recognized as the lad he thought was smuggling. He approached, identified himself as a retired civil servant and pleaded for the boy to tell him what it was he smuggled. The boy denied he had done anything illegal. The guard could not make him change his mind. The young man said he had to go, but as he passed, he uttered one word—bicycles."

Iris turned to me, a look of anger on her face and said, "How do we know Donny Worth actually was on the airplane?"

"His ticket was used. You couldn't get on an airplane without a ticket."

"Who held the ticket?"

"Him."

"Who says? Why couldn't he have sold it or given it away. It was no good to him if he was coming home early, like the day before. We've been looking in the bag of sand, not at the transportation."

I didn't have an answer since neither of us had tried to identify the holder as not being Donny Worth. It was assumed he was. "You want to re-open the case?"

"The wrong Worth is in jail."

"Shit woman, she confessed!"

"Her husband pulled the trigger."

Exasperated, I asked, "Who's going to remember the guy among thousands after all these months if he got on an airplane?"

"The cab driver might that picked him up at the airport the night he came home early. He wouldn't have covered his tracks because he had no reason. There has to be a record of someone dropping him off a night before he was expected. That would be Thursday. That's motive."

"OK, tomorrow we'll do the rounds of the cabs and limo's.

It took four days and nights of checking, but we finally found the cab that delivered a man to the Worth address on a Thursday night, not long after a flight from Edmonton had landed. We had checked every Thursday for two months before the killing to make sure, but we found it the week before the shooting. The cab driver remembered him as the man who told him that he was coming home early to celebrate with his wife. Won't she be surprised, he had said?

Unfortunately, yes.

Donny's in jail awaiting trial, Suzie's out.

Since Iris was right, I never did find where the itch was, but then I never expected to, anyway. Maybe she'll get another one?

SHARON FIENNES-CLINTON was born and raised in Toronto. She began to write short stories when she was in grade school and had dreams of following in the footsteps of Gordon Korman. This is the first year that she is pursuing writing as a career, although she does still maintain a contract position. She writes poems, short stories, and is in the midst of writing two paranormal romance novels. When not writing she loves to read and spend quality time with a close knit circle of friends in the city or in Muskoka. She lives in Toronto with her husband of six years.

Time Game • Sharon Fiennes-Clinton

Toronto, Ontario.

Nothing about this day had really made any sense, but Katherine Nelson knew that she would have to make sense of it if she was to survive. The deadly hiss that the bullets had made as they scattered around her should have been warning enough. The ominous nature of the letter that she had found tacked to her apartment door should have sent her running. Yet still she had stayed. Determined to prove that none of these threats were intended for her. Why would anyone want to harm her? She was a receptionist at a nondescript dental office. Her interests were in reading and walks in the country. There was no way that her or her lifestyle could instigate this reign of terror.

She rose from the couch where she had been making a list of any possible enemies, glanced down at the pad of paper in her hand and grimaced. It was still blank. It had been in that state when she came up with the idea an hour ago as well. There was no one that she knew of who hated her. Even as a child she had always hated conflict and so had gone out of her way, if necessary, to keep the peace. Her yearbook graduation comment even held her nickname 'Amnesty' as she was affectionately referred to by teachers and peers alike. The reference to Amnesty International had at first made her cringe, but as time went on she had grown quite fond of it and actually had decided long ago that her first born daughter would bear the name.

She marvelled still further. No known enemies, no jilted lovers (she would just like a lover), no angered clients (honestly, who took out their animosity for their dentist on his receptionist!). She was back on the bench and she hadn't even seen first base. There had to be someone. No, there was no one because this was not about her. If it wasn't about her then who was it about? Could it really just be mistaken identity? That wasn't really a good possibility either because she had lived and worked in the same place for the last ten years since finishing high-school.

Getting a job within a week of graduation had been great. Within two months she had moved out on her own and not looked back. She loved her parents, they had respected her need and desire for increased independence. Her father had even helped her move. They had given her the furniture in her room to help her get started and later she had bought everything else bit by bit. Even now, she wasn't rich by any stretch of the imagination, but she was comfortable and she had a few dollars saved just in case. Her thoughts were wandering and she needed to focus. It had been almost twenty-four hours since the shooting and nearly twelve since the letter.

The letter. Wait a moment. Katherine let her thoughts race back to the evening before as she arrived home from a day spent at the police station. The letter had been taped to her front door, folded in half to hide the message it contained. Even now, she could clearly recall the feeling of dread that had washed over her as she read the words: "YOU WILL DIE. STRIKE ONE! STRIKE TWO! ARE YOU READY FOR THREE?" Who wouldn't be rattled by that after what had happened earlier?

She had been on her way to work when everything went crazy, so it would have been 8:54 a.m. The same time that she left every morning in order to make the fifteen minute drive to the office and be at her desk for 9:15 a.m. on the dot. Due to the attempt on her life and the start of the police investigation, she had been with the police almost a half a day. By the time that she had gotten home it was nearly nine in the evening. If her theory was correct there would be another threat to her well being in just over an hour. If she was lucky, then she would be wrong, but her skin was prickling and everything in her said to get her things together and get out of her apartment.

Trying to forget how tired she was feeling from lack of sleep she hurried to her room and started tossing some things into the backpack that she took on her nature hikes. She knew how to pack with speed and precision from years of camping, but what to take left her wondering for several minutes. One thing that she did know was that she was not facing this day without a shower. Stripping off her pyjamas she headed for the bathroom to shower and form her mental list of travel necessities. If someone was indeed after her she would not only have to be prepared to be gone for a while, but she also needed to be gone before they got here. Finishing with her shower and comfortable with the items she had decided were best to pack she headed for the kitchen.

Secretly she was proud of herself for keeping a stash of cash out of the bank even after all the Y2K nonsense had been shown to be a hoax. Climbing up on the step stool and reaching for the tin above the cupboards, she pulled out five hundred dollars in various denominations and coins. She was not going to be caught unprepared. Replacing the tin, she grabbed some fruit and trail mix from the pantry and returned to her room to pack. She stopped in her trek and doubled back to her desk. She opened the middle drawer and removed the small fireproof box that contained all of her important documents and the key to her safety deposit box. She tucked it under her arm and resumed her original path to her room. She stopped once more, only long enough to grab her ready packed cosmetic case from the bathroom.

In ten minutes she was packed and pulling on jeans and a sweater. Although it was warm out she took the afghan from the couch and her fall jacket. By this time, Katherine was working purely on instinct and hers was screaming at her that in less than ten minutes she had better be far from where she now stood. She saw the letter on the coffee table where she had dropped it with the blank list and she quickly retrieved it before leaving the apartment and locking the door. She took the stairs to the underground parking lot and went the long way to her car instead of taking the door that was three spaces from her own spot.

As she gunned the engine and drove out of the garage she looked into the rear-view mirror and saw an orange glow reflected in her third floor window. Disbelief and anguish quickly spread throughout her body as she realised that she was watching was her apartment go up in flames. She stopped at the curb to glance at the clock and was not surprised to see the time was 8:52 a.m. She reached into the pocket of her coat and took out her cell-phone and called the fire department, placing the call as anonymous just in case someone actually was tracing her every step. Why was this happening, but more importantly who was behind it all? Katherine hoped that by distancing herself from the familiar and predictable she would be safe. Only eleven hours and fifty-seven or so minutes before she knew for sure!

She headed north. It seemed to make sense, although why she didn't know. Her regular hiking trails were in Collingwood or in upstate New York when time permitted a longer trip, so maybe if she headed toward North Bay she would be OK. She knew no one up there, that was her only concern. If she really ran into trouble there was nowhere for her to turn. The more she thought about the whole situation she had to admit that she was completely isolated. Contacting her parents or any friends might put them in danger as well. Danger from what and who was the big question? A shudder ran through her and inexplicably she knew that she was being followed.

A glance in the rear-view mirror revealed an endless sea of cars, but none that stood out. Most of the cars were like her own, Fords, Gms, Chryslers, Toyotas, and the odd Honda and Volkswagen. Nothing indicated the vehicles or their drivers were to be feared more than any other. There was nothing that she could do except to keep going and pray that she figured out what was going on before the next strike.

Katherine stopped at the McDonalds in Orillia to eat. Her energy was waning from hunger and she couldn't afford to not be alert. She sat in a far corner of the restaurant and scanned the room constantly as more patrons came and went. No one looked suspicious or the least bit familiar. Fear was consuming her and she knew that if she didn't get back on the road soon she would just curl up here and wait for the evening to come and bring her signed death warrant with it. As she approached her car she saw what looked like a flyer on the windshield. Orillia was no booming metropolis, but it seemed strange that the paper was there all the same. A quick check of the cars on either side of her own proved her instincts were right once more, no flyers graced them.

Before she had even reached within five feet of the car, she could read the message clearly. It read "I ONLY MISS THRICE!" Immediately all her self defense training went into action and she circled the car twice, looking underneath, checking under the hood, peering through the window, before she reluctantly unlocked the door and slid into the driver's seat. Even then, she was loath to start the car, but somehow she knew that it was all pointless. Whatever this person had planned for her it wasn't going to happen before tonight. All the cards were in their favour and right now, she was checked. Only time would tell if it was game over completely.

She drove straight through, passing her original stop point in Huntsville and continued on to Burke's Falls. Near exhaustion from the hours of driving and stress of examining every car around her for a potential threat, Katherine found that she had difficulty exiting her vehicle. Opening the door she swung her feet out and paused to allow for the tingling sensation to pass. As she stood, her legs cramped at varying muscle groups and refused to hold her weight. Swinging her upper body around she clung to the roof of her car and sighed in relief when her arms managed where her legs had failed. A minute passed and the shooting pain subsided considerably. Straightening once more she bent and reached over to the passenger seat for her purse. A figure passed close behind her and a shadow filled the car as the person stopped. She froze.

Every muscle in her body tensed up. Had she been wrong? Would her assailant finish this game right here in the open parking lot of a motel? Trapped and not sure what else to do she backed out slowly and turned to face the being that was blocking the sun's warmth and remaining eerily quiet. Her eyes fell level on an upper torso covered in a pale blue shirt. Slowly her vision took in the full sight and she was greeted by the smiling face of a local law enforcement officer. The older gentleman was tall, at least six four, but his height was offset by an expanse of stomach that would quite easily and obviously slow him considerably in any real pursuit. Katherine found it hard not to laugh at the look of concern that reflected on his face as he watched her.

He greeted her stating his name as Officer Burke, which only increased her amusement. How original, she smirked inwardly. They chatted for a few short moments and after he was assured that she posed no threat to his home town and that it was nothing more ominous than fatigue that has caused her graceless exit from her car, he bid her good day and strolled off towards his own car. The encounter left her feeling strangely calm and she didn't even flinch at the forty dollar rate that she was asked for to rent a room for a few hours of rest. She needed sleep or she would only be a danger to herself for the remainder of the trip. Her instincts once again assured her that the place to be at the expected time of attack was on the road surrounded by other travellers and so she would rest.

It was just before eight that evening when she got back on the road. The hairs on the back of her neck were standing straight up and she felt like her skin was crawling from an unseen and unwelcome leer. Looking around her there was not much difference from several hours before except that now she was alert and edgy. There weren't nearly as many people on the road as she had hoped, but she pulled into a steady line of traffic headed north along highway eleven. A sensation of real loneliness began to gather around her once more so she turned on the radio and settled into singing with Shania Twain and her throaty wail of The Woman In Me. Oddly enough she found the thoughts that this evoked comforting as the first smile in over twenty four hours spread over her face.

Katherine had just passed through South River and was going to go until Trout Creek before stopping for a break. She hit the brake to slow down for a man on a tractor when she found that her foot went straight to the floor, but the car continued at its accelerated pace. Swerving she went onto the shoulder to avoid colliding with the hulking contraption and manoeuvred back to the roadway. Her glance went to the clock and the illuminated numbers seemed to glare the time of 8:51 p.m. She knew then. Sometime during her time away from the car, her fate had been sealed and she would never even know why or by whom. There were supposed to be ways to avoid crashing when the brakes ran out, but she could think of none of them at this time.

On one side there was rock face and on the other a ditch. She could aim the car for the ditch and hope for the best, but there was just no way to know for sure. Not surprising, her inner voice instructed her to keep going and to stay with the car no matter what. She drove on managing rather well to not seem more erratic than most drivers as she continued down the highway. As she came to an interchange she saw the massive outline of a trailer and sensed that she was about to meet her match for the roadway. The load must have been heavy because the driver was taking it slow and steady as he brought the truck into traffic. There was no way for Katherine to stop, the shoulder held part of the truck as did the lane and the ditch was no longer an option. There was a kilometre-long opening in the rock face leading to a secondary road. Realising that this was her only salvation, she veered off and drove into the darkness to parts unknown.

North Bay, Ontario

Amnesty Quinn stood outside the North Bay Regional High School and grinned to herself. She was free and life was just as she would want. Today she would begin her position as a teacher in this pleasant northern city. It had taken ten years of living in Katherine's shadow to get her here, but no one would ever think to look for her. No one knew that she existed and there was nothing left of Katherine to trace. The apartment was burned, the car was at the bottom of a secluded lake and Katherine ... well, she was taken care of forever. A new home, a varied routine, and no voice telling her what she had to do to keep the peace. She looked down into her briefcase where the top of a small fireproof box was just barely visible in all the papers. A new beginning. How timely as the school bell sounded it was 8:55 a.m.

BERNICE LEVER, poet and prose writer, lives in Richmond Hill and teaches English at Seneca College. She is active in the League of Canadian Poets, the Canadian Authors Association and Canadian Poetry Association. Her work has been in dozens of anthologies and she has six books of poetry. She was the editor of Waves from 1972-1987. She has also written a grammar text. These two poems will be in her next collection. From 1998-1999, she was the Writer-in-Residence for Metro Toronto CAA branch.

Klepto • Bernice Lever

Who me? Well, maybe sometimes
I just clip a few things
little things, usually
just one at a time, you know,
pocket-sizers or less
whatever is palm size.

I'm not a magician
no Copperfield, nor Houdini
Now you really have to admire
those guys who can disappear
—right on stage, before your eyes—
an elephant. Wow!

"Seeing is believing" so it goes, but
no one believes this curly-haired
granny takes things,
another's things, I mean
so others never see me.

Really this matching pair
of purple linen napkins
—for your new apartment—
were just a lark,
please, laugh now,
no harm done, that restaurant's
got lots of 'em,
'cause for you I'd steal
the world, well,
whatever bits would fit
in my handbag!

Really, sometimes, it's too easy
to even be fun, anymore.
Please, don't use that 'maniac' word!
I'm not a keepo-maniac.
Why sometimes I don't even keep
the bright baubles,
the tip money on café tables
'cause now I find more
challenges in returning
them without anyone noticing me.

Double duty, twice the pleasure.
How did I become invisible?
Mental Murder

Mental Murder

Murder's not funny,
at least, the victim never gets
the joke, just the punch line.
    Aren't puns killers?
Often the victim's family is not laughing,
even close friends   are not smiling,
perhaps a nervous hiccup or giggle
at awkward lines in the eulogy.

But—as long as the murderer
remains outside barred cells—
she or he can enjoy success,
having committed the ultimate
that final stage of robbery,
taking another's life—not just for a holiday—
but permanently out of this world.
    Punchy, yet, dear readers?

Well, there's little reward, not much gain
in accidental homicides
(buses and bombs are so impersonal)
nor angry-fight manslaughters
    or is it person-slaughters now?
nor careless fatal accidents

like some curious bystander
gets our bullet meant for a cop.

What really tickles a murderer's funny bone
—deserving a wide-eyed grin—
is when the foolproof, months-long
plan works,   so headlines read
    "No Known Suspects"!

Don't frown at me, judgmental readers.
If murderers aren't humorous,
how come so many cartoon characters
are always trying to knock each other off,
Road Runner or Popeye,
each plan more ridiculous than the last episode?
    Is it plausible that jokes are
    based on mass-avoided truths?
 Most of us are too afraid
to even think of murdering:
    our wayward spouse, our annoying child,
    our demanding parents,
that loud-mouthed mayor, THE aggravating agent,
those garbage dumping neighbours

add your own favourite target,
as we've all been warned,
　　"To think it is to do it, to be guilty."

Well, some few people—murderers—think the joke is on
　　us,
lily-livered readers of mysteries, only living vicariously
through hundreds of murderous tales
'cause we're too scared to plan crimes of our own.

Ever wonder, why romances are the most sold
books—crime stories come in second—
yet editors keep asking for humour?
Guess more of us crave love than harm, still
maybe many readers need a perfect plan
for their personal, private murder.

What is your weapon of choice:
　　razor blades, mustard gas or acid brownies?

Just fill in the blank, if you dare!
Yet we all enjoy the horror, the suspense, the power,
even admire the cleverness of devilish plans,
become in awe of another's brutal passions,
murderers seeming so focussed, so alive.

Do we, dear readers, hope for justice before the last page,
so we can continue to believe
that the crime is NOT worth the punishment?
   Well, if we use someone else's illicit thoughts
   OK—second hand, repeat crimes are not so bad,
but if we live backwards, we are evil.
   What if we face eternity in hell   with our victim(s)?

It is enough to murder our minds, ·
and then who's laughing?

LORRAINE DUNCAN: An avid reader since she could first form words, it was inevitable she would eventually attempt to achieve her favourite pastime. Now retired, she writes as a hobby and is currently awaiting the decision of her latest endeavour. Although rejection slips keep piling up, she has not given up hope and with the help and patience of her literary friends keeps plugging away. A Bad Seed is her seventh contribution to *Wordscape* anthologies.

A Bad Seed • L.D. Duncan

"May I be of assistance?" Emily politely inquired, addressing the man's back. She could not tell if he was looking outside or at the window display. It was past time for closing, though she would not dream of turning a prospective customer away.

When he had entered the shop, she was in the process of attending Mrs. Friedmont, a very valued patron whom Emily would not have dared to ignore. Out of the corner of her eye she saw him pause in front of the locked glass cabinet where jewellery and curios were displayed, then amble on to browse amongst the oddments and antique furnishings before coming to a halt where he now stood. For some unexplained reason he made her nervous and she was reluctant to see Mrs. Friedmont depart.

Robberies were common, which was why less than a hundred dollars was kept on hand to make change. Most items were high ticketed and paid for by cheque or Visa. The money was kept in a desk drawer at the back of the shop as the proprietor believed a visible cash register tempted thieves. A security system was linked to the nearest police station and a hidden video-camera captured everyone who entered the front door. Good for twenty-four hours, the film was replaced every night by Emily.

When he failed to respond she was about to speak again, but then he turned and angrily asked, "What did you say?"

"May I be of assistance?" she repeated, stepping back as she sensed a black aura surrounding him. Yet, when he suddenly smiled his whole appearance altered making Emily wonder if her imagination was playing tricks. After all, she was tired. She shouldn't have stayed up late watching that horror movie. It had made her edgy all day. She judged him to be in his late twenties. Closer scrutiny revealed neat, clean attire and in an off-beat way he was quite good looking. Her initial impression ebbed and she listened to his reply.

"I noticed the sign in the window, 'Interior Designer, enquire within'. My aunt is considering changing the decor of her house and asked me to find a qualified person."

"You've come to the right place," she stated while trying to hide her excitement. "I'm quite sure my qualifications will meet with her approval. Let me get examples of my work that you can give her." She hurried to the desk and deftly removed a folder containing photographs of her achievements. Selecting those she thought would apply, she attached her business card and placed them into a large envelope, then returned and handed it to him. "I'll be happy to answer any questions your aunt may have. Please tell her to ring at any time, day or evening."

"I will. Thank you," he said, accepting the envelope.

After he had gone, she locked the door and pulled the shade, then stood a moment anticipating the possibility of an assignment. They were few and far between. During her three years of full employment, having worked part-time in the shop prior to this, there had been only about a half dozen: an architectural firm in Don Mills, once an entire house in Rosedale and the rest were single room jobs.

The last commission had finally paid off the balance of her student loans. Often she debated whether a different career with fewer hours would have been better—obviously she was not going to become rich at this rate. On graduating from OAC other offers with higher salaries had been forthcoming, mainly from conglomerates such as Ikea. The salaries, however, did not entice her because the obligations to use just their products limited her artistic scope. Emily liked to mix the old with the new and always attempted to reflect the owner's personality. At least her present position allowed this and more to the point, the commissions were solely hers.

In spite of the desire for more contracts she realized the advantage of having access to items in the shop that normally she would probably never encounter in her search for just the right

piece to complete a project. Mr. Bellamy was most cooperative since it was profitable to him as well. Although the hours were long, where else would a nicely furnished apartment be part of the wage packet. The weekly stipend was small, but still enough to subsist on.

Emily moved to check the window display. She would know immediately if any articles were missing. Part of her job involved the redressing of it every two weeks. Satisfied everything was there, she drew a black velvet drape across the width of the window shutting out the interior to anyone outside. Only the lighted display could be seen.

Her watch showed six-twenty as she removed the video film and inserted a new one. Taking the used film to view later she made her way behind a screen that blocked sight of the door leading to her apartment. This she unlocked and mounted the stairs. Halfway up the phone started to ring and she rushed to answer.

"How did it go today?" Mr. Bellamy's gentle voice asked after she breathlessly said, "Hello." It was his habit to inquire on the days he didn't come into the shop. At first she was resentful that he seemed to be checking on her until she realized his concern was more for herself when he gave sound advice on how to handle a particularly eccentric client.

Catching her breath, she replied, "Normal for a Monday. The couple who were deciding about the Queen Anne chairs phoned to confirm the order and are mailing their cheque. I notified Mr. Kowalski and he's promised to come tomorrow to fix the wobbly leg on the one chair."

Mr. Kowalski was the craftsman they used to restore and repair furniture.

"Good," Mr. Bellamy responded. "Anything else?"

"Several people came in to browse. I sold a broach and Mrs. Friedmont bought a set of candlestick holders."

"Bless her heart. I have an appointment in the west end tomorrow afternoon to see a dining suite they claim is a genuine antiquity. But you know how often they are mistaken," he sighed.

"Also, a fellow came in for his aunt who wants to redo her house. I gave him the usual photographic samples and my card," unable to hide the hopefulness in her voice.

"Don't despair, my dear. I have great faith in your abilities. You're young. It takes time to build a reputation. It will happen, believe me."

His optimism always bolstered her ego. As she hung up, she realized how lucky she was to have a boss who believed in her and was willing to let her use the shop as the base for her own business.

Bruce Templer walked swiftly, heading north on Mount Pleasant Avenue to where he had parked his new Nissan Infiniti. His headache, which had been one of the reasons he had not driven off at once, had finally gone. His other reason for not driving off at once had been to take attention from himself. There were two people in the lobby and the car always attracted admiration and they were bound to remember if they saw him get into it.

It had been rather unfortunate to have had to share the elevator. He had stood facing the door, in order to obstruct a view of his face, but the man in the lobby had seen him clearly. Still, he analyzed, he probably saw so many in a day it was doubtful he would recall him. He felt confident a connection couldn't be made as neither he or she ever met anyone they knew no matter where they went. They were always discreet. For obvious purposes the situation suited him and seemed to suit her, too.

The impulse to duck into that shop had been a good one. It gave him time to recover and make sure no one had followed. He wryly smiled to himself thinking of the young lady waiting for a call that would never come. To his satisfaction there were no pedestrians on the street as he approached the car. Sliding behind the wheel, he threw the envelope onto the passenger seat to discard later. A quick glance showed the apartment lobby was empty. He pulled away to get out of the area fast as he could.

Patrick Buchanen gazed out the window of the superintendent's ground floor apartment at the cream-coloured car wishing he could afford one. He was surprised to see the man who unlocked it and drive away. It was the same man who rode down in the elevator from the sixth floor with Mrs. Jones. Strangers made him uneasy, what with all the vandalism and break-ins one heard about.

He had a good memory for faces and wondered whom the man had visited. Other than Mr. & Mrs. Jones the rest of the tenants on that floor were single females who worked and rarely home before six, except possibly Miss Harding, a student. She shared an apartment with her friend, Miss Kennedy. About to graduate, she would be leaving the end of the month. A shame to lose a good tenant, he thought and hoped Miss Kennedy replaced her with one equally as good. Patrick wanted no ruffians in the building.

Curled on top of the bed Bruce felt ill. For the first time he wished his mother was here. Not since arriving in Canada had he suffered a headache. He knew why. He had become angry. Since a small child his mother had always cautioned and protected him. And he had tried only someone always taunted or ridiculed, then his headaches would begin and he would lose control. His father had constantly berated him.

His mind drifted to when he was at Oxford and so happy. The fellows liked him. Nobody thought of him as a bad seed there. He was the star of the rugby team. It seemed nothing could go wrong. Then halfway through his third year, David Chambers, jealous of Bruce's girlfriend, started to needle and accuse him of being conceited. He shouldn't have lost his temper, but the headaches began and he couldn't help himself.

"To think a son of mine has been sent down," his furious father shouted. "I suppose we should be grateful the lad refused to prosecute. You almost killed him. I'll never live down the scandal."

"Does Mother know?"

"Not yet. She's visiting her parents and is not here to defend you this time."

Bruce could feel the headache mounting. Barely aware he reached out and grabbed his father by the throat. He squeezed hard and then harder. His father's flailing body went limp. The blackness came. When his senses finally returned, he realized what he had done and panicked. But, after mulling it over, he deduced no one would know it was him. Only his father knew of his arrival as servants no longer lived in. Domestic help came in by the day to clean and cook. His father's body wouldn't be discovered until tomorrow. He'd go to Paris and write his mother a letter claiming he had been there all the time. She would believe him. An hour later Bruce left the estate after emptying the safe leaving it open so it would be presumed a robber committed the crime.

In Paris, after selling his mother's valuable jewels, he was able to procure false documents and a passport. Bruce Worthington became Bruce Templer, a qualified professor of modern history. He arrived in

Canada with sixty-two thousand dollars. The timing couldn't have been better. A position was open at the university for a history teacher. The head of the faculty felt an Oxford graduate would add prestige.

This led to him being introduced to a professor who was leaving on a two-year sabbatical in Europe. The professor agreed to lease his tastefully furnished condo situated on the lake-shore. The rent was steep and Bruce had to pay six months in advance, but felt the money well spent.

A vision of Jennifer came to him as he lay in the curled position. He recalled how they had met. Rounding an aisle in the university library, he had bumped into her and knocked a book from her hand. When he stooped to retrieve it, he noticed her nicely shaped legs and was even more impressed by her attractive smiling face. Aware the rules forbid the faculty to become involved with students socially he suggested they meet off campus so he could properly apologize. With no hesitation she agreed.

Bruce learned it was her last year and would be returning to Niagara Falls where her parents resided when she obtained her degree. She was an only child like himself. Her father was sufficiently affluent to afford her education, accommodation and monthly allowance. There was no necessity for her to work to contribute to the cost, which gave her lots of spare time to the delight of Bruce.

A date was arranged and followed by many more. By Christmas they were sleeping together. The time flew by. The deadline for her departure was nearing. Bruce didn't want the affair to end. He was in love. He bought the car in anticipation of driving her to Niagara Falls to meet her parents. It was only proper to declare his intentions to them.

Today he meant to propose, which was why, since he had no afternoon class and Jennifer was home studying, he had gone to her apartment. He had never been inside and she was startled when she opened the door.

It was all a big mistake. She laughed in his face. To her he had only been a passing fancy, someone to fill the time until she returned to her fiancé, a dentist with a prosperous practice in Niagara Falls. A heart-shaped, silver picture frame of the man sat on her night table. Bruce wanted to smash it.

She laughed again.

Blood rushed to his head and it began to pound. Afterwards, when he calmed, he searched for the pictures she had taken at Centre Island where they had gone a month ago. None could be found, not even negatives. Then he reasoned, Jennifer would have thrown them out. She would not want pictures of him for her future husband to see.

He turned on the television to hear the eleven o'clock news. There was no mention of a Jennifer Harding. He assumed her roommate, who sometimes stayed overnight at her boyfriend's, had not made the discovery yet. The more he thought the more convinced he became no one could place them together. He felt reprieved as he undressed and went to bed.

Just as the video was nearing the end, the phone rang, breaking the silence. Emily jumped in surprise before pushing the button to stop the reel from winding while she answered.

"Hi," Phil Prescott said. "I'm just up the street and could use a drink. Do you mind a late-night visitor?"

Emily had met Phil when he was a cop on the beat before being promoted to detective. He had come into the shop seeking sponsors for the police baseball game. The donations went toward the fund for police widows who had been left with young families to raise. Mr. Bellamy gave a generous cheque and feeling it a good cause, Emily attended the game with a couple of girlfriends to give support. Phil had spotted her in the crowd and made a point of thanking her. A friendship developed and they occasionally dated. Emily would have been happy for it to be more than friendship.

"Not if the visitor is you," she answered. "You know where the back entrance is. I'll wait there to unlock the door for you."

Hanging up the phone, she ran to the washroom to brush her hair, apply lipstick and a faint dab of perfume.

He looked exhausted as she led him into the kitchen.

"Gin or rum is all I have."

"If you have tonic, gin would be great," he replied, sitting on a kitchen chair while she mixed the drink.

She joined him at the kitchen table and inquired, "So what brings you out so late?"

"A nasty murder."

"Oh, no! Who? Where?"

"A young lady was strangled in her apartment up the street north of Eglinton. Her roommate is quite shook up. Blames herself for not finding her sooner, thinks she could have saved her. No chance. She was dead. Nothing could have saved her."

"Why would she think that, then?"

"Well, as near as I can gather the phone was ringing just as she got home. It was the corner store calling. They were holding photographs from a film her friend had taken in for developing several weeks ago and they were phoning to remind her. They thought she might have forgotten. She decided to go right then to pick them up to save her friend the trouble. It was mere chance she opened the bedroom door. Normally she wouldn't have intruded, but she thought her friend was out and wanted to leave the package on her dresser so she would see it. That's when she discovered the body and called us."

"When do you think she was killed?"

"The pathologist estimated anywhere between three and six. Miss Kennedy's arrival enabled the time to be narrowed down."

"Do you have any clues?"

"There's a possible suspect. Miss Kennedy felt she was seeing someone but was quite secretive about it. Seems she was engaged to a guy back home. Miss Kennedy didn't think it serious or the engagement would have been called off. The victim was a student about to graduate and was giving up her share of the apartment at the end of the month. We think it might be a jealous lover. When we talked to the superintendent, we showed him pictures from those Miss Kennedy had collected. She didn't recognize the man in the photos but the superintendent remembered him as leaving the building earlier about five-thirty and then coming back about an hour later to drive off in a new cream coloured Nissan Infiniti. We'll be talking with teachers and class mates tomorrow. If a car like the one described is in the parking lot, we'll spot it."

"Will it be on the late news?"

"No. Her parents have to be informed first."

Emily noticed his drink was finished and asked, "Want another?"

"No, I'm driving."

"Do you mind sitting in the living room while I wind off the rest of a video? I like to check to make sure the film didn't break or run out before the shop closed."

Phil sat beside her on the chesterfield. She pushed the 'play' button. The reel started to roll. Bruce Templer's face came on the screen.

"Stop," Phil suddenly commanded. Startled, she responded to the urgency in his voice and pushed the button immediately. "Do you know him?" he asked.

"I've never seen him before today. He came in just before closing inquiring about an interior decorator. His aunt is thinking of redoing her house. He has an unmistakable British accent."

"Take a look at these," he instructed, handing her several snapshots taken from his inside jacket pocket.

Slowly she studied each, then glanced at the screen. "It's him!" she gasped.

"I'd say so," he agreed.

"Now that I think about it, I found him disturbing. He seemed distracted and quite angry when he first spoke."

"Just lucky he didn't take his anger out on you."

Phil placed his arm around her protectively, then bent his head to kiss her upturned mouth.

Emily, forgot the loss of a possible commission.

Next morning, after speaking to the head of the faculty, Phil waited in the parking lot. When the unsuspecting Bruce emerged from his car, he and his partner approached. "How is your aunt?" Phil asked.

Bruce's shoulders slumped. He knew he'd been found out. "Is it permissible to place a long distance call?" he asked.

Lady Worthington picked up the receiver and listened with dread to the voice of her son.

"Mother," he cried. "I'm in terrible trouble."

"I'm not surprised. I'm only sorry I didn't have you committed as your father wanted when you were a child. He'd be alive today if I had."

At the age of eleven, SHARON CRAWFORD won second prize in a creative writing contest. Since then, she has wanted to write and her creative writing career, spanning twenty-four years, has taken some strange twists—from newspaper and magazine article writing (both serious and humorous), poetry, PR work, book proposals, short stories, mystery novels, the latter two under the name S.A. Langevin. The latest turn of the word processor, together with brain and heart is creative non-fiction. Sharon is also a freelance editor, and as with her own writing, her goal is to make the words sing so that they grab the reader by the heart and keep the reader engrossed to the end.

CREATIVE NON-FICTION

Justice, Canadian Style?
• Sharon Langevin Crawford

I lost my innocence in October 1980. No, not rape in its traditional sense, I mean, strangers entering my home uninvited to take and trash. They left me bearing an unholy trinity of violation, betrayal and insecurity.

The year is important because two years later the law changed and the accused would have been treated differently because of their age. Maybe, the old law could have worked better for me, but my case spawned such bizarre tentacles, that I wonder if the old or new law could make any difference.

None of these legalities dance through my head that October night. Instead, love scenes pirouette and fly through my mind, body and spirit as I turn the key in my front door. Behind me, my new love carries a poster. I pay more attention to him, than to the job at hand.

Until the front door swings open to reveal light. I don't leave lights on in the house. Saving electricity translates into saving dollars for this single mother. The upstairs hallway light glares down into the living and dining room. Did my ex-husband visit for some reason? Then I see the fridge door hanging open, its light blaring onto the kitchen floor. My ex would never do that. My dancing mind halts, perched for a fall.

"Stay here," Eric* says, as he speeds down the back stairs.

He returns in ten seconds.

"Call the police," he says.

My fingers drag through the seven-digit number on my rotary phone and my mind begins its fall, stopping at bewilderment. I'm dreaming and I will wake up. Reality intervenes as Eric leads me to his car. He is not brave enough to check out the whole house and I am still stumbling around, lost between never-never land and a bad TV drama.

One lone constable rides in and dismounts from his white police car. After he scrawls a few particulars in his notebook, he leads us on a house tour. I follow, like the proverbial lamb going to slaughter. But it is not me who gets slaughtered, at least not yet. The house will never pass real estate inspection. The back door stands open; a candle lies on the mat just inside. The two-piece powder room, a selling point for the house, now sports a broken window lock. The toilet seat stands in the up position. I never leave the toilet seat up. A whiff of insecurity slides through me.

The two other rooms on that level appear untouched, but I hang onto my insecurity, like a shield from the next exhibits.

The constable leads our search party down into the bowels of the house. He flicks on the main light. Shadows flicker on the walls of my office but my books and typewriter still rest untouched, unscathed. We check out the laundry room and it appears as its normal musty self. The constable shines his flashlight into the crawl space and I see empty boxes ready to attack. The only sounds are the furnace and my irregular breathing.

We climb three sets of stairs to the pinnacle. Lights shine from my room. My armour shatters. I clutch the remnants of my insecurity and feel them swirl around inside my stomach. The constable and Eric sandwich my entry to my bedroom. When I lean out and peek, the remnants try to mix with my heart.

My room resembles the rummage sale at the church. Clothes are scattered everywhere. Drawers gape open, their contents askew. Like a madwoman, I dig in. I need to know my birth control pills are safe. Twelve years before, when I took birth control pills to regulate my cycle, my mother threw them into the garbage.

My pills are safe. Then, I find the empty case for my late dad's antique pocket watch. I begin shrieking and jumping until I remember. I had moved the watch to a velvet bag in another drawer. It is safe. The missing treasure is my late mother's centennial coin collection. It is as if someone has desecrated her grave and cut me off from her spirit. Just like her death, sudden and quick. My stomach's remnants have chewed up my heart and I am hollow.

The watch, coins and the stamp collection (the latter stashed among the boxes in the crawl space) only reside in my home because none of the banks in town had any spare safety deposit boxes.

Town is the key word here. Not big bad city with drugs, murders, and break and enters. Small town, 30 miles north of the big city, a town in transition from close community to bedroom suburbia. The evil city spirit breezed in and entered the bodies and minds of some of its inhabitants. The result leaves me a mute victim.

The C.I.B detectives arrive, bland faced and black-haired, flicking their cameras and dusting for prints, adding one more item of disorder to my bedroom. This is nothing compared to the disorder that will come later. But that night, I sleep in shock, shuddering awake from monster dreams to the comfort of Eric's arms.

The taste of shock follows me like a ghost through the next few days. Eric installs dead-bolt locks in both doors and fixes the window. My home, my fortress has straw walls and thin-skinned windows. I tell my ex-husband, but not my son. How do you tell a two and a half-year-old that his home is not safe? I thank God my son was at his dad's when our home was invaded. But then, I wonder where was God?

My mute victim begins changing to vigilante victim. I buy timers. The house will no longer stand bare and open to the evils outside. Lights appear at different times in different locations. The sounds of music mingle with bad de-jay jokes and the news of the day. My anxiety levels drop until the next minute appears, leaving me tottering in yo-yo land.

The detectives return with more information and questions.

"Do you remember what year those coins were?" Detective No. 1 asks.

"I think they were the centennial," I reply. I try to appear co-operative. Maybe that decides them to tell all, so far. No, it is my real deep down looks that get to them. I wear my face as if it is carved from porcelain and my eyes plead "help me."

"We think it is a gang of youths, trying to pay for their drug habit,"

Detective No. 1 says. "There have been several b and e's in Aurora."

I stare wide-eyed.

"One place on Kennedy, they took a painting out of the frame and then made a return visit for the frame," Detective No. 2 tells me.

"And they pelted eggs in another place, broke liquor bottles in another and hurled pickled beets in another," says Detective No. 1. "You were lucky. They just lit a candle to guide them through the house and threw it on the floor when they heard you return."

That first part sticks in my mind. I see my house filled with flames. I try to mouth the words, "did they blow it out?" but of course they must have.

"When they heard you return" grabs my brain after the police leave. I am glad it is not summer and I don't go out to the patio from the back door. Occasionally, I find myself creeping up to the door, pushing aside its window curtain and staring outside. Do I think I'll find the culprits that way? I do not use the second washroom.

The detective duo returns with more questions and more news. This time they get specific.

"We figure there were three teenagers. Two crawled in through the back bathroom window. One of them fell in the toilet. We figure the third one got scared and didn't come in."

I am still scared, too and I don't want to have any alliance, even in feelings, with the culprits. Whenever I leave the house I double-check timers. I even brave the back door, but from the outside. I hurry through the garage out onto the patio. When I reach the back door, I touch it like a hot stove burner. It is locked, so I don't get burned, then. Once my friend, Dale, is over and for some reason we have to go out the back door, maybe to get something from the garage. I can't get the back dead bolt locked from the inside and I refuse to go anywhere until it locks. Dale fixes it.

The detectives make another visit.

"We know who the culprits are. Five teenagers and a thirty-one year old truck driver who acted as their driver," says Detective No. 1. He smirks.

"A couple of the teens were overheard bragging in Doane Hall Pharmacy," the other detective says.

"We've made some arrests and we'll get the others," his partner adds.

Some of their confidence rubs off on me. I want to catch these thieves and see them dangle by their balls. I want to see the fright in their faces.

What I get to see is justice, Canadian style.

A few months later, I receive a subpoena to appear in court as a witness. I read the subpoena. I know the accused, at least by name. His father is well known in local soccer and writes a column for the local newspaper. His older sister is in the army. What happened with the accused? Then, I notice the accused's address.

He lives three blocks from me.

My hands shake and my stomach and my heart prepare for another encounter.

Not in my backyard, I think. I remember I moved to this town to escape the crime in the city. I remember the town's quieter moods and friendlier people and hoard these thoughts as if to keep away thugs who go bump in my house in the night.

I look at the subpoena, take a deep breath. My turn to smirk. I will do battle in court and see these no-good bastards rot in jail.

On the day of the trial, in May 1981, I arrive at the courthouse and check in with the clerk.

"How long do you think this case will take?" I ask.

"Oh," she tells me. "Some of them go on late into the evening."

"What? I have my son in daycare and have to pick him up by six. I don't drive and had to take the bus here and have to take the bus back to Aurora."

I blind storm into the main waiting area beside the courtroom, latch onto the first person I see and start whining. Tears hide behind my eyelashes.

A tall blond man intercepts. He introduces himself as Sergeant Bill MacPherson.

"Let us go and get a cup of coffee," he says. I follow him into the elevator.

Inside the elevator, he explains a few facts.

"That was the Crown Attorney you were talking to. He is prosecuting the two accused being tried today," MacPherson informs me. He soft-peddles it, but I still feel like an incompetent fool. Now, the tears flow.

"If you have any questions or problems with this trial, ask me," he continues.

"I have a son in daycare. I have to take the bus to get him and the clerk said the trial could go late into the evening," I whine up at this six foot something blond hunk.

"This is family court," he says. "It finishes by 4.30." He smiles back.

By now, we have our coffees and return to the courtroom waiting area. I strangle my tears and anxieties, and prepare for the battlefield.

"All those with subpoenas for George Caron, please enter the courtroom," the bailiff says.

Four of us are left sitting with deflated looks on our faces.

The young fellow wearing glasses begins the storytelling:

"I was visiting my parents in Aurora and parked my car on the street. When I went to leave, it was gone. The police told me it ended up in a scrap yard in Virginia."

He adds that his name is Patrick and he works for the Thompson newspaper chain. I stare at him and wonder why he hasn't pursued this further as any good journalist would. But then, neither have I. However, my invasion was more intimate. He only lost his car, not even parked at his own place.

The elderly Scottish couple have a car tale, too.

"My wife and I were sitting having dinner, when I heard a car out in the driveway," he begins. "When I looked outside, I saw my van being driven away." He licks his lips, fingers his sparse white hair and continues. "I ran out, jumped in the car and chased after them."

Good for you.

"But, I lost them," he adds.

The courtroom door opens and everyone pours out. Lunch time. I head off by myself to McDonald's across the street. A few of the others have the same idea, but I sit alone, mulling over what I will say when I finally sit in the witness box. With every rehearsed word, I stuff another French fry into my mouth and chew it as if it gives me inspiration. Instead, it gives me gas.

After lunch, the same crowd shuffles into the courtroom, and the four of us are again left warming our seats on the chairs and trying to still the butterflies within. Not for long, because the bailiff soon sticks his head out the door and announces, "All those here for Peter Diosis, please come in."

We march in. Now, we will see some action.

The judge's bench yawns with emptiness and the courtroom crowd squawks with a jumble of voices.

"Holidays are the first week in June," and "remand, probably," filter through the mumbled mess of police and witnesses. I shrink into my seat. I'm going to have to come back?

The judge strides in from the front, sits down and bangs his gavel.

"Quiet. I have had enough of this stalling by the police because they want the case remanded to fit in with their holidays. Those here for Peter Diosis only can leave. The Diosis case is remanded until next Monday. The rest of you stay here and we will continue now."

Four of us exit. Patrick drives me home, where I can stew until Monday.

Monday morning I return to the courthouse and check in. This time, I am going to get that bastard, Diosis. I will tell the court how shocked I felt when I realized my house had been broken into and how violated I felt when I discovered he and his cohorts had gone through my underwear. I may even shed a few tears. I know I will stare at Diosis and pretend I am sticking a knife into his eyeballs.

I never get the chance.

The Crown Attorney herds the four of us into his office.

"Diosis has changed his plea to guilty," he tells us. "We threatened to try him in adult court because he turns 16 next month."

I am stunned. This means I cannot tell my story. I cannot let that creep know what he has done to me. He may be pleading guilty, but he doesn't feel guilty. I know I could have made him feel guilty. I have lost not only my security, but also my rights.

But I can still take action. And I do. I start a Neighbourhood Watch program on my small block. My neighbours and I become closer. But we cannot keep away the wolves that stalk the neighbourhood at night. Two doors down, the family, with their three teens, sits watching TV, when they hear someone in their garage. On a humid night, the retired couple on the corner across the street leave their inside door open. They lock the outside door. During the night their collie's barking wakes them. My neighbour runs downstairs and finds an unfamiliar lout jemmying the back outside door. When he sees my neighbour, the lout scoots. My neighbour takes chase after him, but doesn't catch him.

"I was scared he'd get hurt," his wife tells me later.

Peter Diosis' family sells their house and holds a garage sale. As I trudge up their driveway, I wish I had a truck to haul away all their stuff. Didn't their son rob me of mine? That's the point. It was their son, not them. I don't believe it's all the parents' fault. Some people are born evil. It's like the devil spawned their soul.

A few years pass. My son is eleven. We are sitting down to supper, when we hear something at the front door. I open the door and see nothing and nobody, so I close the door. Back at the table, I finally tell my son about the break and enters. Some of the remnants of fear, holed away in my brain's backyard, shift to the front yard. My words rake them away, and my grass appears a cooler green.

The next night, the doorbell rings. This time, an obscene picture, hand drawn, sticks between the doors. It is the middle of winter and we see footprints in the snow. My son wants to play detective. I remember Peter Diosis and decide to follow suit. We quickly don our coats and boots. I grab a magnifying glass and my son, a flashlight. We follow the footsteps across the road to the hedge belonging to the retired couple. The footsteps stop there. My son shines the flashlight on the hedge. A few branches are broken.

Peter Diosis?

I never did find out what happened to him. Perhaps I don't care. No, that's not true. Sometimes I think of him, but I spend more time mulling over the consequences of the Young Offender's Act, which replaced the old Juvenile Delinquents Act in 1982. The YOA covers young people between 12 and 17 years, *covers* being the key word here. It covers *their* rights, not the rights of their *victims*. The most these youthful offenders can get for heinous crimes is three years in jail.

Over the last few years, the content of youth's crimes has intensified. My break and enter may seem tame today because culprits now enter homes when the residents are in. I shudder to think what I would have done if Diosis and friends had entered when I was home. This thought sometimes penetrates my dreams, waking me up to a loud bang. I get up and grab whatever is handy, a hairbrush maybe. For several years after my b & e, I kept a steak knife and a flashlight in the drawer by my bed. Any noise in the night roused me and by rote, I grabbed knife and flashlight, stomped down the stairs, flicking on lights and singing off key as I went.

I never found anyone.

* The names of the innocent and the guilty have been changed to protect me. I remain myself, whichever name I use. The events, however, are all true.

ELIZABETH CLARK is a registered nurse currently working for a private medical information company counselling patients. She began writing in 1998. Nine of her stories were featured on "The Life Rattle Story Show," *CKLN Radio* in the spring of 1999. An excerpt of one of the stories was featured on CBC's program Outfront in December 1999. In March, one story was featured in *CBC*'s "First Person Singular."

Good Night, Mrs. Golden • Elizabeth Clark

Last night the yellow light flashed on and off over room 414. I pushed open the door and walked inside. Mrs. Kennedy, the heavy, forty-eight year old, was lying in the foetal position on her bed, crying. I turned the call light off by pushing a button on the panel above the bed, then pulled the chain to the over-bed light. "What's wrong, Mrs. Kennedy?"

"My back hurts and I don't why I am crying," she wailed.

"I just gave you a pain killer an hour ago. I can't give you anymore till almost six o'clock."

"I know nurse. I'm not crying over the pain," she sobbed. "I don't know what's wrong."

"Mrs. Kennedy, it's not uncommon for women who've had a complete hysterectomy to be emotional. It takes the body a while to adjust to the hormone loss. Don't worry, everything is progressing normally. Why don't you let me rub your back? That might help the pain." I massaged her back, straightened her bedclothes, turned out the light over the bed, turned on the light in the bathroom, leaving the door slightly ajar.

"Good night Mrs. Kennedy," I said leaving. "Ring if you need me."

Inside the nurse's station I sat in front of a stack of paperwork twisting my braid which hung over my shoulder. I put on my gold-frame reading glasses and pulled off the lilac-coloured stethoscope draped around my neck like a stole and placed it on the desk beside me.

Lynne walked into the nurse's station from the east corridor. "Where have you been all this time?" I said picking up a page to read.

"Mrs. Golden," she said shaking her head and wiping excess hand lotion on the blue hospital gown she wore over her pink uniform.

"Ah, say no more."

Lynne walked over to the table across the room, pulled out a chart from the rack, opened it and wrote.

Jennifer walked in the door from the west corridor and came toward me with keys in her outstretched freckled hand; her red hair tightly French-braided. "I'm going for my break," she said.

"All right," I said taking the keys. "Everybody on your side OK?"

"Yeah, they're good. You'll have to change Mr. Rik's IV bag at three-thirty and Sam, that young tonsillectomy patient in 408, might need something for pain at four. Other-wise they shouldn't give you any problems."

"OK, Jenn, have a good sleep."

"You sure you aren't going to take a sleep break tonight?" Jennifer asked.

"No, I have so much paperwork," I said, motioning to the stack on the desk in front of me.

"Leave it for the next shift."

"They left it for me! Anyway, come hell or high water it gets done tonight."

"Well, don't kill yourself. Nobody'll thank you for it," Jennifer said, crossing to the nurse's lounge door. She walked into the small room off the station and closed the door.

I stared at the radio on the desk. Jennifer had it tuned to Ciss FM. I hate that station. I can't stand country music. To me it sounds like whining with a tune. I changed the station to Q107. The choice of radio station causes constant conflict between Jennifer and me.

Jennifer and Lynne both love nights; nights are definitely quieter than days. I don't love nights. I eat too much, get nauseated, vomit, don't eat. I swallow drugs to sleep in the day and stimulants to stay up at night. I cry, get depressed and generally go out of my mind on the night shift. The hospital set a policy: no more than three twelve-hour night-shifts in a row without a day off, but that doesn't help me. My problems start after one shift and by the third shift I feel wacky. Last night was number three.

'Bink.' I looked at the call bell panel. #412, Mrs. Golden. What does that old battle-axe want now? Lynne was just in there. Damn! She is the worst nuisance.

Eight months ago Mrs. Golden came to the hospital suffering from dehydration. She can't manage herself at home anymore and sometimes it takes over a year to get a nursing home bed. I looked again at the call panel, then at the stack of paperwork on the desk, then over at Lynne sitting with her head down on an open chart, snoring.

I'll never get my paperwork done if I get stuck in there with that nit-picking, old bugger. Should I wake Lynne? "Damn it!" I threw my hands in the air and stood. I have to change her IV bag anyway; I might as well kill two birds with one stone. "I'll let Lynne sleep."

Mrs. Golden's blood work showed her potassium to be low so she needs fluid replacement with potassium for a couple of days.

As I pulled one of the red, adhesive labels from a jar on top of the medication cart, I glanced at the clock on the wall. 2:50 a.m. A fluorescent light flickered out in the semi-dark, empty corridor. Lynne's snoring was getting louder.

The elevator bell rang, the red arrow pointed down, the doors slid open but no one was there. The doors closed. I looked around the corner at Lynne snoring, one hand twisted through her shoulder length Afro; black skin glowing under the harsh lights of the nurse's station.

It's a good thing she isn't awake or she'd prattle on the rest of the night about the hospital being haunted.

Blue Oyster Cult's metallic, eerie strains came from the radio on the desk as they sang, *Don't Fear The Reaper*. The sink in the bathroom behind me dripped deafeningly.

Pulling open the top drawer of the medication cart I took out a small, ten millilitre, purple bottle and read the label. "Forty meq of potassium chloride." I read out loud while flicking off the purple, round, plastic top with my nail. I watched it spin in the air before falling to the floor. I picked it up and threw it into the paper bag hanging on the side of the cart, then screwed a large bore needle onto a ten c.c. syringe, drew up the contents of the bottle, and replaced the needle cap. On the label I wrote: Mrs. Golden, 40 meq of KCL/ 1000cc of normal saline, S. Jones RN, March 15/99, 0300 hundred hours.

'Three o'clock in the morning; the witching hour.' I recalled reading somewhere that three a.m. is the time most people are born and the time most people die.

My Ojibwa friend, Althea, always said that this is the time when spirits move between worlds, when the portal between the physical world and the spirit world is widest open. I smiled thinking, I don't know about any of that crap. Most of the deaths I have attended have been on the night shift. I don't really mind preparing the dead for the morgue. The worst part is when I have to prepare someone whom I have never looked after alive. I only had to do that once, but after it was done I had to go to medical records and read his file just so I could put it behind me. I needed to know one thing to make the man human to me: an occupation, a wife, a child, something to keep him from becoming road-kill on the highway of life.

It's as if I need to own a little piece of each person's life that I see die, so the thought of the nothingness of death doesn't drive me insane, like the sound of a dripping tap or ticking clock in the night when I can't fall asleep. I shook my head and said "One thing I know for sure, I'm thinking about some creepy shit in the middle of the night and I have work to do."

I shuddered and walked into the almost dark corridor with my syringe and label. The flickering fluorescent light gave the hall a horror film atmosphere. "I'll have to make a requisition to fix that," I whispered, walking toward Mrs. Golden's room at the end of the hall.

The Portuguese housekeepers keep the place meticulously clean. The cream floor tiles shone. The walls were spotlessly white, each numbered door painted bright orange.

Halfway down the hall, I switched on the light in the utility room and walked over to the wall of shelves. From the bin marked 'normal saline', I lifted out a one thousand millilitre bag, wrapped in cloudy see-though plastic and read the label. "Five percent dextrose and water. Shit!" I tossed it into the bin marked D5W and lifted out another and read, "0.9% Normal Saline." Nodding, I placed the bag on the counter next to the sink.

A wave of dizziness passed over me. "Shit!" I leaned forward dropping the syringe on the counter and gripped the sink with both hands. "Damn it!" I felt my heart beating that horrible rhythm again.

Doctor Maldonado had told me to stay away from caffeine. He'd be angry if he knew I had been guzzling coffee all night especially after he went to all that trouble to book those heart tests. If Juan wasn't my friend I'd have had to wait months for those tests.

"I shouldn't have drank the coffee. Shit!" But it's easy for him to say. When does he ever have to sit up all night? I continued looking at the closed doctor's room door across the hall with no light coming from under it.

After fourteen years my body has never been able to adjust to shifts. Taking pills to sleep in the day gives me a fuzzy head for hours after I get up and drinking caffeine to keep a clear head at night also takes its toll. "I better find myself a new racket before I kill myself," I said out loud. "Three nights without proper rest. It'll take me my whole four days off to recover." I took a few deep breaths while wiping my face with a cool, damp cloth, I then switched off the light and walked toward the last room at the end of the partially lit hall.

My heart beat out its disconcerting rhythm; the squeak of each step of my shoes on the shiny wax floor sounded ear-splitting. Blue Oyster Cult rattled around in my head like an insane thought. *Don't fear the reaper, don't fear the reaper.*

In front of Mrs. Golden's door I stopped and shook my head violently. "Get out of my head," I said to the song, then pushed open the door and walked inside.

A stream of light from the street lamps poured in through the partially opened drapes of the window opposite me on the far side of the room. It revealed the outline of a frail, old woman propped up with several pillows as she lay in the middle of the hospital bed.

"Where have you been?" said a voice that seemed too deep and loud to be coming from a frail, old woman.

I reached across the bed and pulled the chain of the over-bed light. Bright fluorescent light filled the room. Ignoring Mrs. Golden's question, I said "What do you want, Mrs. Golden?" I looked down at the prune-like bag of bones glaring at me through icy, pale blue eyes, a flowered kerchief covered her newly set and recently blue-rinsed hair.

Mrs. Golden's daughter pays a hairdresser to come into the hospital to keep her mother looking respectable.

"I have been ringing a long time!" She clamped her thin lips together, a permanently etched frown on her face. Reaching up to the panel over the bed, I shut off the call light then repeated, "What do you want, Mrs. Golden?" I pulled the plastic cover off the IV bag, tossed the cover in the garbage basket near the sink behind me, then stuck the label to the bag.

"I want a glass of water."

"You have water right in front of you on the over-bed table. Pour yourself some."

"I want you to do it."

"You're capable of pouring your own water."

"It's your job," she said folding her arms across her chest. "I'm not a servant. That's not my job. I'm not here to do things for you that you can do for yourself. I'm here to provide for your medical needs."

"I want water."

"Then pour yourself some," I said pointing to the bottle in front of her.

"Are you going to pour it for me?" Mrs. Golden demanded.

"No!" I said lifting the syringe to inject the medication into the rubber port of the IV bag.

Mrs. Golden lifted the blue bottle and poured water into the glass in front of her. The sound of ice hitting glass rushed through my brain like an avalanche.

Ice cold water splashed across my face then ran down the front of my uniform. I slammed the syringe down on the table and took off my dripping glasses and set them next to it. I pressed my hands to my face and pushed my fingers into my closed eyes, as if by doing so I could have stopped the rage boiling in my brain from spilling out of my head. I walked over to the sink, yanked two paper towels from the silver canister and wiped my face and the front of the green scrubs. I caught a glimpse of my mascara-streaked face in the mirror: dirty brown tears ran out of my eyes and dried on my cheeks, pieces of wet hair were falling out of the braid at the back of my head, sunken eyes were ringed with dark circles. I picked up the clean white towel folded on the edge of the sink for morning, dampened it under the tap and cleaned my face, then I turned back to the table and pulled two tissues from the box to dry my glasses before putting them back on.

I held the syringe in one hand and cleaned the injection port on the new IV bag with an alcohol swab from my pocket.

"Pour me a glass of water," Mrs. Golden said sternly.

I didn't look at her. I didn't speak. The swab dropped and fluttered to the floor between my feet. Closing the roller clamp below the drip chamber of the IV, I wound the tubing around my finger above the injection port closest to Mrs. Golden's wrist. I pierced the rubber injection port with the needle of the syringe. I gave her the full ten millilitres of potassium chloride IV push in five seconds, instead of mixing it with one thousand millilitres of fluid, to be given slowly over many hours. I released my finger from the tubing, opened the clamp to the drip chamber, pulled up a chair to the bedside and sat with my hands clutching the side rails; I watched her, my chin resting on the rail between my hands.

She clutched her chest. Her helpless eyes fixed on mine. Air gurgled in her throat; white foam collected in the corners of her mouth; her breaths came too rapid to count. Her skin paled as beads of perspiration formed on her cheeks and forehead.

I didn't move. I didn't feel. I didn't think. I watched as her hands went limp and her eyes rolled back in her head. Her chest rose, fell, rose, fell, rose, fell, rose then fell slowly. Blue eyes crystallized. The body lay on the bed like an empty shell on the beach, the living part had crept away.

The death smell hung in the air. Not the putrefying stench of decay, a smell that might even be pleasant if there were not so much of it; but a scent similar to violets, but much more pungent; a smell only medical personnel, undertakers and serial killers know.

I washed the spittle from her slack mouth, then closed it by pushing up under her chin. I gripped her lashes between my fingers, closed the dead eyes then rested the dead hands across the old woman's stomach. After straightening the bed clothes, tidying the table, putting the syringe in the yellow container on the window sill, I hung the new IV bag, threw the empty one in the waste basket near the sink, turned out the light over the bed, and switched on the bathroom light, leaving the door slightly ajar.

"Good night Mrs. Golden," I said as I left. "Ring if you need me."

MARY E. MARTIN has written two books: *Conduct Unbecoming* and *Prime Paradox*. She is presently working on a third novel, which forms a trilogy that may be read in any order. While murder and fraud are the events that drive her writing, the universal themes of pride, greed and lust for power are explored. Several summers ago, she attended the Humber School for Writers and was very fortunate to be placed in Wayson Choy's class, the author of the *Jade Peony* and *Paper Shadows*. She received considerable encouragement from him. She is also a member of the Crime Writers Association of Canada. She practiced primarily estate and real estate law in Toronto for the past twenty six years.

An Act of Kindness • Mary E Martin

In his law practice, Harry Jenkins frequently visited the elderly and infirm at their homes. Occasionally, he attended upon the wealthy in their mansions. Today, he was visiting Miss Alicia Markley and her friend of many years, Sarah Carmichael. Affluence and infirmity were married in one appointment.

Dirty slush spattered his windshield. He slowed until the wipers had cleared his view. The road was an isolated stretch winding through a deep ravine in the centre of Toronto. Opening his window to clear the mist, he heard the hollow boom of traffic on the span of concrete bridges above. Forests of branches, waving against the bleak winter sky, reminded him of wild spirits fleeing the night. He checked his watch. He was late.

The two women shared a small house wedged between the mansions of Binscarth Road in Rosedale. Alicia had called to say they wanted to open a business. Its nature was unclear. Harry thought the inquiry unusual, since both of them were well in their sixties and financially well-off. Known for their charm and devotion to charity, the ladies were paragons of social propriety. Harry smiled as he tried to visualize them, sleeves rolled up and embroiled in the daily mess of business affairs. But he knew torrents, raging beneath a calm exterior, could silently foment major upheavals.

He frowned in recollection. Last year, Sarah had suddenly taken to her bed after a funeral to remain there ever since. Perhaps she had miraculously recovered. Otherwise, a business venture did seem strange. Such enquiries were often idle notions created by bored minds.

He slowed down to catch the turn into Rosedale. His bleak thoughts were mirrored by the dismal February afternoon.

He had seen the ladies last year at the funeral of Ronald Hobbs, City Councillor. His funeral was a side-show, partially paid from the public purse. Half the city's police force had escorted the hearse and a long line of limousines. In an age of declared fiscal responsibility, Harry wondered at such profligacy. Nonetheless, the show had gone on. Since he was advising city council on various planning issues, Harry considered it politic to attend.

The funeral was held at the cavernous St. Bartholomew's Church on Sherbourne Street, south of Rosedale. The crush of media had attracted overflow crowds. Harry was relieved to squeeze into a pew near the front. Low chuckles rose from behind him. Harry winced. The press was at its post.

"Know where they found Hobbs?" Harry half-turned in his seat.

"Floating in his swimming pool."

"Really?"

"Ya." Harry could hear the reporter cracking his gum in excitement. "Pictures will be in tonight's paper."

"He drowned?"

"Looks like. But the real story is, he was stark naked. Floating ass-up in his pool!"

More chuckles followed. "But get this." Harry craned his neck. "Right at his indoor pool, near the cabana, they found champagne on ice and two glasses."

"Open?"

"What?"

"Was the champagne open?"

"I don't know."

More low chuckles followed. "Wonder who the guest was?"

Hobbs reputation as a womanizer was legendary. But Harry wondered what city councillor could afford not only an indoor pool, but also a cabana.

Across the aisle, in the front pew, the Hobbs family sat in stony silence. The watch of the dead, thought Harry. Directly behind them, Alicia Markley and Sarah Carmichael were huddled. Sarah was crouched in the pew sobbing steadily. With a penetrating glare, Mrs. Hobbs turned about at the sound of Sarah's sniffles. Alicia wound a consoling arm around her friend to no avail. Rarely had Harry witnessed such a public display of grief from someone unrelated. Sarah's sobs continued unabated as she rested her head against her friend's shoulder. What sort of relationship with Hobbs could bring on such sorrow? Harry had no answer. When the minister took the pulpit, Sarah's weeping diminished. Harry breathed a sigh of relief. Alicia gently brushed a damp strand of hair from Sarah's cheek.

Black chunks of sludge flew up at Harry's car as he turned down into the quiet streets of Rosedale. Across the park, the frozen trees looked pen-sketched against the grey patches of snow. Binscarth Road ran along the southerly side of the park near the rink. In the dim light, he squinted to read the numbers on the houses. There was the Markley house; small, but constructed entirely of stone. The long driveway had not been shovelled for weeks. Once the snow had drifted in sleek, sculpted patterns. Now it had shrunk into muddy patches. Careful to read the signs, Harry parked on the street. When he opened the gate of the stone fence, his spirits rose. The house was only a storey and a half, but lights glowed and welcomed him inward. He knocked. Within moments, Alicia Markley answered.

Catching his breath, Harry stepped back. Miss Markley was a tall woman. Her soft and slender form was silhouetted by the light. Harry had remembered her as sharp-edged and angular. Except when it came to Sarah, she was usually surly.

"Mr. Jenkins!" She sounded delighted at his presence. Her smile was broad. "Please do come in."

Harry stepped forward and shook her hand. She drew him in.

They were close in the narrow hall. She helped him remove his coat. Miss Markley's appearance was more pleasant than he recalled. On past occasions, she had seemed like a gawky child, whose features were not yet fully developed; a nose too big, a mouth too wide. Not at all gawky now, he thought. Her long floral-patterned skirt and silk blouse did not square with his memory of severe tweed suits and sensible shoes.

Something had changed. He hung up his coat and followed her inward to the living room.

A log blazed in the fireplace and sherry glasses were set on a silver tray. The scene was one of comfort and pleasure. Setting his case beside the coffee table, he sank into a chair.

"How kind of you to come on such a dismal day, Mr. Jenkins." She beamed at him.

"Not at all. You have a very pleasant home." Harry relaxed in the quiet peace surrounding him.

"You'll have a sherry once we've discussed business?" The intensity of her request made him look up from his legal pad. He smiled and nodded. "Of course, I'd like that."

Her gaze was somewhat distracting. In the flickering light, her face had acquired sharp angles, he had not first noticed. But then she smiled. Warmth and softness radiated from her. He sat back.

"Mr. Jenkins, I have a business proposal to discuss with you."

"Certainly. What is it?" He picked up his pen.

"My friend Sarah and I have been considering opening an artist studio." She paused to study the heavy silver rings on her fingers.

Harry was surprised. "For yourselves?"

Alicia shook her head wearily and said, "No. Sarah's never been very creative. Too timid for her own good. However, we've shared a love of art throughout our lives." Alicia stopped, as if lost in recollection. Then she said, "In fact, we've shared a great deal together, Mr. Jenkins."

Harry had made only one note. 'Artist studio'. He looked up. "And?" he prompted.

"I'm very concerned about her. I think she needs a project to bring her back to life."

"She's been ill for some time?"

"She's lost her passion for life. She needs an interest to revive her." Alicia rose swiftly to the mantelpiece. Her motions reminded Harry of an awkward bird alighting a branch. "And so, I've decided," she said, fiddling with the clock, "we should open a studio where young artists can work." She took the sherry decanter from the coffee table and poured two glasses. She spilled several drops.

Harry waited as she dabbed at the tiny pool of liquid. "They'd pay a fee for the use of the space?" he asked.

"I suppose." Alicia shrugged. "Something like that." She handed

Harry his glass. "The money's not important. I just want her back."

Harry reflected upon her words. "It's a charitable enterprise, which is good for tax purposes." He smiled. Clients always liked to hear of tax savings. "You should incorporate the business as a non-profit company. So, anything you earn above expenses, gets paid out tax free." Easily enough done, he thought.

Alicia nodded absently. "Then do it, Mr. Jenkins. Please." Obviously she had no interest in detailed legal advice. Harry knew he was missing something.

Alicia began to pace slowly about the coffee table. "You've heard of Ronald Hobbs?"

"Yes, the City Councillor who died last year."

Alicia nodded. "After his funeral, Sarah took to her bed and simply, for no physical reason, became an invalid." Alicia's face grew pinched in thought. Suddenly she turned away from Harry and rushed to the foot of the stairs. She cocked her head and motioned him to remain silent. After a moment, she shook her head. "I thought I heard her upstairs. I did so hope she'd come down." She returned to stand behind his chair and rested her hand on his shoulder. He glanced up at her.

"Mr. Jenkins," she began quietly. With her closeness, Harry contemplated the loneliness of elderly spinsters. "I want to show you something, so you'll understand the problem."

She moved to the sideboard. Opening a drawer, she lifted out a heavy package wrapped up in brown paper. Carefully she untied the string and drew out two frames. In them were two photographs, which she handed to him.

Harry searched for his reading glasses. The room seemed to darken as he examined the first one, a photograph of a man in a business suit. Harry's mouth dropped open. He could think of no words. He handed the photograph back to her and said at last, "But why?"

With great precision, the head of the man in the photograph had been neatly clipped out and then crudely pasted at the bottom. No doubt, it was the City Councillor, Ronald Hobbs.

She handed him the second photograph. Again, Hobbs, dressed in a casual shirt had been beheaded. Again, his face was pasted at the bottom, this time, upside down.

"After the funeral," Alicia began quietly, "we returned to the house. Sarah was inconsolable. I took her upstairs and put her to bed." Alicia's voice was devoid of emotion as if she were reporting a distant and mildly curious event. "I went downstairs to make her some tea and when I got back, she was sitting up in bed snipping out the heads with a pair of nail scissors." Alicia smoothed her skirt, then continued, "She had such a strange look on her face, Mr. Jenkins, and she hummed a little tune. She wasn't herself at all, you see."

Harry could picture the scene with clarity. "But who pasted them back in?" he asked.

Alicia shrugged as if the question were unimportant. "Oh, she did several days later."

Harry rose from his chair and went to the bay window. The significance of legal issues surrounding taxation of charitable corporations was paling. The snow had started. Huge soft flakes drifted down, swiftly covering the walk and muddy patches on the lawn. The world was coated in silence.

The story fascinated him. He could almost hear Sarah's sing-song voice and see her vacant smile. Apparently normal minds could turn themselves inside out. He turned and spoke to Alicia. "So she took to her bed and never got up?"

Alicia nodded. "Perhaps I was wrong, but then I thought she must hear the truth about Mr. Hobbs."

"Which was?"

Alicia's voice became bitter. "He was a philanderer, Mr. Jenkins."

Harry almost smiled at the old fashioned word. Surely everyone knew of Hobbs' exploits. He asked, "Sarah and he were lovers?"

"Yes. Sarah was less than faithful."

Harry was confused. "You mean he was unfaithful?"

Anger flashed in Alicia's eyes. She rushed on. "What could anyone expect? After all, he was a man."

Harry ignored the slight. "What did you tell her?" he asked
Alicia sighed deeply. Her dark eyes bore into him. Harry sank into his chair. Her intensity compelled him to listen.

"I saw Mr. Hobbs with another woman. Not his wife." Alicia stiffened in her chair. "I thought Sarah should know."

Harry waited in silence. The room once warm and inviting was growing hot and oppressive. He was drawn to hear the story.

"You know the arcade downtown?" she began.

Harry knew it well. He nodded.

"One day, I was shopping there. Just picking up a few things."

Harry instantly pictured her marching through the narrow passages of shops in her severe tweed suit and heavy shoes.

"When I finished, I stopped for coffee. I sat at a table on the mews."

Harry could see her, eyes darting suspiciously about nearby tables.

"While I was waiting, I looked inside through the glass." Alicia pursed her lips in distaste. "There he sat at a table with a woman."

Harry could visualize Alicia's ill-disguised attempt at nonchalance.

Disgust mounted in Alicia's voice. "There was no mistaking him." She shook her head. "Leering over her with his hand on her knee." Alicia's face was suffused with anger. "She was a common slut!"

Harry was shocked. He could easily envision the groping City Councillor and the woman. But he could not comprehend Alicia's mounting fury. White-faced, she stood in front of the fire. Glaring, she pointed at him. "He was a licentious and immoral fraud, Mr. Jenkins!" Harry felt accused of aeons of male perfidy.

At last she continued. "When he saw me, he got the waiter, paid the bill and slunk out with his woman."

"He knew you?" Harry asked in surprise.

"We had met once or twice before," she said carefully. Then she added darkly, "I followed them, Mr. Jenkins."

So powerful was the story, Harry had the odd sensation of voyeurism. He saw poor Hobbs rushing from the café. His woman stumbled after him in her stiletto heels and tight skirt. He saw Alicia in her sensible shoes striding mercilessly after them. He saw them hurrying down tiled hallways surrounded by brass and marble. He heard the muted rush of the noontime crowds underneath the opaque skylight. In the distance, he saw the couple hand in hand, desperately seeking sanctuary in the twisting passages.

Harry closed his eyes and asked weakly, "Did you see anything more?" Alicia shook her head. "No. They escaped."

Harry felt strangely frustrated at the inconclusiveness of the story.

"I had to tell her, Mr. Jenkins." Crouched in her chair, Alicia bit her lip.

"What was Sarah's reaction?"

"She said she wanted to die," said Alicia weakly. "She's said almost nothing since. Not even 'thank you' for all the nursing, bathing and meals I cook her." Alicia looked up helplessly. Her eye were rimmed with red. "Was I wrong, Mr. Jenkins?" she asked.

Harry squirmed in the role of moral arbiter. He had no idea what to say. But he had an uncanny ability to picture scenes vividly. The images of Alicia, the avenging angel, and Sarah, the determined decapitator, were emblazoned on his memory.

At last Alicia spoke. "So, you see, I thought I might divert her with a project."

Harry was relieved to return to legal matters. "Then you want to proceed with the incorporation?" His pen was poised over his pad.

"First, I want you to talk to Sarah. Perhaps she'll listen to you." With determination, Alicia stood up. "Let's go upstairs, Mr. Jenkins."

Harry had no idea why the uncommunicative Sarah would want his advice. Alicia led the way up the stairs. The stairwell was lined with photographs of ancient relatives. Fortunately, he observed, all the heads were intact. Sarah's bedroom was down the hall at the back of the house. A grey light seeped from her door, which was slightly ajar. Harry's chest constricted. He hated unannounced bedside visits. No sound could be heard from within.

Suddenly, Harry became aware of a faint, yet foul odour. Alicia stepped inside the room and closed the door behind her. With bile rising in his throat, Harry hung back and stared at the ceiling.

"Darling?" said Alicia. There was no reply.

"Sarah, you must sit up and look at me," Harry heard Alicia say. There was rustling of curtains and a sigh, but Sarah had not yet replied. Alicia's voice grew insistent. "Mr. Jenkins is here. I want you to discuss our plan with him."

Harry stared at his shoes. The room was silent. "If you won't co-operate," Alicia hissed, "there won't be any dinner for you!" Harry frowned. "Now sit up at once and stop this nonsense." Harry could hear the mounting desperation in Alicia's voice.

The door flew open. Alicia's gaunt form swayed in the doorway. Harry was almost knocked over by the stench emanating from the bedroom.

"Mr. Jenkins," Alicia's face was white and strained, "something is terribly wrong with Sarah!"

Harry stepped into the room. Sarah's head lolled awkwardly to one side of the pillow. Her unseeing eyes stared upward at the ceiling.

Alicia clenched her hands and cried in desperation, "She refuses to speak to me after all I've done for her. She won't eat, although I've begged her." In her misery, she clutched at Harry's hands and dragged him toward the bed.

Harry could scarcely get his breath. At last he spoke, "Alicia, she's dead. She's been dead for days."

Alicia's expression was uncomprehending. "No, Mr. Jenkins!" Violently she shook her head. "That cannot be. I've given my life for her. She cannot die."

Staggered by the rancid air, Harry grasped Alicia's shoulders and marched her into the next bedroom. Immediately, he opened the window and took deep, greedy breaths of the cold night air. He was amazed to find the steady breeze fanned his anger. He turned on her. "How in God's name could you not know she's been dead for days?"

He was prepared for anger, but not her sweet and patient smile. "That isn't true, Mr. Jenkins. Last night, we toasted our new venture with a glass of champagne and had a lovely chat before bedtime." She glanced down at her rings. "Granted, she hasn't eaten much today. I was going to bring her dinner after you'd gone."

Her smile of innocence and fond gaze made Harry understand. In that moment, he realized she was completely mad. Why had he been so slow to understand? He sat on the bed and gently took her hand. "We'll have to call for help, Alicia."

"Help?" she laughed. "I don't need any help. I'll start her dinner as soon as I've had a little rest." She slumped back on the pillow and shut her eyes.

Harry stood. He walked down the hall to the bathroom and shut the door. On the ledge above the sink sat two champagne glasses. Beside them were three bottles of pills. His head was beginning to throb. He gripped the sink. Then he saw the empty capsules strewn on the ledge. He straightened up. How easy, he thought, to give an overdose with champagne.

Wearily he returned to the bedroom. "Alicia," he said quietly. Her eyes flew open. "How many capsules did you give her?"

"Quite a few," Alicia replied. "She wanted to leave. So I let her. It was an act of kindness." A tiny sob escaped Alicia. "But, I miss her so."

If he tried hard, Harry could imagine the circumstances leading up to so called mercy killing. Had Sarah begged her friend to put an end to suffering? Had Sarah been driven to death by the unfaithfulness of men? Regardless, such an act of kindness was definitely against the law.

"She tortured me so," said Alicia angrily. "She never could decide between the two of us."

Harry turned sharply to face her. "What? Between whom?"

"Between me and that man, Mr. Hobbs."

At last Harry understood. He remembered the champagne glasses beside Mr. Hobbs' cabana. Death with champagne. "You were jealous of him?" Harry prodded. "You gave him the capsules with champagne." Poor unsuspecting Hobbs. What a price for his dalliance.

"I devoted my life to her! What did I get in return?" Fury flashed in Alicia's eyes. "Nothing but heartache waiting for her to decide." She drew herself up. "No matter what I had to offer, she wanted him even in death." Pride rang in her voice. "I loved her enough to let her go."

He left her sitting on the bed. As he passed through the downstairs hallway to the kitchen, he marvelled at the normality of the scene. The fire still blazed and the sherry glasses sat on the coffee table. Not forty-five minutes ago, he had sat in the living room enjoying the company of a charming woman. In the kitchen he picked up the telephone and dialled the police.

After graduating with a BFA in drama, BARBARA HOLLERAN began a career as a stage and television actress in the US and Canada. Writing for television seemed a natural progression, and Barbara has written extensively for such series as "The Littlest Hobo," (seen in more than thirty countries) "Once Upon A Hamster," "Snow Job," "The Campbells" and "The Elizabeth Manley Special," among others. Barbara has also written for the *Atlanta Journal/Constitution*, the *Toronto Star*, and *Dance Scene*, as well as penning advertising and publicity copy. She is a member of the Writers' Guild of Canada, the Canadian Authors Association and ACTRA. In her spare time, Barbara is an avid ballroom dance competitor.

The Beginning • Barbara Holleran

Virginia Shelton felt her aging features collapse into an exasperated frown as she pointed a painful, arthritic finger at a large wooden crate being struggled past her by two elderly men, the nursing home's part-time staff.

"What the hell is that?"

"Dunno," one of them said, puffing. "Truck left it here this morning. Got your name on it."

"Not mine. All my things got here last week."

"Now, Virginia ... " She didn't have to turn to know that the voice slithering from the doorway belonged to Miss Blanchard, head nurse at the Autumn Valley Retirement Residence. Despite the condescending tone, Miss Blanchard crackled into the room, seeming to move independently of her starched-armour uniform. "If the name on the address label is yours, then it must belong to you. Isn't that right?" The nurse shoved the corners of her wide mouth into a familiar smirk and without waiting for an answer, motioned for the helpers to open the crate.

After some tugging of nails and splintering of wood, the old men withdrew a large oil painting. Virginia leaned forward and even squinted but couldn't see anything familiar. The soft-hued farm scene featured a young girl, a small white dog and a farmhouse.

"My, what a pretty picture," oozed Miss Blanchard, glancing briefly at the canvas. "I want it hung over the dresser tomorrow morning." Her command decision followed the helpers into the hall.

"Forget it, Blanchard," Virginia barked. "That canvas goes back to wherever it came from. I told you all my stuff they were 'kind enough' to let me keep is already here in my cage."

"Now, Virginia." The nurse's professional demeanour settled over the woman like a shroud. "Remember what your son said. You often forget things. A lot of things."

Straightening uneasily in her chair, Virginia turned again toward the painting. She felt the nurse start to move toward the bathroom, bent on her daily efforts to sanitize and control her own universe, then hesitate.

"All your things are very nice," she said, running her fingers along the polished arm of Virginia's favorite French chair. "We don't always see such nice things here." The nurse turned her appraising eyes back to the canvas. "That painting must have cost a lot. It's so fine."

Virginia smiled softly, then looked at the nurse's face. "It's crap. It's crap and it's not mine." With satisfaction she watched the younger woman's lips stretch tersely, underlining the rapier-point of her nose.

The old woman knew she had hit home when Miss Blanchard, fending off the blow to her artistic integrity, carefully thrust the sword. "But you're not sure of that." She gazed steadily at Virginia for a moment. "Never mind, at your age, we all expect to become a little uncertain, don't we?"

"For God's sake, don't you think I know my own property? I was a painter myself, and a damn good one." Virginia flung the announcement in the direction of the bathroom and turned to squint at the painting. But as she peered, it did seem to have a familiar look. Not a look, a feeling. Something she'd definitely known before. She felt worry lines begin to creep across her brow.

Meanwhile, the nurse's voice rail-roaded into the room. "Now, look here, Virginia, you've forgotten to put the cap back on the toothpaste again, and I reminded you just yesterday."

Virginia's thoughts scattered. She had difficulty collecting the pieces. "What? Oh ... the toothpaste ... I'm sorry, I ... " For a moment, the painting, the pink roses on the bedspread, the window casement all blurred into a waving background. What was it she was trying to remember? Something about a dog ...

"Well, 'sorry' doesn't neaten our quarters, does it?" Blanchard said. The white armour swivelled from the bathroom to the door, then clanked to face her. "The help are coming tomorrow to hang your picture." The woman's stare bored into Virginia's confusion. "Maybe you painted it yourself ... a long time ago ... only now you can't ... Oh, well. Good night, Virginia."

Motionless, the old woman watched the nurse's temporary retreat. Her hands over her ears, she tried to press away the sound of rubber heels thumping relentlessly down the darkening hall.

One week later, Virginia lay in bed, her body making barely a ripple under the smooth covers. She was aware of her gaze moving like a dust moat in a shaft of light, aimlessly drifting across the counterpane, by the empty wheelchair, finally coming to rest on the painting. She squinted with sudden attention. Why did it now seem familiar, as though she had owned it all her life? Maybe Blanchard was right, maybe ... Her eyes strained as she traced the contours of the white clapboard farmhouse. Of course. It was like her grandfather's place in the country. Summer. Her childhood was a mosaic of summers with the whole family laughing and free. Even now she could feel the sun-warmed mud squishing through her newly bared toes after a sudden silvery rain. If one could only lift the door-latch today ... Saddened by an inexplicable wave of exclusion, her mind started to push against the painting's static figures, the image frozen in another time. Her fragile body stiff and contorted with effort, she began at last to feel the lines of the tall trees, of the long grasses, softening. Swaying. Beckoning.

"Virginia!" That was Mother calling me, her voice tinkling past our rose-heavy wall trellis, right through the low, spreading branches of our old crabapple tree. And there I was, perched on the sturdiest limb, munching on fresh-baked chocolate cookies I'd sneaked out of the kitchen. I was a wiry eight-year-old, tow-headed and stubborn as a mule. Mother tried to keep me out of the tree—she thought I'd break an arm or something—but I liked to go there to be alone and watch the shifting colors of the leaves as the wind tipped them this way and that. Then I'd go inside and draw them the way I remembered. I was always drawing. Cassandra, my dog, would sit at the bottom of the tree and wait for me, her nose twitching, filling her little lungs with the soft spring air. The apples from that tree were so tart and good. Mother made them into jelly and …

"Virginia?"

"Oh, Mama, don't make me come down."

"What?" Miss Langer, the home's hearty, round-faced crafts teacher, stepped cautiously over the threshold, but Virginia's disoriented glance halted her approach. The old woman's eyes narrowed suspiciously. Here she was again, she thought, always trying to conscript as many infirm bodies as possible to work on that woven monstrosity she calls 'our Spring project'. Who else would make a floor mat in neon orange and puke green?

"I do not weave," muttered Virginia before Miss Langer could issue the daily invitation. "Neither do I spin." But her voice sounded hollow and far away. She turned her face to the wall again, hearing Miss Langer's perplexed sigh as the door clicked behind her.

Ten minutes later, Virginia heard the swish of an opening door and felt a breeze brush by her still-averted cheek. Like a bird's wing, she thought, idly. Like a bird's wing in an apple tree.

Miss Blanchard tip-toed across the room. Virginia felt her body become part of the bed, the covers, the walls. Briefly, she fluttered against the painting, but she was too weak to soften its contours. She could not enter.

"You're going to have a visitor tomorrow," whispered Miss Blanchard nervously. "Won't that be nice?"

She's getting worried, mused Virginia. Thinks I'll die on her. Her eyes glazed as the late afternoon sun flicked at them from the window. Well, for once, maybe we'll give the old battle-axe her way.

"You'll never guess who I am." The voice, chirping from the door behind her, pecked around the edges of her reverie. So the mysterious visitor had arrived. Well, she could wait. Virginia's whined complaints had been almost an afterthought when Miss Blanchard had bullied her into a dressing gown, smoothed the tangled strands of white hair and lifted her into the wheelchair. If she had cared enough, Virginia mused, she would have resented these nurturing attentions, but it was becoming increasingly comfortable to surrender her body bit by bit. As she would soon be surrendering her mind.

She turned the chair. A girl, perhaps twenty-one, with a mass of smoky curls floating aimlessly about her shoulders, was smiling out at her with the bland, uncomprehending eyes of youth.

"No," Virginia replied, "I won't guess who you are." She was surprised at her own vehemence, which seemed to go unnoticed.

The young woman grinned broadly as though presenting a gift. "I'm Virginia Shelton." The announcement hung in the air untouched as Virginia reassembled her thoughts. The girl giggled. "They call me Ginny. May I sit down?" Without waiting, she dropped into the French chair. Virginia watched the iridescent flash of pink nail enamel against baby blue cashmere as the girl slid easily out of her sweater. Against her will, Virginia's eyes dropped to the wrinkled hand lying among the folds of her robe—and then she was seeing, at the bottom of a dishevelled dresser drawer, a small red bottle. "Try SHORT FUSE for Long Nails," the advertisement had said. She smiled. It had been her favorite when she was sixteen. Quickly, she looked back at the girl, who had settled in, seemingly to appraise the contents of the room.

Was it her imagination, thought Virginia, or had this stranger's eyes rested too long on her new painting?

"This is a really nice room," the young woman was saying. "With your own furniture and everything." The scrutinizing glance now seemed to avoid the entire wall where the painting hung. "My grandmother was in a place like this. She really liked it." The pink fingernails plucked nervously at a gold button. "They brought her meals and helped her dress and took her for walks in the park. It was great. She didn't have to do a single thing for herself."

"Was she paralyzed?" Virginia felt the corners of her mouth twitch downward.

"Oh, no. She was just fine."

The old woman allowed a wedge of silence to slice between them. Without moving, she stared at the girl until Ginny rose uneasily.

"So we share a name, do we?" Virginia said, finally. "And is that why you've come, to see what happens to Virginia Sheltons when they are too old and venerable to be known as 'Ginny'?"

The girl seemed not to have heard. She stood in front of the painting. "This scene is really pretty," Ginny said quietly. "Last month I bought a picture just like it from a place in New Orleans. They said they'd send it to me, but it never came."

Virginia found the sudden dampness of her palms unpleasant. She tried to steady them, to dry them on the chenille robe.

"I feel really bad, but I have to tell you something," Ginny was saying. She turned, the smoky tendrils of her hair blending into the painting in a twisting swirl of curls, leaves and darkening clouds. "You see, because our names are the same, there was a mistake." The girl seemed to be explaining something. Virginia tried to concentrate. "Ms. Shelton, this picture belongs to me." Ginny was staring at her, a little worry line darting between her eyebrows. "I'm sorry, but you'll have to give it up."

Fifty-nine. Yes, there had been exactly fifty-nine gleaming acrylic tiles lining the ceiling of her hospital room. Those ten days spent flat on her back, the fractured hip imprisoned in its cast, the insistent sound of clanking gurney wheels and the ascetically sterile smells of a world disinfected had made her seem a hostage drawn from the warm womb of her life, her back now pressed against the chilling steel of an alien existence.

The cast was removed and she had sat up in bed, watching shadows darken across his face, her friend since grammar school, Doug Stevens— Dr. Doug Stevens. She had watched him painfully peel away his fear for her, taking refuge in the safe folds of medical jargon.

She would never walk again unaided.

Watching his lips move, passing sentence, she looked at the way his pewter hair hung in tired threads across the valleys of his forehead. One breathless day in early June, when she was eighteen, a classroom ceiling fan had teased his auburn hair, making it restless and moving and infinitely desirable. Her fingers had ached for him.

Silently, he removed his glasses and wiped them. "We gain, then we lose throughout our lives, Virginia." She remembered his nearing retirement. How could a little boy in the third grade retire? Now, with careful concentration, she watched him replace the glasses and adjust them. "Eventually—gracefully—we must let others help us," he was saying. "We must give it up."

And then, blessedly, she was home. Blanketed in the protective nest of her own living-room, she had, with her eyes, caressed each familiar object, many older than she. The damask-covered Queen Anne sofa, her mother's, her grandmother's, the crystal hurricane lamps, even the old chewed-on needlepoint pillow, mauled and adored by Cassandra's progeny. And her paintings.

She had lost. But not all.

"Mrs. Shelton? Are you OK?" Ginny was asking. So she had worried this heedless child, whose anxious face floated toward her. Good. "It's just that my father gave me that picture for my new condo and the sky colour exactly matches this adorable little love-seat I bought. Otherwise, you could keep the old thing. I really don't like farms anyway."

Virginia heard her voice slap out at the girl. "You may not have my painting!"

"What? They sent it to you by mistake from the gallery," Ginny was speaking slowly, loud. "Because of our names. Don't you see?"

Virginia felt her hands grip the wheelchair, their distorted knuckles paling. "The mistake is yours." Old lips stretched into a defiant line. "I brought that painting here from my home."

Cassandra seemed to give a little whimper. Virginia comforted the dog with her eyes. "I had many paintings there, all fine. But this," she whispered, "this was my favorite."

She felt herself pushing the wheelchair toward the window, toward the manicured lawns beyond, toward the blossoming trees and old homes, protecting.

"But Mom," her son had pleaded, perched uneasily on the edge of her chintz-covered wing chair, "I'm scared for you all the time. And so is Jane. What if you should fall again? That walker's no help." Virginia had watched his foot tap nervously against the carved chair leg. She and his father had brought that chair from England. As a small boy, her son had crouched between its sheltering wings, shot 'canons' from its rampart-arms, and they all called it 'Richard's Fort'. She reached for his hand, trying to bridge the years. "You must understand, Richard, this is my home, your father's home, for fifty years. This house is ..."

"I know just how you feel, Mom. It's rough. But Dad's dead and you can take most of the stuff with you. Well, some of it. You just can't handle things anymore. Let us take care of you. You've got to give it up, Mom. We worry."

With a start, Virginia felt Ginny's words, like sprayed bullets, grazing her reverie.

"You're not telling the truth, Ms. Shelton! You know it's my picture!"

Virginia stared at the girl. Even now she knew surrender was settling over her like a drugged sleep. Exhausted, she watched the girl's mouth move, strongly, passionately.

"Why don't you just give it up? Relax, enjoy life the way my grandmother did."

The laughing voices of children in the school playground across the street from the Autumn Valley Retirement Residence rose like bouncing clowns, springing higher and higher from myriad throaty trampolines. As Virginia looked down, even through her malaise she felt she could almost catch some of the stronger tones, which somersaulted, through the open window, landing in a giggling heap in her lap. One high-pitched little girl sound tumbled in her hair and rolled across her face, easing the numbness.

Below her, a young mother pushed a carriage whose occupant squirmed happily, even gleefully. Helpless, nurtured, controlled. Virginia remembered how effortless it had been to have Blanchard lift her and dress her that very morning. Two months ago, when Doug had released her from the hospital, Richard had driven her home. Someone else to watch the traffic lights, out-guess other motorists, be responsible. She had hated the knowledge that she would never drive again, but wasn't it easier? To lean. Pushed around in a baby carriage, pushed around in a wheelchair. What was the difference?

The drone of Ginny's continuing barrage began to bee-sting her consciousness. She shifted uncomfortably. The girl was at her again. Virginia felt queasy. Where was Blanchard, she whimpered to herself. Why didn't they protect old, sick people from…

" … and not make trouble!" Ginny was saying. Virginia noticed the pink fingernails extending beyond the upturned palms. The girl was pleading. "You can go to those classes they have for old people. Don't you crochet, or something? Anyway, they'll do it for you."

Do it for me?

Eyes narrowed, Virginia began to grow taller in her chair. The sickness in her stomach started to subside. Ginny was going on, "Stop, Ms. Shelton. Stop trying to be a … a … " The old woman's hand seemed somehow disembodied as it tightened on the chair's arm.

"A what, Ginny?" Virginia breathed. "A what?"

"A … person!"

The words exploded into the air. "Oh, I'm so sorry—I didn't mean …" Virginia stared at the girl silently. Now it was easy. She turned the chair around and looked at the painting. Her spine tingled as old vertebrae stretched upward. For a moment, she studied the cottage, the trees, the animal—all static and strange.

"Of course the painting is yours," she said finally. "I have no need for it."

The room suddenly seemed uncomfortably filled with gratitude. "Oh, Ms. Shelton, thank you! And I'm so sorry I said ... Can I at least help you?"

Virginia wheeled her chair to the night table and withdrew from its drawer a dog-eared catalogue. She gently smoothed its yellow cover, then smiled up at the girl. Instinctively, she patted the bed. "Come here, please," she requested, noticing with surprise a long abandoned lilt in her voice. "I want you to do something for me."

The next afternoon, the image in the mirror returned her saucy wink as Virginia adjusted the rose that sprouted from over her left ear. Her gaze slid to the large vase of flowers on the dresser. "My daughter sings your praises and I join her. Many thanks from both Ginny and me. Ralph Shelton," read the accompanying card. Virginia was pleased to note that when she started to hum, her voice was, as always, off key. My old self again, she thought with satisfaction.

"What beautiful roses!" exclaimed Miss Blanchard, stepping into the room. Strange, thought Virginia, she's losing her abrasiveness. Wonder if she knows. "Did your son send them?" the nurse asked.

"No," whispered Virginia, tenderly caressing the flowers with her gaze, "My lover."

"Your ... oh ... I didn't think you ... " Blanchard's voice trailed away in confusion. Virginia's blue eyes twinkled mischievously. Would she ever be able to resist the challenge of a literal mind?

Without further questions, Nurse Blanchard plunked a large cardboard carton down on the bed. "That young girl, Ginny, left this box this morning. She doesn't waste time." Virginia stared silently at the box for a moment. "She said it was for you," said Blanchard impatiently.

"It's Pandora's," replied Virginia quietly.

Blanchard frowned at the label. "Nope. Got your name on it."

After arranging the sketch-pads, brushes, and paints on a side table, Virginia looked for the first time at the space where the painting had hung. It seemed empty. She blinked moistly, washing away images, which, for a moment, seemed burned into the wall.

"What are you going to put up there?" Blanchard's question seeped through her mind's mist.

Virginia blinked sharply, then fired the younger woman a look. "A painting, of course. My own, this time." She picked up a sketch-pad and pencil from the table and started to draw, snorting in disgust at old fingers which resumed too slowly their life's purpose. But soon the drawing was recognizable. "The dog in that other painting never did really look like mine," she muttered. "Too small. Cassandra was taller and her tail had a kind of bushiness to it ... "

Virginia felt Blanchard move closer, her breath warming the artist's ear.

"You know," Blanchard said finally, "I knew that picture didn't belong to you the minute I saw it. Not a bit like something you'd have."

The pencil stopped mid-stroke. With great deliberation, Virginia leaned back in her chair and stared frostily up at the nurse. Suddenly, the corners of her mouth twitched upward. "Blanchard," she proclaimed, "you're the biggest liar I ever met." Rewarded by the nurse's startled glance, she continued. "But you know something, I'm beginning to like you." She turned back to the pad. "Must be getting senile."

Through her thin shoulders, Virginia could feel Blanchard's wry smile. "I told you that all along," the nurse growled quietly. Virginia felt stubby fingers lightly brush her bent white head. Abruptly, Blanchard withdrew the hand and marched into the hall. Still sketching, Virginia chuckled softly. "Maybe there's hope for her yet," she informed an emerging Cassandra.

With a final flourish, she held up the pad for appraisal. After a moment, the corners of her eyes crinkled with satisfaction. As she carefully placed the pad and pencil on the table, she became aware of other eyes, peering. A slight motion from across the room flicked at her attention and she raised her gaze to the mirror, where, with a start, she saw that someone else was occupying her space. A young woman with blond hair and challenging blue eyes. Virginia blinked, but the apparition remained fixed, permanent. She smiled a welcome. She thought of the sketch.

"Not bad," she whispered to the young Virginia. "Not bad. For a beginning."

TRUDY SCOTT IS a geologist by profession and spent 22 years managing the publishing of scientific reports and maps for the Ontario government. Upon her early retirement in 1988 she started to devote all her time to writing fiction. She has had seven short crime stories published in Canadian Authors Association Anthologies, one in *SISTERS IN CRIME* Anthology in Germany, and articles in various publications. Ten completed novels and numerous short stories in a variety of genres are awaiting far-sighted publishers. She has been recently widowed; her husband, James VanEvery Scott, wrote science fiction stories and Trudy is continuing his series under his name.

Casino • Trudy Scott

Missy would have bounced on the seat if Hilda hadn't been sitting beside her in grim silence.

The little lady had to hold back the giggles that were trying to force their way out her closely held lips. Hoist on her own petard. Hoist on her own petard.

That described Hilda exactly. She had been claiming in a loud voice for months that everyone should support the efforts at entertainment the committee provided. Well ... she had been unable to refuse this bus trip to the new casino opened up north. Hoist on her own petard. Served her right.

Hilda had been speaking out against gambling all her life and now she was on her way to a casino. Missy was ecstatic; she had been wanting to go to a casino ever since the first one had opened a couple of years before, but Hilda ruled her with an iron hand, without the softening of the velvet glove to be sure; she had for years. In fact all her siblings thought they had the right to order her life.

Her family had voted, when their father had suffered his first stroke that Missy, youngest of the family and the only one unmarried, should give up her schooling and look after the parents. She had not been given veto rights and the force of family opinion had been enough to make her toe the line.

From eighteen to sixty-five was really more line toeing than Missy considered fair. Her only romance had failed because he had to look after his parents and refused to take on Missy's as well and Missy's family pressure made leaving the older people unthinkable. If she had it to do over, she would have gone. Who would have thought that her father would live into his late nineties; changed from a kindly parent into a tyrant who ruled both Missy and her meek mother? The mother had been lucky, she had died thirty years before but Missy was too healthy to die.

As soon as the old man died, Hilda, recently widowed, had swept in and moved Missy into her apartment. From one prison to another; Missy had hoped she would be left alone finally but the family brought pressure on her again. Poor, poor Hilda so lonely and recently widowed. As far as Missy could tell Hilda hadn't even noticed her husband's death; why should she when she never paid any attention to him when he was alive?

Hilda demanded Missy's old age pension to pay for her keep; she didn't know about the small cheque Missy received from the grocery store she had clerked in those many long years. Missy took great care to keep it from her. She had the cheque sent to an accommodation address near the library; so far it had worked well and she had her gambling money tucked into a small pocket in the handbag she clutched to her chest.

Missy had been reading up on the different games and thought that she would like Blackjack; it sounded fun. But it wouldn't be like breaking the bank at Monte Carlo; as soon as a table lost some fairly small amount it closed so no one could continue a good luck run. You were allowed greater leeway if you were on a losing streak.

The bus moved quickly through the flat landscape; the day was dismal, no sun but no rain either, just miserable and raw. Missy didn't care, she was going to enjoy herself, she planned to lose Hilda the very first opportunity and hoped it would be crowded.

It was, very crowded; and Hilda wanted to eat immediately. The casino offered free lunch to bus loads so that they would feel more like gambling, no doubt. Hilda claimed that neither of them was going to gamble but Missy had other ideas although she wisely didn't disagree with her sister.

They ate the buffet luncheon and before they left their table the crowd was lined up for fifty feet or more. They were lucky they had eaten early.

"We will just wander around now that we have eaten; make sure you stay right beside me, you don't want to get lost do you?"

Missy felt like yelling "Yes, yes, I want to get lost far away from you and my whole selfish family." But she didn't have the nerve to do it so she just looked as if she didn't quite hear what Hilda was saying and as soon as her sister turned her head Missy slipped between people standing behind the group playing the slot machines.

Missy had pretended to be interested in the slot machines and acted as if she would be frightened to play any of the card games. Hilda evidently didn't know that she had played almost all the card games ever invented with her stricken father; it was all he could comfortably do. Sometimes they even played poker for money and Missy always won. That made her parent very angry, so they didn't play that game very often.

Missy was small and drably clothed so that she got lost very quickly in any group of people. She had taken note of the position of the Blackjack tables when they had first entered and worked her way to them quickly. She had to find a five dollar table or she wouldn't have enough money to play very long unless she was lucky.

The signs on the tables were easy to read and she quickly found the right priced table but all the seats were filled, as were the seats at the surrounding tables. Well, she would be patient and try to guess who would give up first and then slide into their vacated seat. She stood behind a woman who appeared to be losing the small pile of chips she had in front of her. Missy was right, the woman gave up in another half-hour and Missy took over the empty spot.

She handed the dealer fifty dollars and asked for five dollar chips; she cuddled the ten chips in her hand and then gingerly placed one in the correct betting spot; the dealer passed out one card to each player twice and one man had Blackjack; the dealer paid him three to two and swept away his cards. He then signaled each player to see if they wanted additional cards; Missy watched closely so that she would use the correct gestures. Tap the table if you wanted a card and show a clean palm to the dealer if you didn't.

Missy only had fourteen so she signaled for a card, which was an ace, so naturally she counted it as a one not eleven. She tapped the table again and was thrilled to get a six. She had twenty-one and as long as the dealer didn't get twenty-one with his cards she had won. Her eyes sparkled as she waited.

The dealer paid out to all winners, his cards had added up to twenty-two; and he swept the losers' chips and the cards back to his side of the table.

Although Missy was caught up in the game she had time to take note of all the other players and the observers who crowded against the seated players. She also casually checked the adjacent tables to see how they were going. This was fun.

The bus wasn't to leave for another three hours so Missy settled down to play in earnest. She won often enough that she never had to augment her original stake; she was pleased by that.

She never took long to make up her mind on whether or not she wanted additional cards dealt to her so she had plenty of time to look at the mixed group around her table. The older man standing behind the good-looking blonde was surreptitiously petting her shoulder but the blonde either didn't notice or didn't care. More men than women were playing and kibitzing but all were quiet. It was a serious game; after all it was for money.

Missy was winning but not much, large wins were impossible at a five-dollar table; oh to be able to play at the five hundred table like the one to the left of them. All those players grim-faced; it was much worse to lose the larger amount but then the winnings were so much better. Missy tried to calculate how much she would have won if each of the bets had been five hundred but it was beyond her at the moment. On the way home she would have plenty of time for that mental arithmetic.

Hilda loomed behind Missy, "What are you doing? You are not supposed to gamble." And then it dawned on her, "Where did you get the chips? Did you steal from the housekeeping money?"

Missy was furious, to accuse her of stealing, just like Hilda.

"No I didn't and please leave, you are interrupting play and disturbing all these other people." Before Hilda could demand that she accompany her elsewhere, Missy added. "I'm staying here until the bus goes so you leave me alone." She turned back to the waiting dealer.

Hilda's mouth gaped, never had she expected the meek Missy to turn on her like that. How dare she?

"Everyone placed their bets?" The dealer called and started laying out the cards in front of each player.

Hilda shook Missy's arm and Missy tore it out of her grasp; as the irate older woman started to harangue her the others at the table told her to shut up and leave. Hilda had never been spoken to in that tone in her life. She backed off trembling. Wait until she got her crazy sister back in their apartment. She had always said gambling was a sin, look what it had done to little Missy in only an hour or two, dreadful, dreadful, she might never be the same again. Hilda depended on the service she received from Missy; she needed someone to order about now her husband had the nerve to die on her. You couldn't count on anyone any more, not on anyone.

She had thought that Missy had been tamed sufficiently by their father but evidently not. Well she'd see to it when they left this devil's den.

Hilda decided on a cup of coffee but all the eating places were still crowded; disgraceful; she wanted coffee not alcohol but alcohol was the only beverage available at the bar. If you wanted a soft drink you had to be playing the slot machines or the tables; they wouldn't take money at the bar but they would give it to her free if she would gamble. She'd just have to go thirsty. Hilda looked impatiently at her watch, would this day never end?

Missy thought that getting rid of Hilda had been easy. She would have to try it back home and insist on being able to live alone; she seemed to be lucky at Blackjack, perhaps she should move near the casino and augment her funds that way. It was one way of keeping her family away from her.

The man next to Missy suddenly gasped, his eyes opened wide and he shuddered before he slumped sideways taking the slight Missy to the floor with him. She struggled to get away from him but he was a dead weight.

She found out, once the spectators managed to get her free of his body, that he was truly dead. Had it been a heart attack?

The management rushed up and had security remove the still form to one of the offices. Missy straightened her rumpled dress thinking that moving the body was a no-no.

It didn't seem right to go on playing but then again, why was it wrong? The management would prefer that they go on gambling but most of her table-mates wandered off, some joining another table and others looking for the bar.

After picking up her chips Missy stood around feeling useless, at this time of day, this was the only five-dollar table and she couldn't afford to play any higher could she? She surreptitiously counted her winnings; she had won more than one hundred dollars; maybe she could play at the ten-dollar table for a little while, after all she hadn't known the man seated beside her.

While she was considering her next move a discreet voice asked her to step into the office for a moment? She looked up startled at the tuxedo-clad young man.

"Why? I don't want anything from the office. What's wrong?'

As she was standing undecided Hilda grabbed her arm; she shook her off again and thought that she would go with the polite young man.

"Where are you going? Come away, the bus will be here shortly and you must visit the washroom."

Missy frowned at her sister, what made her think that Missy had to be told when to go to the washroom? Really, Hilda was ridiculous, simply ridiculous.

"You did say I was wanted in the office, didn't you? Well come along, what are we waiting for. I'll see you on the bus Hilda but don't wait for me. If you want to go to the washroom, don't let me stop you. Come along, young man, where is that office of yours?"

"You can't go off with a strange man, Missy, come back."

"Really Hilda, you are absurd." Missy sniffed and followed the tuxedoed back across the floor.

They entered a crowded room and the guard on the door turned back a determined Hilda. The door closed, cutting off her sister's shrill voice berating the uncaring sentry.

Missy looked around with interest, were they big gamblers like they had in Las Vegas? Or just the home-grown variety? She had never really wondered about that before, she had been so excited at getting a chance to visit a casino without actually running away to do it; imagine having to plan to run off at 69 to get away from a bossy sister.

A paunchy man smoking a black cigar snarled; "How did you become acquainted with Sammy the Mark? You're a little old for his usual broad. Well speak up! Speak up!"

"I don't know what you are talking about and I object to your tone of voice, please change it." Missy was not about to put up with being hectored by a complete stranger; she had put up with a thousand years of family browbeating it seemed, but she refused to give in to this treatment by a big tyrant who was so discourteous as to blow smoke at her. She coughed in protest but it made no difference.

"When Mr. Francis asks you a question you answer nice and polite, you hear me?" A scar-faced tough growled at her.

"Indeed, and who is Mr. Francis when he is at home, Mr. Mob?" Good Heavens at her age Missy wasn't afraid of TV villains, no way.

"Mr. Francis runs this joint, you understand?" The thug, regardless of his tuxedo, he was just a cheap punk to Missy. He appeared shocked at her levity.

"So what?" Missy was enjoying herself; these people didn't scare her after putting up with her miserable father for over fifty years. And Hilda could out-snarl the best of them; they'd have to do better than this to worry Missy. She laughed out loud at her thoughts and the men in the office gasped at her defiance.

A little old lady facing down a Don; what was the world coming to?

"Answer me, you old filly." She guessed 'filly' was better than 'bitch' but she didn't like the paunchy man's tone one bit.

"Word your question in a way I can understand and I'll think about it. Was Sammy the Mark the man who fell on me? Well? You answer me for a change." She grinned at their nonplussed faces; they appeared to be use to yes-women as well as yes-men.

"Ya. He was killed by something injected into his back; you were next to him and could have done it. Who paid you? Come on talk or you'll be sorry." The leader waved to his tough to use physical force on the fragile body in front of him,

"Don't you touch me, you ruffian, I have a bad heart," she lied, "and I'm liable to die on your hands, you wouldn't like that, would you?"

She continued, "Two bodies in one day at your bountiful casino would make even sympathetic police suspicious. So keep your hands to yourself, you big brave bully boy." She snapped her fingers at them. She had never had so much fun in her whole long life. "Tell me what you know or suspect and I may answer you or then again, I may not. But I won't, if you don't cooperate."

The boss's eyes bulged; who was this old broad? Maybe she belonged to the Family, she sounded as if she did. Maybe she was some brother Don's mother or aunt or some close relative. Easy does it, Guglielmo Francicetti, some old broads have powerful connections, don't make any mistake about this.

He waved away his hireling. Maybe he should deal with the old dame as if she was someone important? It wouldn't hurt. He didn't want any bad publicity interfering with this very successful venture.

"Sammy the Mark was on the run from some people that he had cheated many miles away. We didn't expect him to land here and we would have warned him off as soon as one of my people had recognized him. But someone stuck a needle into him first. What do you know about it? Please help us if you can. We'll have to call the cops within a very little while and if we can hand over the murderer along with the victim that will quiet the furore. Be a nice old broad. Hmm?"

She liked him even less, now that he was being conciliating but the bus would be leaving soon and she had better be on it or Hilda would burst. "I didn't see anyone do anything to him but a short slim man, who looked like a teenager except he had wrinkles, stood behind him just before he took a header off his chair. The man had a good tan and was dressed in designer clothes. And oh, yes, he had one blue eye and one hazel. Know him?"

The boss looked around at his staff and two of them nodded their heads. One burst out with, "That's Johnny l'Infanti. Bruno's hit man. He never uses a gun and no one pays any attention to him 'cause he looks like a kid, until you see him real close."

The scarred tough dashed out the door and made a beeline for the parking lot, he hailed a cruising security car and they sped away.

"He'll be easy to catch, boss. He won't expect us to be after him so fast. The old dame has good eyes for her age."

"Not so much AGE, young fellow, you can over-do it."

Hilda pushed her way into the crowded room, past the startled guard who was busy looking after the rushing figure heading out the main doors.

"Come with me now, Missy, how dare you run away from me? You must be crazier than usual, come along."

The paunchy man took Hilda's arm in a strong grip, "Who the hell are you to be talking like that to this old broad, I mean lady?"

"I am her older sister and her guardian." Hilda told only partial truth, Missy had never needed a guardian and certainly didn't need one now.

"Why would a nice old dame like this need a guardian? She's bright as a new penny and has just solved a murder that was baffling the police." He could inflate the truth too and he needed this old bag to talk to the cops and get the casino off the hook. No one bothered with a solved crime, not like they had to question all these nice generous people losing money at all the machines and tables.

"You go away, old lady, and leave your sister to us. I'll see she gets home in my own limousine with my own chauffeur looking after her. Go on, shoo, don't keep the bus waiting. They got a schedule to keep and we will look after your sister real good. She's an important witness. She'll probably be home tonight but don't you worry about any little thing. She's very important to us and we wouldn't let anyone harm a hair of her head. See the lady out, Joseph. See she makes her bus and tell the driver this old girl is staying with us until after the police get here."

"Say good bye to your sister, Missy, that's your name isn't it? Missy what?" Mr. Francis was being affable now his problem was solved so easily. Hand the authorities the guilty man and everything is copecetic. Easy as rolling off a log if you knew what you were doing.

"No! My name is Caroline McCormick and I'll never answer to Missy again, a ridiculous name. Missy indeed." She sniffed.

"Missy, you can't stay with these rough men, you can't. It just isn't done. Come with me this instant, Missy." Hilda was almost wringing her hands in her despair and shock.

"Mr. Francis, please tell this woman that there is no Missy here any more, only Ms. Caroline McCormick." She drew herself up to her full five foot, one inch, "and she is perfectly willing to stay here with you until after the police get here." the new Caroline looked around arrogantly. "Get rid of this person, she doesn't even know my name?"

BARBARA RITSON'S love for writing ignited when she was in high school. She pursued a career as a software analyst for eleven years after graduating from Ryerson Polytechnic University. Retiring in 1994 after the birth of her third daughter, she brushed off her love of writing and began a new chapter in her life. Her writing credits include both creative fiction and non-fiction as well as numerous inspirational articles published in national religious magazines. She currently writes monthly for a national woman's magazine. This is her second contribution to *Wordscape*.

The Knocking • Barbara Ritson

"Gargie, Pargie, puddin' n' pie," Otto teased as he lobbed the red hairpin over George's head to George's older brother, Walt.

"Kiss the girls and made 'em cry," Walt continued the children's taunt, as he tossed the coveted hair clip back to Otto. George lunged for the flying pin only to end up in a heap in the muddy blueberry patch.

"Give it back, you foul-smellin' codfish!" George yelled in the loudest twelve-year-old voice he could muster. "Right now, I tells ya, or you'll be sorry the day yer were born, byes!"

Otto and Walt stopped their banter to assume an 'I'm shaking in my thigh rubbers,' pose when they heard their father's voice behind them.

"Give George back his hair barrette," Father said. "Knock off the teasin'. Olive's a good girl and if George takes a fancy to her then leave them alone. Let's walk up to see how Uncle Josiah is getting on with his boat."

Frank Hicks started down the path toward the ocean, stooped to pluck a couple blueberries and tossed them in his mouth. The three brothers followed the leader, and fell in behind.

Otto tossed Olive's ruddy hued clip nonchalantly to George. OK, things were good again. George caught the pin and felt for its familiar ridges and curves. Still in one piece. He carefully placed it in his jersey pocket, and gave it a final pat before bending down to pick a blueberry in his path.

"That Jig's dinner was some good today, eh, Father?" Walt commented, as they neared the main road in the small out port of Musgrave Harbour, Newfoundland. He patted his slightly protruding belly. "I say Mother's apple dumplings are a little taste of heaven."

"Ah, Walt, grow up. All you ever talk about is food," George answered.

"Shut yer face, George," Walt said. "I don't need no little boy's advice. You tink yer so special."

Otto piped up. "Hey, Walt, cut the bye some slack. He is special. Who else do you know who's made so peculiar, his nose does the runnin' and his feet does the smellin'?"

Walt slapped Otto on his back as he broke into laughter. George, teased beyond what his twelve years could bear, took a run at Walt's shaking frame, rammed his head into his jiggling abdomen and toppled forward into the muddy road with Walt as his cushion.

"Knock it off, the three of ya!" Father yelled. "Git up and act like men." George and Walt picked themselves up and wiped the sticky mud off their clothes and hands. Father turned to George and placed a stern hand on George's shoulder. "Son, should I be sendin' ya 'ome to the women, or are you ready to behave like a man?"

Colour crept up the back of George's neck. "Yes, Father."

"Good enough, me son. Then let's keep goin'."

They crossed the dirt road to their fish stage where they dried and salted cod. The wood stage, supported by sturdy rafters and stilts, jutted out into the rocky harbour like a long wide dock. At high tide, Frank and his sons moored alongside the stage and unloaded their daily catch of fish. At fourteen and eighteen years of age, Otto and Walt helped in the family fishing business.

Frank checked on the drying cod that was laid out on the flake. The fishing season was almost over and the fish would soon be ready to load for its trip to St. John's for sale.

Back out on the road, the small party of Hicks men resumed their walk, patting Aunt Mariah's cow as she wandered looking for a good clump of grass. The main road in the nestled community hugged the shore and it was only a couple of minutes before they reached Uncle Josiah's stage. They stamped the muddy mess of yesterday's rainstorm off their boots as they headed toward the back end of the stage, just behind Uncle Josiah's workshop where he was building a new punt.

Eerie sounds pierced the salty air. The men hesitated. An anguished voice shouting for water echoed off the incoming tide. Heart wrenching wails and the sound of a man weeping sent the men bolting down Josiah's stage. They stopped dead. And witnessed Hell.

A bonfire roared, licking and leaping in its hunger for food. There was wood scattered about; the hull of a new boat sat in its cradle, and a small bench was toppled over, along with a dinner pot with its nourishment a sawdust stew on the wood floor.

Two men huddled over a moaning black figure that squirmed on the floor just in front of the fire. As George neared the commotion he saw the figure was a man, or what used to be a man. It was Uncle Josiah, and his legs were twitching, and he was moaning, but there wasn't much more. The smell of roasted flesh, boiled codfish, burnt wood and singed hair and clothes produced a sickly aroma. Flaky black skin hung from Uncle Jos' face, his silver hair and beard were gone, and what was left of his overalls was melted into his body, a shade of grey that matched the ocean on an angry day. George gagged, and stumbled back, bumping into his father.

"Oh, God, byes, it's some bad," the first of the two men stammered, wiping tears from his eyes. "We needs the nurse, fast."

Father looked at George. He didn't say a word, and George took off. Musgrave Harbour didn't have a doctor, but they had a good substitute: a nurse who stitched, delivered babies, and set broken bones.

It seemed seconds for George to sprint up the nurse's back garden, bang on the door, and get her attention. The round trip took only seven minutes with the nurse in hot pursuit of George.

"She's comin', she's comin'," George huffed out, as he descended on the now larger but quiet group. Uncle Josiah lied deathly silent and still. The fire crackled. The sun's rays, lengthening with the day, spread across the wood-shop roof, casting a shadow over Josiah's burned body. The tide continued its incoming spirited flow. Death hung in the air.

The nurse gingerly knelt down over Uncle Jos' body and hesitated. A pulse was needed. But where? She grimaced when she touched his left wrist and grey skin flaked off into her palm. His muscle, spongy in texture, met her fingertips on her next touch.

She stood back up. "There's nothin' there, byes. He's gone." A catch in her voice brought a lump to George's young throat.

Soft murmurs drifted through the crowd of men.

"What's we gonna do?" one asked.

Father turned to Walt and Otto, who watched from the gathered shadows.

"Fetch Ol' Nance and the wagon, me sons. And grab the shovels." Frank then turned to Uncle Sammy who shuffled his feet by the dying fire.

"Sammy, we needs a casket. Do you gots one?"

"Aye, but we needs to lay 'im out, and have a wake. It's the proper ting to do, bye."

"He's no good to lay out, me son. I say we just takes 'im and puts 'im to rest today."

Murmurs of 'Proper ting, proper ting' and 'Poor bye, some bad I say' moved through the crowd.

Ol' Uncle Sammy headed down the flake, and called after his sons who had congregated with the crowd.

George, the lump in his throat grown gum-ball size, fought hot tears. Be a man. Be a man. He slowly moved away from Uncle Josiah's charred body, and listened to the town's men as they recounted the grisly event.

"Gasoline? Why would 'e use gasoline?" one fellow asked.

"I don't know, bye, but the can was still in his hand," another offered. "I heard one buddy say that Uncle Sammy was 'ere with 'im when it happened and he had to put 'im out with his coat."

"Some sad, some sad. He's the last of his family," another said.

George tried to piece the horrific event together as best as his distraught brain would allow. He made a mental note to never use gasoline to stoke a fire. He turned the toppled stool upright, and sat down by the fire to warm himself. A wind off the water had turned the air chilly, and George had to fight not only an ever-growing lump in his throat but the threat of chattering teeth as well.

Walt and Otto, who had changed into work overalls and heavy boots, returned less than a half an hour later with the horse and wagon. The casket arrived right behind them.

A neighbour yelled down the stage to announce the arrival of the wagon and casket. Frank jumped, startled by the loud voice. He took a deep breath and started the walk to meet Uncle Sammy. The dull rhythmic shuffling of footsteps along the stage boards told everyone that the casket was coming.

George was still sitting by the fire. He thought how funny that the very fire that devoured Uncle Josiah was keeping the men warm as they stood watch over his ravaged body. The clunking sound of fresh wood as it was thrown onto the simmering embers sent shivers down George's hunched over frame.

George watched as the wood box was laid down about a foot from Uncle Jos.

Frank, a leader in the small community, crouched down at Uncle Josiah's feet and wrapped his hands around the old man's ankles. His fingers sunk into the fused mix of shrivelled flesh and overalls. Otto and Walt, looking worn, soberly squatted down on either side of Jos. Two other men joined the ensemble and they transferred the body into the waiting casket. They smoothed out and tucked in hanging shreds of overalls. Josiah's breast pocket was untouched in the incineration, and Frank reached in. He pulled out a wrinkled picture of Aunt Sarah. She smiled out at Frank. He placed the black and white treasure in Josiah's grey hands and folded them across his body. The gathered men removed their caps and bowed their heads. Frank offered a short prayer. Rough unpolished voices joined him as he sang Amazing Grace in his lilting Newfoundland brogue.

"Someone gots a hammer and nails?" Frank asked the men.

Solemnly, Walt and Otto lifted the rough lid of the casket into place. Father worked his way around the box, driving in nails. The clank of the hammer hitting its mark echoed through the stage bouncing off the advancing tide. The men watched silently as the lid was securely fastened to its grave counterpart.

It only took moments before Frank, Walt, Otto and Uncle Sammy gathered around the coffin, picked it up, and began their slow retreat away from the high sea, stepping toward the front of the stage and waiting wagon.

Ol' Nance whinnied and bobbed her head as she stomped in the dirt, eager to be underway. The men carried Josiah's casket around to the back of the wagon and began the awkward shift of weight from shoulder to wagon floor.

Young saucer eyes peeked from behind curtains in homes set back from the main road. The women of the houses were less shy and stood in the doorways.

"Father, I wants to come," George's voice was quiet beside his father. George and the other men had followed the procession and milled about talking quietly.

The casket met the wagon floor with a thump, and they slid it in.

Father turned to George.

"Do you tink you can handle this, me son?"

"Yes, Father."

With a nod of his head, Frank motioned his boys to board the wagon. He climbed aboard and took the reins. Walt, Otto, and George piled into the back with the casket.

Ol' Nance gave a snort, and the wagon lurched forward. They pulled away from the main road, heading inland to the ridge.

George pulled his knees up to his chest, in a vain attempt to keep warm against the increasing wind coming in off the sea. He was still in his good clothes crusted in mud from his earlier romp with Walt eons ago. The sun was starting its lazy descent, and he had to shield his eyes to look across the wagon at his brothers. Walt and Otto had pulled their caps low over their brows. He couldn't tell but they looked like they were sleeping.

George relaxed to the musical sounds that tugged at his ears. There was Ol' Nance's melodic clomp of her hooves against the dirt path. Waves crashed in the distance. The wind rustled the bushes by the side of the path and the front wagon wheel hit the underbelly of the carriage producing a light tapping sound.

Wait. That's odd, he thought. The wheel never made that noise before. George sat up a little, and listened more intently. Yes, there it was. Tap ... tap. No wait. As George brought his mind to full attention, he realized it was more of a knocking sound, muffled, heavy, and closer to him than the front wheel.

He sat up on his haunches from his spot against the side of the wagon, and strained to unravel the sound from all the others vying for his attention. He rested his hands on the casket to steady himself.

George glanced at his father. Father faced away, watching the road ahead of him. George looked at his brothers. They hadn't moved, other than their shoulders meeting, as their bodies jostled with the wagon's movement.

Knock ... knock ... The colour drained from George's face. He froze, still on his haunches, still gripping the casket. His dark eyes grew wide, in stark contrast to his ashen face. The sound's origin lay in front of him, under his hands.

Get over it. It's not what you're thinking. Uncle Josiah is dead. Be a man. Be a man.

But George was sure. The knocking was coming from inside the casket.

Walt stirred and readjusted his hat over his eyes to block out the sun's retreating rays.

"Do you hear that," George blurted out, startling all three men. "He's knocking ... the coffin ... it's coming from the coffin ... "

Walt and Otto pushed their hats up out of their eyes, and squinted at their agitated younger brother.

"What knocking? Who's knocking?" Walt asked.

"It's, it's, it's comin' from the casket. Uncle Jos is knockin'."

Otto hooted and slapped his knee. "Wait, wait, don't tell me, little brother," he started, "you mean to tell us that Uncle Josiah is alive and rapping at his coffin lid, asking to come out?"

George looked at his brothers in disbelief. Coming from Otto's lips the idea sounded ridiculous. And yet ...

His hands felt the casket shudder with each knock. "I'm tellin' ya, he's knockin'. Can't you hear that? Just listen."

"Yeah, and the ghost of ol' Uncle Jimmy is bangin' along with 'im," Otto said.

George grimaced. Uncle Jimmy drowned two years ago, and George saw his ghost walking in the harbour at low tide one misty night a few months back. He had mistakenly confided in his brothers. And put up with relentless teasing ever since.

"C'mon Garge, bye, he's dead. Yer hearin' tings," Walt offered.

Father heard George and Otto, and called back.

"Garge tinks Uncle Josiah has come back from the dead and wants out," Otto chortled.

Ruddy tones replaced the paleness of George's skin. "It's not like that, Father. I just hears knockin' and I tinks we should be lookin' inside, just to make sure everyting's OK."

Frank pulled back on Ol' Nance's reins. She stopped and he turned around. He leaned back into the wagon and placed his hand on the casket. Otto and Walt followed their father's lead and placed their hands on the wooden box as well. George's hand still grasped the rough surface.

Silence. Except for the distant roar of the ocean, and the wind rustling the grass by the roadside. Four pairs of dark eyes studied the casket lid. Nothing.

"Father, you gots to believe me," George said, "I heard the knockin', gentle like comin' from inside the box, and I put me hand on the lid and I felt it."

"Yer feelin' the road, you ol' sap," Otto interrupted. He added, "You wants to be treated like a man. Then act like one."

"Father, you gots to believe me," George implored for a second time. "We can't bury Uncle Jos if he's not dead. If there's even one chance, Father, we've gots to do the proper ting." George's eyes locked with his father's. Father kept his hand on the casket.

"There! Did you feel that? It's like a soft scratchin' now, weak scratchin'. You must feel that," George whispered.

"Father, maybe we should cut the lad some slack, and pry off the lid," Walt said. "Then we'll know for sure. You know what happened to ol' Uncle Isaac." The four men stared at each other. They knew. They found claw marks on the inside of his casket lid when they moved him to rest beside Aunt Dorah.

Father's hand moved over the casket's surface. He looked up and studied George's face, a mixture of the exuberance of youth, and the beginnings of wisdom that only comes from years working the sea.

"There! I tells ya, he's scratchin'," George choked. Clearing his throat, he called out, "Hello, are you in there?" and knocked on the lid.

"Yer not gonna believe this little sap are ya, Father?" Otto asked. "He'll keep us here all night, and we'll be digging up everybody else soon enough when he hears from them too."

"I don't feels anyting, me son," Father said. "And we gots to get on, or it'll be dark before we're done. I'm sorry bye, but Uncle Jos is dead. He's not knockin' and he's not scratchin'."

Father turned around and blew kisses to Ol' Nance. The wagon lurched ahead, and they finished their short journey to the town's cemetery.

Tears stung George's eyes but he didn't dare attempt to swipe at them for fear of being caught crying. Each time George felt the casket shiver, or heard scratching, he scratched in response.

They turned into the graveyard, and hopped out of the wagon, grabbing shovels and gloves. George stayed with the casket, listening for scratching, feeling for movement.

The four Hicks men gingerly lifted the casket down from the wagon, and carried it over to Uncle Josiah's family plot. Aunt Sarah's grave was still fresh, only six months old.

Father, Walt and Otto plunged their shovels into the rain-softened soil and dug the grave quickly.

George, with his heart lodged in his throat, squatted by the casket. He pressed his ear flush against the side. He could hear the chunking sound as the shovels hit the dirt. The ocean's roar and the rustling grass were still there. But no sound came from the casket.

"Hello," George's voice cracked against the casket wall. Silence. He knocked on the lid lightly. "Hello?" he pleaded. He looked up to make sure his father and brothers didn't hear him. Weak scratching brought him down against the casket again. George scratched back.

He was interrupted when his brothers squatted down with their father to pick up the casket.

"Father, I knows I hear scratchin'," George started. "'E's alive I tells ya. We can't bury him. We just can't."

Walt and Otto, tired from digging the grave, plopped down on the ground. No one spoke.

They listened. To the ocean. To the wind. To the silent wooden box.

"Father, listen when I knock," George said. He knocked. He scratched. He tapped. Nothing.

George, desperate to prove he was right, leaned up to the casket and with his voice cracking, called out "Hello?" Still silence.

"Garge, you saw Uncle Jos. You know he was some bad. He didn't live, bye." Father's words were little comfort to George. He stood up and paced behind Walt and Otto.

"Com'on, byes, let's get this done," Father declared. "We needs to get 'ome."

"Yeah, supper'll be spoiled fer sure," Walt agreed. "Mother's cookin' up cod tongues."

George watched as his father and brothers gathered up the casket and struggled to lower it into the grave. George shut his eyes tight, crossed his fingers, and wished the box would topple over jarring the lid off.

It didn't. His eyes still tightly closed, he eventually heard the sounds of shovels scooping and dirt thumping as it hit wood. He covered his ears. The thumping sounded like knocking.

The job was soon done. Walt and Otto patted down the dirt on the new grave with their boots.

As the troupe walked silently back to the wagon, Otto swung his arm across George's shoulder.

"C'mon ol' man, it'll be alright. Let's go 'ome."

They climbed aboard the wagon and Walt and Otto pulled their caps down over their eyes again. Father sang a tune to Ol' Nance.

George gathered his knees up to his chin and bowed his head. His hands were chilled and he tucked them under his arms to warm them. Coming back over the ridge, he looked up to see the wide expanse of the Atlantic that matched the sounds of its swells. The wind had died down. Ol' Nance's hooves clopped along the path. And there was no knocking. That sound was buried back up the road.

Be a man. Be a man. George decided he didn't like being a man. Men not only buried men, but they buried hearts too, including their own.

George fumbled to fit his hands into his pockets in an attempt to find warmth. What he found though, tucked in the folds of his woolen jersey, was a simple red hair clip. Grasping it in his fingers, his haggard thoughts drifted to a sweet girl and to the town dance next week. He thought of licorice sticks and gum-balls. And he thought of tomorrow when he'd be out on the sea again, bringing in a new catch of cod.

Tomorrow was a new day. Maybe he'd be a man tomorrow.

Once his responsibilities are over during a seven-day work week, BILL BELFONTAINE is most comfortable writing short stories and poetry. He is president and general manager of the Toronto and Central Branch of the Canadian Authors Association (CAA), a writers' group of over 260 members. He manages The Abbeyfield Companies Ltd., business consultants, who are a specialty book publisher producing five to seven author-controlled books a year. His creative writing life has been influenced by a love of people, self-employment as a marketing and business consultant, being an adjudicator for an Ontario Government Board for five years, a 19 year stint on Scarborough and Metropolitan Toronto councils, being an advertising agency account executive and serving as an RCAF pilot in his teenage years. He is listed in Who's Who in Ontario.

Tobias • Bill Belfontaine

I imagined that the old duffer I saw on Jarvis Street just above Queen had seen more of life than I would ever want to.

He was lean, slightly bent like a willow bough, and walked with a slight snap to his left leg. As I waited for the traffic light to change, I watched from the corner of my eye as he drifted across Jarvis street at an angle to traffic, causing cars of all shapes and sizes to dodge around him as they would an island in a midway fun ride. His slightly-imperfect step made me imagine a hidden prosthesis but that was not the reason my stare remained fixed on him. His chest was extended by thick straps pulling at his drawn-back shoulders, as if he was wearing medieval armour under his shabby coat.

I paused, dwelling on the strange weight of his burden, and my eyes followed him for too long before I decided to step off the curb to cross to the other side of the road. A yellow light joined the green, and below them an orange hand joined the challenge that prevented me from moving to the side of the road the was also the old man's destination.

My breath shortened when I realized the danger he was in and I couldn't shake off my apprehension at his imminent death as the traffic began its headlong careen around him once again as he moved to the curb lane. I then got the foolish notion that he would stop, face the irritation of the noon-hour motorists, jamb a middle finger to the sky in his defiance. Yet his pace remained unchecked as the closest car slowed, unable to get by after failing to inject it's chromium snout into the outer lane of barrelling traffic. It followed a yard from his slowly moving legs, horn beeping sharply to announce each step he took. Musical accompaniment or not, his pace was unchanged. If anything, the angle of his direction flattened out so that he appeared to be treading an invisible line in the middle of the lane that he would follow for the next five miles, as long as the beeping continued.

By now a small bevy of drunks, drawn to the beeping confusion and cursing drivers, moved off the retaining wall in front of the Salvation Army Lighthouse and wove their way to the curb edge on the opposite side of the road. The one with a crusty grey beard and shaggy overcoat shouted in a voice easily heard above the roar of traffic, "Hey, Tobi, get your gympie ass outta the goddamn traffic. Don'cha know these poor sonsabitches can't afford the time your wasting?" He was soundly ignored and the walk to Canada's Northland continued. "Hey! Let 'em get home so they can park their high-priced asses in front of their eighteen-foot TV set for the rest a' the day."

The walker turned and stepped sideways onto the newly-whitened traffic line which let me see the reason for his protruding chest. The backpack of a mountain hiker hung from his shoulders to just above his waist, the weight in the bottom caused it to droop so that the top angled steeply away from his shoulders. His frame came to full height as he faced them directly and raised his hand level with his forehead, his thumb and first two fingers extended and as if he was the most solemn of popes making the sign of the cross to a multitude. Greybeard roared, slapped his knee and bent over in a coughing fit as his companions couldn't wait to get into the act.

"Bless me, Father, for I have sinned," screamed one in a high falsetto and grabbed a handful of his fly.

"Me, too, Father, pray for me!" yelled another.

"Shay, me too, Father Gimp," slurred a third and hopped into a high-stepping rendition of an east-coast jig holding his baggy hips outward and bending back so far that his hat fell to the sidewalk.

The "Pope" remained impassive on his narrow white dais as the jammed up traffic flew by and left the street empty. The old man stared down his long patrician nose until they finished laughing and stood like panting dogs, tongues licking dried lips. "Hey, Father Gimp, how the hell's Mount Everest doin'? Why ain't yer friggin' Sherpa carryin' that sto-o-o-o-pid pack of yers?"

The message came clearly, "Don't bide your time on that, my children," his voice surprised me with its mellow, educated tone as if he'd recently hung up a teacher's gown at the best British university. "The Lord will soon have work for your idle hands. Be glad the Lord loves you, for I'm sure your mothers did not or you wouldn't be here blaspheming." Hoots of laughter filled the street as he turned, hupped the pack higher on his shoulders, and in three quick steps reached the curb and wended his way laboriously down the street.

"Ah, you're fulla shit like always, you goddamn phony," yelled Greybeard who turned with a scowl to his buddies then swung his upper body around, "Give my love to the friggin' Pope, *if* you ever see him again." His opponent's hand appeared in a peace sign and remained on high until he turned the corner of Queen Street and was gone.

I crossed the street and hurried past the four sinners fearful of being tapped 'for a little change for something to eat,' but they were too engrossed with their recent encounter to notice me.

"Silly bloody, shit," I overheard one fume, "who does he think he is? Loses his leg to a mountain then comes down here acting the high and mighty. I got a good mind to take a round outta the sonuvabitch."

This wasn't the kind of territory where I chose to stop, as I would have done in my own neighbourhood a few miles further north in a middle-class utopia, and ease my curiosity with a nearby stranger. I didn't need it satisfied, least of all from these unpredictable four. My five-foot-four physique couldn't help me to develop enough nerve to talk to four rounders like these, especially when I suspected they had their noses in a bottle not an hour before and would look to me as the benefactor of their next one.

I knew a seed of curiosity had been planted that, no matter how much I ignored it, would grow and keep growing until I harvested it, bad blooms and all. What was there about that little flick in his leg and the droop of the pack that caught with me? "Tobias," that name could come from anywhere in the world or even be totally unrelated to the person's birth name. In university, my roommate, because he loved to quote Hamlet, which we couldn't stand, carried the nickname, "Too-be" until he learned to love Chaucer more and became something else. Trying to track down a Tobias in downtown Toronto was not my game but my newspaper man's nose said there was a story in that man and I just couldn't let go until I knew more.

Was, or had Tobias been, a minister? No, not a minister, that's too Protestant for what I had seen. From the invectives hurled by the drunks, the Pope had to be in the equation. Roman Catholic would do until I knew better. Yet a lay Catholic would not have given such a fine blessing that was laid on that motley group. A former priest? That didn't fit because I reasoned the church would keep these kind of misfits under lock and key, either actually or mentally.

I stared across the rooftops as the day darkened and sipped at the rest of my post-meal brandy. Why not a former priest? But with suicide not an option for a Catholic, what gives with the death-wish walking pattern on Jarvis Street, especially with an artificial leg?

Before I slept, I had Mount Everest on my mind because I had glanced in my encyclopedia and found how little I knew about that mountainous region. I also checked out the massive rock of the Matterhorn. Now where does that fit in? I finally faded into the obscurity of sleep with the vision of two long, slender fingers held in a vee above an expanse of faded blue canvas. I knew I would awaken with the query still working within me the following morning because I trusted my mind to work overnight solutions to my dilemmas.

To continue, or not? The morning would show me. Usually my waking hours, especially after the shower and coffee take-off point, would present a reasoned solution to the problem that had become entangled in my grey matter the hours before.

But it took another week before I reached for the telephone to make the call that I knew would help unlock the box of questions I had filled to the brim about a man named Tobias.

Just after lunch the following day I was seated across from Inspector Bert O'Rawlins who ran 51 Division of the Toronto Police Department. He filled the space behind his well-ordered desk, arms projecting thigh-like from the sleeves of his white summer shirt. We got into the topic right away and I listened, with very little interruption, to a great story teller performing the magic of the Irish art. I toyed with an empty mug during most of my allotted time. I'd listened to a most amazing tale that continually opened doors to new questions after the ones brought with me had been satisfied.

When his secretary tapped lightly on the office door an hour later, I rose knowing my time was up just as O'Rawlins finished his monologue. "As a practicing Catholic, the extra eye looking out for them priestly boys belongs to me. I don't see the dear man ever returning to a state of grace, but the Lord works in mysterious ways so I try to keep him out of harm's way. That can be a full-time job, unfortunately."

After I closed a notebook on my thanks, he walked me to the door. "Take care of yourself, we need newspaper men like you. The guys on the job appreciate the way you tell it like it is, good and fair." I waved a hand in embarrassment, blarney or not. "That upstart punk, Joey Meyers from Now magazine was in here last year sniffing around. He got so much bullshit and high-rolling stories from me and the boys that he didn't know if his butt was punched or bored. He finally got the hint, gave him a few more reasons to put in his column why he hates cops, and went after the Minister of Highways instead."

"Thanks for your time, Jim," I said, "who needs to go to Hollywood for stories when we've got 51 Division?" He crushed my hand again in farewell. I wouldn't be able to keyboard with it for a week.

I stored what I had learned in my mind for a month and researched more, until I became too obsessed with it and incapable of writing anything else but his story. During ten days of furious activity it reached novella length. By the time it was all on my hard drive I realized what I had written was hard newspaper copy, not a story full of the respect and colour that I felt the man deserved. 'Respect' for a destitute mental patient? I saw little of it on the page. I rewrote for another two weeks, then more again until I felt it was right. I made one hard copy, then, after transferring the story to a diskette I cleaned every last comma from my data base. I decided in some distant year, after he'd found his last resting place, I would file it with a publisher who specialized in small books. Or see both disk and paper go up in smoke in my fireplace.

After almost five years, that day of decision arrived. O'Rawlins called to say they'd found Tobias at the foot of Jarvis Street, frozen to death at the back of a parking lot. When his backpack was released from his shoulders and inspected, it was found to be full of worthless weight. A few personal items included a small leather-bound bible with the name August Tobias Schumacher listing him as a member of the Jesuit Order. Birthplace Austria. He'd been educated in Rome and brought to Canada by a cousin after recovering as much as he could from his fall.

For the first time since writing the story I reached into the bottom of my desk and drew out a bright red folder. Yet, rarely did a day pass that my thoughts weren't drawn to the contents of that desk drawer. I felt his life deserved to be stored in Cardinal's red, a colour that he would have suitably worn if he'd been allowed to fulfil his destiny. As I thumbed through the file, still pristine from the imprisonment, tears pooled at the corner of my eyes as my fingers turned the pages that had made a man's life so worthwhile to me. His name would not be seen in the death notices if it was left to those that reside in the seats of power.

No one would take my story seriously. I cursed and rankled words with every editor in sight. I said to hell with it and went as high up in the tower of the newspaper as one could go, shouting like a madman at senior editors and administrators as if they were copy boys. Finally an enormous oak door, one of a pair, was opened to me by a smiling, but white-faced, secretary. As I stomped across the football-field office, the publisher's eyes never left mine. I was too focused even to blink. He waited until I neared his desk then motioned to a plush chair before he spoke. I sat and felt a nerve in my calf start to twitch.

"I'll print it, Dudley," he said, anger just barely concealed. "The only reason being that it's the best I've seen in a helluva lot of years and I can't let it go. Not a bio about a dead bum is it? If you've got the absolute truth this is the eulogy that he rightly deserves, isn't that it?" I moved my head slowly from side to side and let my eyes, now half-closed from the utter exhaustion that had overtaken me, stare into the wood grain of his highly-polished desk.

"Dammit man, say something!" The ache in my chest left a hollow shell as the last of the tension let go leaving me nothing to draw on. It was impossible to raise my face to him.

"I can't let you get away with that undisciplined rant you used to get in here. My managers are farting pure steam from the goddamn boil you've had them in knowing how you got in here. You've done yourself a lot of harm in the newspaper business today." I could sense his words getting softer as they neared the end of his oration. "Time you took it easy, go away for a few days to let this place cool down."

I raised my head feebly and said, "Thank you, Sir. I know what I'm going to say, I shouldn't, but here, today, in the present time, it just doesn't matter."

He continued to stare. I felt slightly dizzy and hesitated before continuing. "As a writer I may never again feel the need to fight so hard for what I believe in as I have today. These words have formed the most significant story I've ever put together. Nothing could ever become as important as that, and terrifying as it may appear to me tomorrow— even the loss of a position I love."

A muffled "humph" said he agreed with me.

"It's enough for me to know that I have written it. It was as if I was guided by a force that had been released from somewhere, the lid having been kept on tight from years ago when I was so damn idealistic."

"A youngster wouldn't know how to put these kinds of words together," he said and sat still, awaiting for my response. Our eyes met. The hostility was gone and he could have been remembering the idealism of his first days on his father's newspaper.

Strength returned slowly to my voice and I could feel it continue its restoring journey through muscle and sinew. Drawing my back ramrod straight on the edge of the chair I said, "What I put on those pages can never be taken away from me even if they were burnt before my eyes. I found such an unnatural energy gather in the writing of that manuscript that even today I say to myself, I wish that I could have felt that passion bounding through all that I had written and could create in the future."

I watched him entwine his fingers and rest their wrinkled pinkness on the green of his blotter. "Look for it to start on the religion page with Tom Harper's column. It will also be a feature on the homeless that we're putting out from our book publishing division." He remained unmoved as I stood. I was undecided whether to reach out to shake his hand or not, and finally determined that a quiet, "Thank you," would express what I felt best.

The Sunday edition hit the newsstands and front porches when I was on an airplane bound for Europe, flying away from the mean streets and corrugated box that had become the sarcophagus of Father Tobias Schumacher. I could not bear to think of him in a pauper's grave in Mount Pleasant Cemetery, even though it meant I could be his visitor from my home nearby. Tobias was going where the brutality of the streets could never touch him again.

In the brightness of a blue-domed afternoon, the crags of his mountain country appeared from beneath an aluminum wing and spread to the horizon like cream-topped bon-bons.

Tobias would never again experience his love of mountain climbing that warmed his Austrian blood when he returned every year from studying in Rome to lead tourist parties into high, wind-lashed canyons and blinding-white snow fields. He'd never again feel the bite of his boots stomping into a rocky crevice. Nor sense again the rough wooden cross that laid against his chest in his small room in Rome, and remained steadfast as he fell from an ice-slicked ledge and lost the one he had lived for.

Tobias never returned to Rome to seek the charity of the church with only one leg to hold him upright. He constantly fainted in pain attempting to adjust to his artificial limb as he kneeled in devotion in the hospital chapel. As he tried to find new footing in the life others had chosen for him, the cross, carved by his father from the handle of an ice axe, remained a constant reminder of the Alps of his childhood. He left the convalescent hospital and became a recluse in his village, refusing the ministrations of the church. Then he disappeared never to be heard of again. They searched for him for three days, then for his body for weeks, but he was never found. But I had. He was at final peace as I accompanied him on his return to his family, lying beneath me in a casket in the baggage hold of the aircraft.

It was only after I turned away from looking at the simple Alpine flowers on his grave with tears on my cheeks that his youngest brother asked if he could walk with me back to their home. As we trod the winding path, the wind tugging at our hair, he said, "August was a hero who would never allow himself to carry that title. He braved so much to help, especially on the day he fell. The person he tried to save was Agatha, his younger sister, who had become exhausted from a climb. He found her and was carrying her on his back when the ledge gave way and she died from their fall. His leg was badly shattered and he left part of his mind behind, if you know what I mean. Can you imagine carrying someone for so many hours, even if she weighed only eighty-five pounds."

I stopped and grasped his shoulder, my eyes blurred as a shock wave of nausea overcame me. Eighty-five pounds. Exactly the weight of the strange rock the Toronto police found in his haversack.

BRUCE VERGE is still residing in Mississauga with the same lovely wife and two interesting sons as noted in the last Wordscape anthology. He is still writing short fiction and poetry and continues to ignore all those snide references to what has been described as a rather skewed outlook on life and a most unusual usage of the English language.

Sinner • Bruce Verge

I deliberately planned a murder, and did so in the name of my Lord. As He is my witness, I had a righteous motive and the means. And, as he provided so many other things, my Saviour afforded me the perfect opportunity. A sign, I was sure, that my work met with His approval.

And with His blessing, as it seemed my time would come sooner than I dared hope.

One evening in the local coffee shop I heard my intended victim gloating because she would, for the first time in her life, get to spend a weekend alone. It seemed her parents were off to Montreal in two weeks for some jazz festival. It was a most auspicious announcement, and I offered a silent prayer of gratitude to Him for ingraining in me the habit of always keeping a concerned eye on those I cared about.

And I *had* cared for her, for quite some time in fact; since she was a child. I remember how charming the delicate pink of her smile, how honest the pale blue of her eyes, in that time of innocence. On more than one occasion I dangled her on my knee, when visiting her parents, and I could never forget the sudden rush of protective love she aroused in me.

And I remember the sudden delicious shock when I first realised that she had ripened into a lovely young lady; a young lady I made every effort to know as a an adult. Yet strangely she rebuffed all advances of friendship. In fact every time I made offers of advice or proposed an intimate chat, away from the un-Christian influence of her peers, she turned me down.

It was then that I realised what was happening. That arrogant sneer that curled her full, red lips every time she said no to me, that look of haughty disdain in her large, expressive eyes as she rebuked my propositions, were ample proofs of her wickedness to one who recognised the signs. There could be only one reason for her treating me in such a manner. Her soul had been given over to the Anti-Christ.

Willingly also, how else to explain her sardonic comments when I approached her, or the almost brutal way she would brush me away if I tried to shake her hand whenever we met. That hand, with those long, tapering fingers and skin so soft and pink, would curl into a deadly talon as soon as she caught sight of me. Truly, to treat someone, who offered only gentle love, in such a callous fashion was proof that Satan lived within her heart.

And there was only one sure way to cast him out forever.

For the longest time I agonized over my decision to take her life, afraid I would lack the courage and will. However, the sight of her strutting around in her tight-fitting T-shirts, and the sound of her humming lyrics to songs that were full of sexual innuendoes, hardened my resolve. To me it was obvious the music she listened to contained hidden messages that advocated moral decay, and those dreadful rock and roll bands were nothing but servants of the Lord of Lies. Better she die now than spend any more of her life ensnared by his unholy temptations, I reasoned.

Old Splitfoot was very busy; his handiwork everywhere you could care to look. Same sex couples; buying alcohol on the Lord's Day; equal rights for women—why, there was even a story in the newspaper about a child who sued its parents. I, for one, would not be taken in by those liberal fools who preached equality and the freedom to 'do your own thing'. There was never a better time to take a stand against Satan and his servants. Never a better time for them to feel the might of a soldier in the army of the Lord. His strength would be my strength, and I would use it to destroy those who sinned against Him.

Especially those who sinned as brazenly as she did and rebuked offers of honest, loving companionship in such a hateful fashion.

The dangers of getting caught carrying out His work held no fear for me. Obviously, I would be protected by Heaven's power, innocent of any wrong doing in His eyes. On a more practical note, there was little to fear from the authorities. I was a familiar sight on the streets of my little neighbourhood, having lived there all my life, except when away at college. I knew, with the utmost certainty, my presence on the day of the murder would go un-remarked. My life was an open book; my manner impeccable, and my demeanour always courteous and respectful. Everyone knew me, and none had ever uttered an unkind word in my company, or behind my back. There was no way I, of all people, would ever be linked to the girl's death.

I had the utmost faith in my ability to kill her and get away with it.

I didn't concern myself with a choice of weapons; God would guide my hand as He had guided all facets of my life. So I waited, with the patience once attributed to Job. Every day I cringed when I saw her with her heathen friends, parading her voluptuous body down the streets. Every night I strengthened myself with prayer in preparation for the inevitable confrontation.

One lonely night, as happens to all men from time to time when they are alone, I tasted the smallness of my place in the plans of the Creator. A tiny spark of doubt ignited itself and rose to cloud my resolve. Who was I to presume the Lord's work? Should I not rather bow my head humbly and beg forgiveness for my arrogance? Was it not the meek that would inherit the earth? My faith wavered; I almost gave up my heinous plans.

The next day I saw her walking into a video store, tight pants moulded to the delicate curves of her buttocks, flaunting her sexuality again. Though I couldn't see her face I was sure she was impudently and wickedly flirting with every male she saw. What a sluttish tramp, I moaned, and with that whispered cry, icy resolve crushed whatever hesitancy I may have felt.

It was no longer possible for me to allow that wicked Jezebel to run free from God's wrath. She had to die, and before her intolerable blasphemy could stain the wholesome reputation of her parents. Blinded as I knew they were by their love for her, they could not see their daughter's true nature. Though they failed to realize how far from the path of righteousness she had strayed, they deserved better than to bear the stigma of her transgressions.

Had any of my fellow man peered into my soul at that moment they would have been quite shocked by the heat of the vengeful fires burning there, I am sure. In my desire to end the little strumpet's profane temptations, I had almost forgotten that my outward behaviour dare not reflect the rage within. It would not do to be noticed in what, for me, was such an unusual state. But for a brief moment it didn't matter—this abomination to the purity of my Lord and the Holy Mother of Christ tried my patience to the limits. It was not an easy task, but I forced myself to calm down. After several deep breaths and a short prayer of forgiveness, I was able to once again projected the kindly, gentle manner people were used to seeing.

On the last few days before the deed was done I continued to suffer a multitude of mood swings. I was the vengeful arm of God fighting His fight; I was Cain, standing over Abel's bloodied form; I was praised by all for the righteousness of my actions; I was reviled throughout history for my bloody deed. It was one of the most unsettling times I ever experienced. Indeed, only my few pitiable and inept attempts at copulation when I was a lad ever came close making me feel this disjointed. Those mishaps I was able to live with, once I realised they were the fault of the coarse whores that tempted me into trying such a filthy act. This time the cure for my unease would be more than quiet introspection and prayer. Much more.

Even the routine of my daily life could not shake my perturbation. During working hours I found myself wandering off on abstract tangents at the most inopportune times. On several occasions people that came to see me went away muttering. My secretary of more than twenty years found herself on the verge of tears several times, due to my lack of attention at times when she needed it most. Things in my once orderly life were far from normal.

Of course it was all the fault of the girl and the demonic spell I knew she was casting. It was only my faith in God and His Son that died for me and my sins that shielded me from any worse harm. In my nightly prayers I asked for the strength to withstand her wickedness and was comforted by the feeling of rightness that talking to God gave me. It was He also, I am sure, who showed me how to feel better by thinking about it as a casting out of demons rather than as the murder of a teenage girl.

And at last it was the weekend. I wisely chose to wait until Saturday morning, knowing full well that she would like as not be out drinking and fornicating and cavorting like the devil on Friday night. The next morning she would be home and in bed, surely besieged by the aftermath of strong drink and illicit drugs.

All that long night I stayed on my knees, head bowed in abject piety before my Lord. I prayed for the strength and courage I would so sorely need over the next while, until the furore over her death quieted down. I confessed the many sins I had committed in my life and begged forgiveness for those transgressions. I pleaded for the soul of the girl who's life I would shortly end. Though she deserved death for her ways, I would not see her soul in Hell, an eternal slave to a fallen Angel.

And I thanked Him for allowing me to be the blessed instrument of His will.

With the rising of the sun came the rising of my spirit. Though not having slept all night, I felt more refreshed, more *alive*, than at any time I could remember. I dressed in my best outfit, which, though fittingly a sombre black, needed something to break its sobriety. On a whim I added a white silk scarf, one of my favourites. I always felt it gave me somewhat of a jocular air. The sight of me in such attire was not unusual in the neighbourhood; indeed, some jokingly referred to it as my uniform. If by chance I was seen, my presence would not seem odd or my appearance out of the norm. It was important that I not draw undue attention to myself when I went to call on the little Lilith.

I broke my fast on a cup of tea and a small Danish pastry, savouring the flavours that my newly heightened senses embellished. Time moved in an exquisite slowness, enhanced by the feeling of surety and power I was experiencing. Indeed, everything in my tiny kitchen, from the crumbs of my meal to the faded wallpaper, seemed to glow; seemed surrounded by an aura of love and serenity. And the knowledge that His will was about to be done.

Outside, the air was clean and sharp, and had a sense of something indescribable to it. The closest I could come to defining it was that the air was filled with *purpose*. Righteous purpose. Emboldened by what I took to be a positive omen, I headed toward her parent's house and our entwined destinies.

At ten on the dot I pushed the buzzer on the door and held it, knowing that the strident noise was sure to wake her. Sure enough, it was not more than five minutes before I heard a shuffle of footsteps on the stairs and a muffled voice saying, "I'm coming, I'm coming. Don't have a cow."

The door swung open and there she was. Wearing nothing but one of her unholy tops, this one of some God-cursed band called the Spice Girls, the brilliant silk-screening emphasising the sinfully tight outfits that revealed what no man save their husbands should see. I could not but help notice that she was as shameless as the tramps depicted on her T-shirt. It was obvious she was not wearing a brassiere by the way her pert young breasts were swinging free under the thin cotton of her top.

The sight enraged me and before she could say anything I pushed her back into the house, slamming the door behind me. Her heel caught on a braided throw rug in the vestibule and she fell. Sprawled out on the floor as she was caused her T-shirt to ride up and I could see the wispy red silk of her bikini panties. Her thick luxurious mane of hair fanned out around her head in a blond mockery of Christ Jesus' halo. My wrath at this wanton spectacle erupted in a mad flurry of violence.

I crouched over her limp body, slipped off my scarf and wrapped it tightly around her neck. Straddling her so as to get maximum leverage I gripped both ends of the satiny material and pulled. She strained against me but I rode her bucking body mercilessly until she went limp and breathed her last. For some reason I felt curiously drained, and was forced to catch my breath before I regained enough strength to rise.

As I stood up I couldn't help but notice, to my great satisfaction, that already her face had changed. In death she once again appeared sweet and innocent, the very picture of glorious youth. My faith was justified. The demon inhabiting her body was no more. Praise be to God, I whispered quietly.

Unbidden, a snippet of vanity slipped into my thoughts. Surely my place in heaven was assured now that I had shown the strength to do the right thing. Quickly I prayed forgiveness for the sin of pride, and immediately felt the flowing warmth of His love permeate my body.

God truly does work in mysterious ways.

Of course I was questioned about the incident. I explained to the police how I had gone over to check on the young lady because I knew her parents were away and I worried for her as I worried about all young people, especially in these violent times. I was unable to adequately convey my horror at what I discovered, I told them. The police took their notes and thanked me for my time and left. They promised me that they would find her killer and told me not to take it so personally.

Later that evening, I was sitting on the steps of my church, seeking solace from my Father, when I saw a sight that chilled my soul. A woman sat on the bench in the park across the street, talking to some children. She had on a plain grey sweat-suit that, though loose fitting, failed to completely conceal the proud thrust of her breasts or the insolent curves of her long legs. She dribbled a basketball idly as she and the youngsters talked.

At that moment I knew that my work hadn't ended. Rather it had just begun. Why, right before my eyes a woman, more than likely a prostitute or drug pusher, was trying to entice children into her heathen ways. I wasn't fooled by the her casual demeanour; visions of depravity and the seduction of innocents swam before my knowing eyes. Thank you Lord for showing me the path I must take, I whispered into the night, I only hope I have the strength to do what is asked of me.

Right then I began to plan the demise of that evil slattern. If God approved my faith and desire, her sins would go unpunished no longer. Once again I would take up arms in the eternal fight against evil, and willingly. I was contemplating the most appropriate means of removing her salacious presence, lost in the desire to feel her struggle vainly against me, when my thoughts were interrupted by one of my neighbours as he strolled past.

"Hey, Reverend MacLeod, did you hear the awful news about the girl that got murdered this morning?"

BRUNA DI GIUSEPPE-BERTONI was born in Rome, Italy. She emigrated to Canada with her family in 1964. She volunteers in many organizations, committee boards, schools and the PTA. She is currently working as the Director of services for the Multiple Sclerosis of Canada, Scarborough Chapter. Writing has been a passion all her life, beginning with poetry when she was young in Italy. Some of her work has been published in Italy. Her first English poem *Italian Element* was published by a women's magazine. She writes mostly of memories and realities of her experiences as an immigrant, and of self-awareness of belonging in her new country.

CREATIVE NON-FICTION

The Evil Eye • Bruna Di Giuseppe-Bertoni

It's not unusual in Italy to see Gypsies begging around the city streets, making their temporary home in parks, farmer's fields and vacant lots. When they first appeared in Europe, Gypsies presented themselves as pilgrims and they told fortunes. They felt that "Gadje" (non-Gypsy) were not to be trusted. As a secret society they made their way in caravans settling all over Western Europe. Before I actually met one, I knew that we were to fear them.

In July 1982 when Italy won the World Cup soccer tournament, I was in Rome visiting family with my son who was only two years old. It was very hot and with no one going anywhere until the soccer tournament was over, the whole family was glued to the T.V. screen each time a game was played; the streets of Rome were deserted. The buildings rocked with each goal scored, and when the game was over the streets were mobbed, from wall to wall, with people celebrating the victory.

One Sunday afternoon, while everyone was watching the soccer match on T.V., I took a walk with my son who happily sat in a stroller. The hot July sun was cooling down, there was no traffic, so we walked straight along the main street to a park nearby that I remembered from the time I had played there as a child. I turned onto a side street, the park was just ahead and I could see the trees from a distance. Across the street, there was an old, abandoned house. The fence with the gate torn down, exposed the courtyard. Under the trees near a parked trailer, people seemed busy. A fire burned and a pot above it steamed at a rolling boil. Camping came to my mind, just like in the parks back in Canada.

I walked slowly until I stopped and gazed at the campers. Huddled around the fire were some people attending to the cooking. I kept staring, my eyes drawn to the flames. Then behind the fire, above the boiling pot, I saw an image. Through the steam, the face of a Gypsy woman rose slowly until her eyes met mine. She stood there staring, and I stared back, absorbing her beauty, which would occasionally fade as the steam rose through the air. I felt the urge to run, but all I could do was take a step. As if locked in slow motion, I took several steps, and kept looking as she followed me with her eyes. The more steps I took, the more her body would stretch to follow my gaze until I disappeared from her sight, around the corner.

I didn't want to forget her. Walking in a hurry, I imagined the image of her beautiful face over and over. A colourful head-scarf kept her long black hair back and over her shoulder. Dust and dirt enhanced her cheek bones. Streaks of black soot covered her forehead as if she had wiped herself with a hand dirty from the ashes. Her deep-set eyes sparkled like candles glowing in the night. A gold chain caught the light from the fire and glittered as she moved. I asked myself why I felt enchanted by her.

Panic engulfed me and I remembered a time when I was only five years old. Fear overpowered me. "Oh my God, could it be her?" I thought out loud. "Could it be that young Gypsy girl whose eyes I can't forget?"

In Italy everyone has a story to tell about the Gypsies. As we grew up we were always afraid and apprehensive over the superstition surrounding them. Nothing fascinated us more, or put the fear of God into us more, than the stories our parents and grandparents would tell us. Sometimes it was too much to handle. Gypsies were meant to be responsible for the thievery that went on around the neighbourhood. Worst of all, they could give you 'il malocchio', the 'evil eye'; people feared Gypsies, for the malediction they were known to carry. When they asked for food or begged out on the streets, people usually gave them money or whatever they wanted. In Italy it was a well-known fact that the curse of the evil eye could be passed on to you by anyone; you could be cursed without even knowing it.

Not believing was just another way of suggesting that perhaps you'd been cursed by someone. Therefore, we grew up with this absurdity, that at times you were unsure whether to believe or not. To protect us from this superstition, our parents would decorate the house with a big red animal horn, or 'corno'. They would also pin a tiny red or gold horn to our clothing. This would symbolize the power that would protect us from the evil eye. So we were told! Luckily, however, if the curse was upon you it could be removed. This ritual would be performed by an old woman who had some kind of healing power. The so-called healer knew the right words to whisper. This ritual still goes on today. It begins with the healer making the sign of the cross on herself three times and muttering unfamiliar words while, with her right hand, she dips her finger in virgin olive oil. Her hand then moves to a dark bowl full of water, and lets fall a drop of oil into it. This is repeated three times over the bowl, keeping up the murmuring in a chanting momentum. The anticipated evil eye is present if the first drop of olive oil falls and scatters quickly across the surface. Following each drop, the oil should hit the water without scattering. By the third drop the oil should be intact: a perfect, undisturbed round drop indicates that the curse is ended. Hard to believe. Yet, I never left the house without my golden horn to protect me from *il Malocchio*.

In the late 1950s until 1964, when my family emigrated to Canada, we lived in a suburb of Rome. Gypsies were seen around, but we tried to avoid them; we would be kept inside if they were nearby, and never allowed to speak to them. "Gypsies steal everything they see," my mother used to tell me. "They also steal children!" she said once. "When you see them coming, you run!" My mother had her reasons for being apprehensive: she had her share of Gypsy encounters.

I remember vividly the day my little sister was baptized, on a hot day, near the end of July. I was almost five years old. My family gathered together at a "*trattoria*" just outside Rome. We were seated outside for our lunch, celebrating this very important Sacrament. The sun was at its peak, there wasn't much of a breeze , but we were well covered from the scorching sun: fruit trees and a grape vine shaded this beautiful courtyard. A fountain was situated in the middle of the garden, and you could hear the water dripping from it, despite all the chattering of the guests and the music playing. Near the end of the meal, when the air was cooling down, people were getting up to enjoy the music and the beautiful scenery. Looking towards the green valley, one could see the ancient city surrounded by the seven hills of Rome.

I waited patiently along with the other kids for the last dish on the menu: Gelato. Espresso would follow. I was losing my patience, it was too long to wait. My dad gave me a stick of pure dark licorice to pacify me. Like a lollipop, it takes time to finish and it kept me occupied. By the age of four I was addicted to caffeine from 'espresso' and licorice; all my father's fault. While the grown-ups were enjoying each other, singing and playing cards, I was busy sucking on the licorice. Someone shouted "Zingari."

My father, who stood beside me, took my brother's hand; I attached myself to his leg where I had a perfect view of what was to occur. There they were, dressed in their colourful outfits, running around touching everything and muttering words to the guests. One Gypsy climbed a fig tree and stood there eating until he was full. Others helped themselves to leftover food and finished all the gelato. I watched a young girl finish a bowl of ice cream. The women held babies on their hips and they were annoying my aunts and taunting my mother who was holding my little sister tightly in her arms.

The owner of the restaurant begged them to leave. My dad however, was calm and in the midst of this excitement, I felt invincible behind my father's leg. Mesmerized by the ordeal, I stood quietly, rapidly rotating the stick of licorice for more flavor. My eyes followed a young girl. How different she was. She reminded me of a peasant girl in my story book. She wore a skirt, vivid in colour; wide and full, it cascaded down to the ground. As she walked her skirt brushed the unpaved yard, lifting the dust and exposing her bare feet. She wore two gold anklets on her right foot and several bracelets on each arm. The jewellery jangled as she walked. She moved gracefully, with a sense of assurance; everything about her was enchanting, bewitching. As she got closer to me, I could admire her even more. Peeking from behind my protector, I was well concealed. She slowly turned her body, exposing her long black, uncombed curly hair. A traditional flower head scarf was tied to her hip. To enhance her beauty, several strings of red coral hung loosely around her neck. And as she walked towards us, the rays of the sun sparkled against the golden loops hanging from her ears. My eyes got bigger with each step she took; I held my father tighter and tighter.

Once in front of my dad and I, she bent down, snatched the licorice out of my hands and walked away. Shocked, I watched her walk to the end of the courtyard. Before she disappeared, she turned to look at me. No words can describe my feelings: breathing vengeance, I resented her bold attitude. She knew; she saw it in my eyes. For a split second I met her green mysterious eyes and she looked at me with envy. I looked at her with hate. Abruptly, she turned her head and walked away with my favorite treat.

As I quickly made my way back to the apartment, my heart was in my throat; I couldn't get the woman out of my mind. More disturbing were my thoughts and my mother's words "They steal children!" God, what if they're after mine! Once inside the lobby, with the door closed shut, I took a look at the court yard. No one was in sight, the steel gate was closed. No one had followed me.

Everyone was still inside watching the soccer game, so no one noticed my ghostly white face. Too busy glued to the T.V. screen! Shaking and perspiring all over, I could still smell the smoke from the camp fire; I couldn't forget the woman. What did she have that reminded me of that young girl? How could I remember? I hadn't thought of her for such a long time, yet if I mentioned or told the story about her, I could see her as if she was standing in front of me. I could re-live that day and feel the excitement, hear the chattering of their voices and my concentration upon her, gazing at her with such a frown.

With one goal, Italy was advancing to the finals. The streets rocked, the buildings were shaking and all Italy was celebrating. We all left for Venice the next day. After waiting forty-four years, that weekend Italy won the World Cup. Italians celebrated this long-awaited day, with all great excitement.

I had three days left of my holidays once we got back to Rome, and I was anxious to get back to Toronto.

The day before I was to leave, with everything packed, my cousin and I had gone to the market first thing in the morning. People were coming to say goodbye to me and some were staying for lunch. My cousin asked me if I would go again to the market before it closed at noon. We needed more fruit and mozzarella. Because it was just around the corner from her home, and I knew people who worked there, I put my son in the stroller and went off.

It didn't cross my mind, or even occur to me until I was standing in front of a fruit stand, but then I remembered. I felt a wave of heat all over. My mind racing, I recalled that Gypsies roam the markets at closing time and sift through the food that the merchants throw away. They loot the market like thieves.

Being so late, not many customers were around, and even as I was remembering, I knew that they were there. I felt them. My eyes moved slowly, my body following, until I saw them. I took my son out of the stroller and held him tightly, pressed his face against my shoulder and told him to be quiet. The closer they got the more I hid his face closer to me. Several of them circled around me. One child was holding hands with another, their dark brown eyes staring at me. I stared back. I lost their gaze when a young mother, holding her baby on her hip, came to stand next to me. Following her was an old woman. She too, stood there, looking me up and down. One little boy took the stroller and started to play with it. The other one started to tug at my shorts. The young mother touched my arm almost caressing it. I could not hear or think. The merchants began shouting at them to move on and let me be. The old woman turned to face me, her wrinkled face there in front of me, staring. She was so close I could smell the scent of mint in her breath. Her eyes were sunken deep into their sockets, barely showing their pupils. She did not speak, but motioned to me to give her my hand. I resisted. Her face, her once beautiful face, turned, and she calmly walked away. So did the rest of them, all moving out quickly, carrying whatever they could.

Holding my son, I prayed that my mother's words were not true, hoping this was a dream and that I would soon wake up in my living room in Toronto. Just as I regained my thoughts, someone brushed me on the back and then moved on to the side. In front of me stood the woman I had seen at the park. She seemed to recognize me. I contemplated her face, her eyes. She must have been in her forties; slim, well proportioned; like a painting of Bouguereau. She would not look in my eyes. She stared at my hands, then my neck. I thought it was jewellery she wanted. If so, whatever it was, she could have it.

She spoke; her head went up and my eyes met hers. "Is that your son?" I stared into her eyes before answering "si," yes. Her green eyes glimmered, speaking to me with a lament. Surprised, I was not afraid; I did not fear her. She said nothing else, just took my hand in hers; gazed into my palm, looked into my eyes, then turned quickly and walked away. I forgot why I was there, not thinking that I did not get any fruit or "mozzarella." I had just experienced a more tense and anxious time than I may ever encounter again. And yet I didn't feel threatened or intimidated.

As I walked back to the apartment's gates, the stroller in one hand, the other one holding my child, I had never felt so strong. When I reached the door that led us to the lobby, I disturbed my son, who had been quietly resting on my shoulder. I put him back into the stroller and smiled at him for being such a good boy. To my astonishment, my son held in his hand a stick of dark licorice ...

S. ANNE MCCORMICK enjoys writing in a variety of genres that include poetry, fiction and articles on environmental and social issues. She is a member of the CAA and the Canadian Poetry Association, and has been published in their anthologies as well as literary journals and magazines in recent years. Her current projects include putting the final touches on a fiction novel and work on a full-length, non-fiction piece.

Bitter One • Anne McCormick

Ugliness
erupts inside
spewing venom from your lips
putrid words hurl blame
anger, cruelty

And when you smile
I see cracks across the
eggshell joy
crinkling holes cave

I watch your face
fragile, false
wait for it to fall in pieces
off the blue ice
of your eyes and veins.
Kay

Kay

Sad, sweet girl

No one knew
behind the shy smile and
kind eyes
you were possessed

Voices
never let you be in
peace
we let you down

Strategic hits on
the magical profession
fulfilled your liberation

A cold soup of
eight components
settled in your blood

Salvation.

FAY FERGUSON is from Jamaica. When she had completed commercial college there, she came to Canada in 1972. She is an associate of the Insurance Institute of Canada. She is divorced with one daughter. She is a Claims Examiner with the Property and Casualty Insurance Company in Toronto.

CREATIVE NON-FICTION

A Thin Line • Fay Ferguson

We often hear people speak about a thin line between love and hate. Or what about the thin line between premonition and vision? Or do we call it extra sensory perception? Sometimes a dream will make you begin to wonder, 'Am I psychic or crazy?'

Saturday afternoon, November 19, 1983, was one of those chilly, overcast fall days when the sun hid behind the clouds. The hard, cold ground was covered by a mosaic of leaves—rust, green, red, yellow, mustard and brown, scattered shapes and sizes strewn everywhere. The trees' naked branches were blowing, twisting and bowing while the leaves swirled and circled in the wind, at times rising up toward the empty branches. It was as though this gloomy day was befitting for the sombre experience that was to occur as the day went by.

I lived with my daughter, Kristal, in a two-storey condominium town-house with a finished basement. Kristal, who was about thirteen at the time, had gone to the library to study with her friends on this particular Saturday afternoon. I had woken up with a slight headache that day, but could not attribute it to anything in particular and figured that it would go away. At around three o'clock, I decided to wash my hair. I usually wash-roll-set it in curlers and then sit under a dryer for more than one hour to achieve a salon-type style. However, this particular Saturday, I was having a rather lethargic, spaced-out, zombie type feeling, so I washed my hair in the laundry tub in the basement. I then decided to part it in two sections from the centre of my forehead down the nape of my neck, made two braids on both sides, and left it to air-dry.

I muddled around the house with my usual weekend cleaning. Within a half an hour, I started to smell something suspicious, and realized that I was smelling gasoline.

I scurried around checking the kitchen, the garage, heating vents and air ducts. Nothing. We used only electricity and there were no gas appliances in the home. Well! There was no doubt that the smell of gas fumes was emanating from the basement, and strongest in the laundry room, which adjoined the furnace room.

I knocked on my neighbours' doors. Lady luck stepped in. My neighbour adjoining the south side of my house, told me that her husband, Jim, had only a few minutes ago, changed the oil in his motorcycle. He then poured about one cup of gasoline down the manhole in the parking lot in front of our homes. Apparently, the fumes were escaping upward into my basement through the drainage outlet for the overflow in the basement. This was situated in the laundry room, which had a built-in, cemented, twin-tub, one large and one small, as opposed to the more modern white plastic tub, and also housed the washer and dryer. They were not in use that day.

My mind raced, what should I do? If I cooked or lit a candle, there might be an explosion. I decided to let the tap run on cold water at full force, contemplating that it would be much more costly to run the hot water tap. I figured that running water would carry the gasoline-filled stagnant water under my basement, away, away, far away. That did not work.

What next? Time was going. More than half an hour had already passed, or so it seemed. I filled the smaller of the two tubs, thinking that when I unplugged it, the deluge would wash the stench away. Well! I filled the tub, but instead of unplugging it, I stood there mesmerized, staring into the water. My heart pounded, my head felt light, and I had goose bumps. I was terribly afraid to put my hand in the water to unplug it. I was like a cat, trying to cross a stream, paw in, then out with a flash. First, it was too cold, then it was too deep, I was sweating but my hands were clammy, my head spinning.

I just stood there, looking, thinking, lost in the tub of water.

I was beamed down to Jamaica instantly, like the cast on 'Star Trek'. It was a bright sunny day at the beach. The sky was blue, the sun was hot. My father had taken us to the beach. My siblings, friends and I were frolicking on the sand and in the water. There were almond and sea-grape trees. Our dogs were chasing the sand-covered, salt-soaked wet sticks that we threw back and forth for them to fetch. My father was foremost on my mind. He was swimming, floating, because he loved the beach. He had a protective look on his face and half-smiled.

BANG! The door slammed and I was beamed back to my basement in Willowdale. I realized that I was standing there in the same spot, mesmerized by the water and afraid to put my hand in to unplug the sink. I had to give myself an ultimatum. I decided to close my eyes and count to three, after which, I unplugged the tub. The water gulped and gurgled until it was all gone. I felt as drained and as empty as the tub.

The slamming of the door meant that Kristal had arrived home. Another fifteen minutes passed, which meant that she had snacked, and was about to settle in the family room in the basement, in front of the television to watch her favourite Saturday afternoon programmes. Twenty minutes passed, the house still stank of the gas. I filled the larger of the two tubs and called Kristal. "Kristal, come in here and look into the water."

"Gosh! Mom, I'm tired, and my programme is just about to start."

"I said, to come here now, and look into the water!"

We both stood there, staring, glaring into the tub of water. Why? We didn't know. Then Kristal said to me. "Mommy, would you prefer to die by water or by fire?"

I was dumfounded, and felt a chill. I shuddered. "What kind of a question is that? I don't know!"

Kristal went on. "Really, Mom, would you prefer to die by water or by fire? Think about it. If you had a choice, which would you prefer?"

I said, "None." But she persisted in going on with the subject.

"Well, if it's by fire, you can drop and roll, or you could douse yourself with water, and if you are outside, someone might see you and douse you with a hose or bucket of water."

I said, "But you would be in such pain, and such a panic knowing that you were being fried alive, with no more chance to do or say the things that you wanted to. Your life would be flashing by there and then, knowing this is the end, a lose-lose situation. That would be sure torture and worst than being in hell. How could one think of what to do in such a frantic situation, except to pray and ask for forgiveness realizing that this is your doomsday? I certainly would not like that kind of death."

Kristal went on, as if totally engrossed in her thoughts. "But you don't necessarily have to die, because you could be saved and treated for burns. And with new technology and plastic surgery, you could be almost normal again. I think that drowning would be worse, because in the water, you know that you have no air, your lungs are being filled with water and it is a much worse death by suffocating, struggling, sinking down, down, and grasping at the very same water which is taking your life."

There was no rationale for this dismal conversation. We both stood there analyzing these two situations for minutes on end, still standing at the filled tub, gawking into the water, engrossed in this depressing discussion and being totally afraid to immerse our hands into the water. I have never felt so very afraid and the most eerie feeling enveloped my whole being.

Finally, I unplugged the tub and the water gushed out. I figured that by now, the worst of the smell was gone.

My headache got progressively worse over the evening and into the night. I went to bed, but sleep was not easy for me. I'm not sure if I slept or not, or whether I had a horrible nightmare or a vision, but this certainly could not be called a dream. It lasted like what seemed, the entire night.

In the nightmare, I was driving my car in Jamaica at a junction called Three Miles, between Spanish Town and Kingston. There were three other family members with me in the car. My sister, Kisha, who in reality was in Florida on vacation, my brother Angus, and his wife, Agnes, who actually live here in Canada, within minutes away from me in Scarborough. As we were driving along this stretch of road called Spanish Town Road approaching the large ice cream manufacturing company called, Cremo Limited at Six Miles, we were held up at gunpoint. The robber ordered us out of the car with our hands above our heads. I, Fay, being the eldest sibling, decided to take action. I told the robber that I had something special in the trunk, which he could have if he would spare our lives. He allowed me to open the trunk. Sneakily, I took out a loose piece from the jack and used it to hit him over the head. He fell down on the ground. I ran into the Cremo building, leaving the other three standing there. What was originally the Cremo building was suddenly transformed into a McDonald's Restaurant. I ran inside to seek help. While standing at the counter, in the reflection of the neon menus, I could see a police cruiser driving into the parking lot. It was the old canary-yellow car that the Metro Toronto police used some years ago. I darted out of the restaurant and started to run after the cruiser, but it just disappeared into mid air, as if it was beamed away. Disappointed, I returned to my car where my siblings were, only to find that my sister had vanished from the scene, my car had also disappeared, and all that remained were the nude, headless bodies of my brother and his wife. They were both hanging from the high overhead electrical wires with two very shiny aluminium-type machetes (the broad ones with the hook used for cutting sugar cane in the fields) hanging beside them and glistening in the sun. There was no blood to be seen anywhere.

I woke up, startled out of this horrible nightmare, and jumped out of bed. My head was now splitting in several pieces, but I would not resort to pain killers, since I realized that there was no cure for this severe headache which was only caused from the events of the last twenty four hours, and was a combination of anxiety, stress and fear. It was now Sunday morning about 9:00 a.m. I was disoriented but I went to wake up Kristal.

She wasn't home so I assumed that she had gone to Church. I grabbed the telephone and called my brother, Angus. My sister-in-law answered the telephone. I asked.

"Are you guys OK?"

"Yes! Why?"

"I just had the weirdest dream about you two."

"Really? Well, we are fine, not quite awake as yet."

"Ok then, talk to you later."

But I could not go back to sleep, so I called my girlfriend, Marla. She said very little, as she did not get a word in edgewise, because I monopolised the entire conversation, talking about my father and his role as a model to his family. After about an hour and a half of using Marla as a sounding board, we said our goodbyes.

I hung up the telephone and as I turned to go downstairs to make breakfast, the telephone rang and I picked it up. I did not recognize the voice at first. The caller sounded very distraught and almost incoherent.

"Hello. Hello!" I said.

"Hi Fay, it's Wanda." Wanda was another sister who lived in New York.

"It doesn't sound like you, what's the matter?" I said.

"Nothing."

"It can't be 'nothing' because you're sniffling. Did you have a fight with Don?"

"No! Where's your daughter?"

"Gone to church."

"Where's Angus?"

"I just spoke to Agnes and they're at home, doing fine."

Then she said the strangest thing. "Give me your phone number."

"Wanda, you called me, therefore you already have my number. What is it? I'm sure that it can't be as bad as my last twenty four hours."

"Ah-em, are you sitting down?"

"Wanda! I am not sitting down. My daughter is at church. Angus is OK, and you already have my phone number. What happened? For goodness sakes, speak up!"

"Daddy is dead."

Not believing my ears, I asked, "Which Daddy?"

"Daddy, our father, he is dead." Then silence at both ends of the phone.

I finally spoke first. "Are you sure? If Daddy is dead, Mama would have called."

"I received the news from Junior. He's in New York. Uncle Wally told him that Daddy's body was found on the beach and that he was reported missing since yesterday. They searched until it was dark but did not find him, so the search continued early this morning. Mom's gone to identify the body."

I started to cry with Wanda on the telephone. I was too stunned to say much more. Then we said our goodbyes and hung up. The rest of the day was filled with telephone calls locally and overseas. I completely forgot to eat and just bawled the whole day. When Kristal got home from church and I told her, she was too shocked to speak and only cried.

I flew home for the funeral on Tuesday. When I arrived home, as soon as the family saw me, we all started crying. Everyone gathered around to relate the events surrounding his death. They said that he left home early in the morning to attend his annual company picnic at Black

River beach on the Saturday. At about 3.00 p.m. he told his co-workers that he was going to order fried fish to take home. He left his towel, clothes, glasses and his car keys wrapped together and went for a swim. That was the last time anyone saw him. He was a good swimmer, so they thought that he was OK, or he had wandered off with some friends. They figured that he would not have gone far because his belongings were all there. After about an hour had passed, and no one had heard from him, they started looking for him and searched until dusk. It was too dark by that time so they reported him missing to the police and everyone left for their respective homes. The search continued at sunrise the next morning.

They found his body washed up on the beach with one of his eyelids eaten away. The fish had him for food overnight. We decided to visit the beach where he was found and spoke to people there. It was then that I had a flashback. I felt as if I had been there before, as if I had seen all this before. It struck home. So that was the feeling of deja vu. All the events from Saturday leading up to this moment flooded my mind, and I knew then, that I had a premonition of my father's death.

I felt a sudden shudder, and I thought of all that spiritual energy which had been transmitted, and I was saddened, yet relieved. Then I wondered, why couldn't I have responded, helped him, why couldn't I have done something to prevent his death? He was reaching out to me and found my home across the seas. But I was not there for him. I was alive, and he was dead. Does this mean that it is in death that we find our spiritual connection is strengthened?

JOHN PRINCE was born in Manchester, UK. He witnessed the 1940 battle of Britain. He was lucky to survive a bombing which destroyed two blocks of houses next to his. He came to Canada in 1959 with his wife and two children and has a Canadian-born son. He retired from work on television production. He roughed out scripts, saved, saw daylight, and now works on them while learning to write thanks to Toronto CAA. John likes different genres with six Wordscape stories published, and is now writing his third *Trilogy For Sparks* book.

A Brood Apart • John Prince

Queen Victoria was in her sixtieth year of reign.

I grew up a nobody; I never knew my unmarried mom and was given at birth to foster parents who had little use for me, other than to belabour me with heavy chores from the moment I was old enough. I would not have minded the chores much if my foster father had not been so free inflicting his birch on me for the least little infraction. His own two daughters, he treated well.

Both girls felt sorry for me, at times, I know, but a lot of good it did to stop his cruelty.

At sixteen, my life took a turn for the better. His daughters, by this time, were in domestic service, and only came home on the weekend. One day, foster mother had prepared mushrooms for a stew she would boil up that afternoon, ready for her spouse when he came home. Before leaving for school that day, I put a handful of other mushroom cuttings into the stew as well. I had looked up a book on mushrooms and had searched for non-edible mushrooms in some parkland near the house. I thought it a good idea to get a little revenge this way. I went to school that day hoping they were both sick as a dog when I got home.

Returning from school, I expected to see them looking pale and ill, and I was ready to secretly gloat at their misery, but it was not to be.

I was surprised to see some policemen together with the two sisters who were crying. I was told that my foster mother had poisoned her spouse and herself in a murder/suicide. I was not about to argue with this train of thought. I do know one thing: I will never again eat mushrooms.

The house was sold and I got a job, working as a clerk, with a Mr. Toller.

For five years I worked hard to please Mr. Toller, then one day he invited me to accompany him to his friend's home to listen to his friend's daughter give a musical recital. This was not my idea of a good afternoon but sometimes it's necessary to do unpleasant things if one wants to progress among the 'uppity', as my late guardians called them.

I sat there listening to a warbling human canary, Millicent. Excruciating. Later on, a serving of food and wine brightened the day. Between the eats and drink, I got introduced to the bird (the daughter). I learned the daughter was to inherit a large sum of money when she married and a good endowment would be the bridegroom's reward. Yes, this was for me.

It wasn't as if she were a beauty. She was not. However, she might have looked picturesque working on a farm if no other farm girls were around.

A few weeks later, I received an invitation to her coming-of-age ball, whatever that meant. I thought a coming-of-old-age-ball more suitable. My boss and his wife were invited, of course, and we all travelled by coach together. It was well attended but I felt out of place because of my dress and manners. I wondered a bit why Mr. Toller got me on the guest list.

The girl's mother had died when she was a mere child and she was adopted when very young. I envied her good fortune and luck to be in the situation.

There were plenty of gentry at the ball. It was my first experience to see young belles fill name cards for partnering.

During the course of the night, Mr. Toller suggested I get my name down on Millicent's dance card before she filled it up. Her adoptive father also encouraged me. The poor girl was dancing with elderly married partners while their spouses looked on, I suppose knowing their own marriages were safe with her.

Millicent's tone was rather sharp-tongued, cutting enough to keep young bucks clear of her. I did get to dance with her, but my clumsy style made my effort short-lived. She limped off the floor to the amusement of guests. I felt even more out of place and wished I was anywhere else. However, in the course of the night, Mr. Toller reminded me about the dowry for the future spouse.

Towards the end of the night, I asked her if I could be permitted to call on her soon and perhaps go riding. I presumed she had horses, or could borrow two. She suggested the following Sunday was free, with no trouble getting a loan of mounts. From that point on, our courtship started, and I gritted my teeth, thinking only of the dowry and family fortune I hoped in time to bring my way. I became more acceptable to her relatives and friends because her father and my boss were in collusion to marry her off to anyone fast, before she finished up a spinster.

Six months later we married and a princely sum of one hundred thousand pounds was made over to me.

Because of my marriage and my money I became more acceptable to Ottawa gentry and even joined a private club, staying out late playing billiards and card games for money. Oh, I held my own at first but then a run of bad luck forced me to quit my gambling, and I become desperate for more money. I didn't know where to turn.

However, summer was upon us, and I thought a trip to Toronto for a few days would do me wonders. Millicent encouraged me as she was tied to her musical teas and other petty past-times.

I arrived at the lake-shore at mid-day and found a nice place to lodge. I took a walk later that afternoon and sat on a bench and looked out over Lake Ontario. The sun warmed on my face and I appreciated being alone to watch water splashing. It was a beautiful day to be alive.

Pedestrians casually strolled along the sidewalk. I was startled. Millicent approached. I nearly fell off the bench in shock. Why had she followed me? I waited for her to get near so I could give her a tongue-lashing for not trusting me enough to take a holiday on my own. These were not the clothes Millicent would normally have worn while strolling a beach front.

She came level with the bench and gave me a big smile, before sitting next to me and said, "Hello." She wiped the smile off her face when I called her Millicent with anger in my voice.

She looked at me, plainly confused and moved to be off. I quickly apologised for my rudeness as I realized it wasn't Millicent and explained to her that she was the double of my wife.

She seemed to find this amusing and told me that she had heard some funny, 'come on' stories by fellows in her time, but this was a new one for her.

I took out my wallet to show her my wife's picture and she interrupted me by saying. "Hey, mister, we haven't discussed the price yet."

The penny dropped as to her profession, but I showed her Millicent's picture anyway. She looked at it and she seemed genuinely surprised. "I ain't never had fancy clothes like your missus in the photograph."

"You from Toronto?"

"Nah. But clientele is better here, love, than around the area I live." I felt as if I were having a conversation with Millicent and it confused me.

"Well, must be going. Time is money as they say." She stood up.

Before I could stop myself, I stammered, "I'll buy some of your time. How much?"

"If you've one pound, I'll spend an hour or so with you."

I gave her four pounds and told her there was more if we spent the night together. She agreed.

After we had settled down in her digs, over a bottle of wine, I made it a point to find out all I could about her.

Her name was Cassie, and she had been fostered as a baby and left with different families until old enough to look after herself. Her uncanny likeness to Millicent bothered me, but we spent the afternoon at her digs. I suggested I should get my bags and I would make it worth her while to spend holiday time with me.

During that time I worried someone would see us together. Bumping into someone I knew could create problems unless I said Cassie was Millicent and that Millicent had a sore throat and was unable to talk.

That night I told Cassie about my marital arrangements, and the dowry I had received and how it had been spent.

"I would kill to own half that," Cassie said.

That was what I had wished to hear; she would be my alibi to murder. But first I had to bring her around to the plan I had in mind. I had two days in Toronto to tell her how nice it was to have money to spend. I told her that I would pay her to take my wife's place. I spoke of holidays in the south of France and Italy, wearing the latest styles.

She did not need much persuading to take the job. She was ready to take Millicent's place if I could guarantee no one would be any the wiser.

There was only one problem and that was the difference in accent, but we could work on it.

We left Toronto and Cassie got a place closer to Ottawa so we could meet me some evenings, in order to make her familiar with her new life. I got her comfortable with Millicent's relatives by showing pictures of them and explaining their traits. We met often during the next three months.

Fortunately, Cassie had customers, and we got by with her customer's donations and my meagre allowance.

I insisted she wear a wig in order to disguise herself. She was not happy about it but we could not risk her meeting one of Millicent's friends or family. Or heaven, Millicent herself.

My idea was easy enough. I'd kill Millicent and get rid of her body. Next, I bring Cassie in the house as Millicent for a while. Later, I pay off the household staff and tell them Millicent had gone to the south of France and wished to settle down there. I terminate my employment with Mr. Toller.

Of course there was the business of Millicent's signatures on documents. I would get around it quite easily. Millicent and I had the same solicitor. If Millicent\Cassie was to suffer a bad hand injury I could sign for her.

My plans got unexpectedly waylaid with the sudden death of Millicent's adoptive stepfather. Well, that was fine, because in the end, there would be more money for me from Millicent.

Millicent had to be quickly eliminated, I told myself. I could wait no longer.

We were in the kitchen and Millicent was nagging about something. This had to be the time. I picked up a sharp kitchen knife and cut her throat. Before I could dispose of the body her late father's servant came into the room and saw me holding the weapon while I stood over it. She ran from the room, screaming.

Throughout the trial and even here in prison, I find it hard to understand why everyone keeps calling me Cassie. During the trial some strange characters from Europe spoke in my defence. They said funny things like schizoid characteristics or split personality, schizophrenia symptoms, delusions, hallucinations and paranoia. The silliest one I thought was schizophrenic condition in which a person appears inhabited by two internally consistent but irreconcilable characters. They said that I had developed a split personality and in the dark recess of my mind, I think people persecute me. 'Delusion of grandeur' was mentioned as well. The visitors had funny names like Freud, and two young men named Jung and Adler.

My biggest confusion though, was being called Cassie all the time, even when I objected.

The prosecution suggested that I had murdered Millicent's spouse, and left his body in the room of a house I had rented. Then I killed Millicent.

The funny-named characters got my sentence commuted from death to life imprisonment.

I felt really put out when I was told that I must serve time in a woman's jail. How can I have murdered Millicent's husband when I am Millicent's husband? I admit I killed her because she stood in my way.

They claimed I would not wait for him to get divorced. I will go to my grave knowing I am Millicent's husband. I don't know whose body they found in my old rental room. I know it was not mine, because I'm here. Right? The split personality idea is mad.

To add insult to injury the trial prosecutors claimed Millicent's spouse had been fostered out at birth. Twins were later born to the same mother. Of the twins, Millicent was adopted and Cassie fostered out. They proved they were Millicent and Cassie. In other words, Millicent had married me, her brother. How disgusting. They claimed I hadn't known that she was my sister. But again, I may have been subconsciously as one with them both.

Strange ideas these schizophrenic doctors have with their assumptions. Putting me in a female prison is outrageous, and I am not through yet. The law will hear about this, and where is Cassie, my future mate? She will hear of my wrongful conviction for murdering myself. So help me, she will.

BEVERLEY RICHMOND has been an assistant publisher at a firm producing employee newsletters, a columnist for a Metroland newspaper, and an advertising rep for a Thomson newspaper.

She has also completed a non-fiction book and has been recently published in *Active Living Magazine*. Bev writes from her Victorian farmhouse in Prince Edward County where she lives with her partner and two hounds. This is Bev's second year in *Wordscape*.

Rhonda Goes Postal • Beverley Richmond

Rhonda shoved the stick into gear and pulled out of the garage. Halfway down the driveway she became acutely aware of the powerful roar under her that, until now, she had only dreamed about. She glanced up at the exhaust rising from the stack. The ride was bumpy but it promised to be the best she'd ever had.

She slowed as she neared the road, checked for traffic, then pulled out of the yard. At the corner she turned right. When she sighted her first target her dark eyes flashed wildly. A sinister smile spread across her face.

Today was going to be a good day. Yesterday began like any other day, just like the past thousand days at the post office had begun.

Rhonda entered through the back door. "Hi, guys," she said as she shoved her purse under the desk and eyed the clutter for any new notes from her supervisor.

"Hi, Rhonda," Pam answered, dumping the incoming mail sack onto the large table. She grabbed a handful of letters and started sorting them onto the carriers' desks, walking back and forth between them as she plunked down ten letters here, fifteen there, and six on the other. "No bulk today, girls, just the regular stuff," she said, continuing her sort.

Pam was the supervisor at the small town post office. She was born and raised in the county and expected to spend the rest of her life there, as did the other women with whom she worked. This was no hardship. It wasn't like being in prison. In fact, it was like being in paradise. The area was known for its miles of coastline, famous sand dune beaches, historic farmsteads, and idyllic country scenes.

Rhonda, like her ancestors, had stayed in the area all her life. At an early age she met and married a man named Brian, and they lived with their three children in an older home on a quiet road two miles north of town. She worked for the post office; Brian worked at the large farm complex at the other end of their road. Life was good.

Just by looking at Rhonda you could tell she enjoyed life. Her round face, framed by a mass of dark curly hair, seemed always ready to burst into a smile. And smile a lot she did. And giggle! In fact, it was that giggle that was her trademark: an infectious laugh ready to bubble out at the slightest hint of humour.

"Bills, bills, bills," Rhonda said, organising the mail for her route. "You know, I feel guilty delivering bills to my customers. I feel like I'm the one who's billing them. I know that's nuts, but that's what I feel."

"Rhonda, you're nuts," Pam cracked, knowing full well that Rhonda was totally sane. She'd never met a woman more dedicated to her husband and family and serious about her job, but who at the same time knew how to have fun. What a great combination; Rhonda was a star employee.

"But I like it when the cheques come through," Rhonda continued, "'cause then I know when people open their mailboxes they get a little thrill seeing some money waiting for them. You know, I feel like Santa or the Tooth Fairy, even."

With that last remark the whole office burst into giggles. Rhonda giggled the loudest and the longest as usual.

Just then the door opened and they heard someone call out behind them. "Oh, Ladies!"

They turned their heads in unison to face the counter at the front of the office. There stood Doug, one of their favourite customers, smiling. "Yes, ladies, I'd like to thank you all for the fine calibre of mail lately. Good quality mail. No junk, no bills. Nice mail. Magazines, cheques, coupons, greeting cards. Very nice."

The women broke into another round of giggles. Pam neared the front counter with a wide grin on her face.

"What'll you have today, sir?"

"Give me ten," Doug said, holding out a five dollar bill. The stamps and money exchanged hands. "Thanks, ladies. Good day."   Soon the carriers had their mail organised and started loading up their cars. Pam stuck her head out the door.

"I hear there's a large bulk order coming in tomorrow. You girls may want to get in here a bit earlier if you want to end your day at a decent hour. It may take some time to sort."

She waved at them as they pulled out of the parking lot, then drew her head back inside the door and turned toward the counter.

"May I help you?" she asked the next customer.

Meanwhile, Rhonda turned up the street that began her rural delivery route. The road was lined with bushes, trees and wild flowers. Fenced fields spotted with cows and acres of golden corn or corn stubble completed the picturesque views. She pulled over at the first mailbox, stuffed a few letters in and raised the red flag. As she pulled away she glanced in the rear-view mirror.

"Oh, oh," she whispered out loud and pulled way off the road so the huge tractor could pass. There was barely enough room but the machine rumbled by. I wonder what field Brian's working today, she thought as she drove down the road.

Rhonda continued on her route much like she had hundreds of times, until she came to a new mailbox: one she hadn't noticed before. It was different than the other fancy mailboxes along her route. There were the red mailboxes; she didn't mind them although she thought they were a bit too urgent looking. There were a few green mailboxes with designs or pretty white flowers painted on them. She liked those. There was the mailbox shaped like a church, the one she opened the front doors of to stuff the church's mail into. That one was quite appropriate. There were blue mailboxes, yellow mailboxes, old rusted metal mailboxes, and plastic mailboxes. All very colourful. The black mailboxes, of course, were the pièce de résistance—functional, yet classic. She liked them the best.

But the ones shaped like a white cow with huge black spots or patches all over them—she didn't like them at all. It seemed to her as if the owners were poking fun at her, at her job, at the seriousness of the mail.

But this one. This one. This was the limit.

She stopped and gazed at the green monster staring back at her through the open window. She reached out of the car and pulled down its jaw. She quickly jammed in the letters and shut the jaw back up. She flipped the red flag indicator to the 'mail's here' vertical position and sat there looking at the mailbox. The green fish eyes and the green fish fin and the green fish tail and the green fish fishiness sat there beside the car looking back at her.

I hate that thing, she thought, and a giggle rose in her throat. But this giggle was a different giggle: an evil giggle. It came from a place Rhonda's giggles had never come from before.

When Rhonda finished her route later that day, she headed for the grocery store in town to pick up a few items. As she got out of the car she reached for her purse. Her purse! She'd left her purse at work. She got back in and drove to the post office. When she pulled into the parking lot she noticed eight skids sitting at the back of the lot, piled high and covered with black plastic tarpaulins.

"What the heck is that?" she spoke out loud, although no one was there to hear her. She stopped the car, got out, and headed inside.

"There's my purse," she said and walked over to her desk. "Stupid, stupid, stupid. Why did I have to leave it here anyway? I've been forgetting it a lot lately. In fact, I've been forgetting lots of things lately. Sometimes I think I'm losing my mind."

Just then a piece of bright pink paper with the words "Bulk Mail Bulletin" on it caught her attention. "Sears has announced it will begin delivery of all Sears catalogues to its individual customers through the postal service. This replaces the reminder cards that were previously mailed to customers, which had instructed customers to pick up their catalogues at their nearest Sears outlet. The first shipment will be for rural route customers; RR #1 catalogues will be the first shipment."

The pink slip of paper floated to the floor.

"RR #1. That's my route. Those are my catalogues. I've got to deliver eight skids of Sears catalogues. Eight skids! What am I, a machine? They want me to deliver eight skids of catalogues. I don't believe it." Rhonda reached down, picked up the pink slip of paper, and looked for the catalogue description.

"Christmas Wish Book" the writing said.

"The Sears Christmas Wish Book," she laughed. Or did she cry?

That night Rhonda's sleep was fitful. She had dreams about the most terrible haunting things: mailboxes shaped like wild animals, their jaw-lids gaping open with the Wish Book stuffed inside. She dreamed that she was caught under a landslide of Wish Book catalogues, lying kicking and screaming as her bulging eyes scanned the catalogues all open at the 'rural mailboxes for sale' section. Mailboxes over, under, behind and in front of her. The images swirled in her brain: mailboxes, catalogues, mailboxes. And that bizarre green fish mailbox, it's jaw gaping open with a Sears Wish Book catalogue wiggling in its mouth like a fat juicy worm.

Rhonda started giggling in her sleep. "Giggle, giggle, giggle." It was an evil giggle again, like the one she'd giggled when she saw that green fish mailbox for the first time. She couldn't stop. "Giggle, giggle, giggle, giggle, giggle."

Morning came. Rhonda woke up, not to the alarm clock but to her own internal clock: a clock that was set on self-destruct although Rhonda didn't know that yet. She felt numb and groggy and sick. She tiptoed past Brian who was still asleep and shuffled down to the kitchen. She lifted two sets of keys off the hook: hers and Brian's. She got in the car and drove.

She didn't have to drive very far, just to the end of the road. She parked the car in the yard and walked over to the beast. She lifted her leg up high, climbed into the cab, slammed the door shut, and put the key in the ignition. She shoved the stick into gear and pulled out of the garage.

Halfway down the driveway she became acutely aware of the powerful roar under her that she had only imagined before. She glanced up at the exhaust puffing out of the exhaust stack. The ride felt bumpy but it would be the best she'd ever had.

She slowed as she neared the road, checked for traffic, then pulled out of the yard. At the corner she turned right. When she sighted her first target her dark eyes flashed wildly. As she neared it the giggle began again. That same evil, sickening giggle—the giggle of a crazed woman. "Giggle, giggle, giggle." She raised the bucket of the tractor and ploughed into her first target, knocking the white-cow-with-black-patches mailbox over and crushing it under the tire as she drove past. The crunching sound it made was very satisfying. "That was easy," she said out loud.

Up the road ahead she spotted the silhouette of a fish, a green fish. "Giggle, giggle, giggle," she giggled and pressed down harder on the gas. "Today's going to be a good day."

BOB SEALEY, Bsc, CA is a self-employed consultant in North York. After twenty-eight years of living and working with an undiagnosed and untreated bipolar mood disorder, he finally learned about restorative mental healthcare using orthomolecular medicine. He has written several layman's guides including the Depression Survivor's Kit and Orthomolecular Healthcare References—A Layman's Guide to New Hope for Mental Health. His mental accounting and consulting work and his depression coaching helps clients and care-givers of people who suffer with involuntary symptoms of depression, anxiety, manic-depression and episodes of other mental illnesses.

Twists & Turns: Around and Through The Mental Healthcare Maze • R Sealey

There are hidden truths
and obvious lies about mental illness.

There is reality,
and lies about reality,
silence about reality,
and reality twisted around into lies.

There are stigmas
and lies about stigmas.
There are silences
and silence about silences.

There are defences
and lies about defences,
silence about defences,
twists around silent defences,
and turns around deceitful silences.
There are silent truths
and twisted truths,

unspoken truths, broken promises,
and lies about all these truths.

There are illusions of truth
and lies about illusions,
shadows of hidden truth,
and truth hidden in dark shadows.

There are twists around truth
and turns around reality,
truth twisted to defend against reality,
and reality twisted into defensive lies.

There are hidden truths and obvious lies
and the plain honest truth.
It is hard to see sense through
the darkness of depression.

While exploring the mental healthcare maze,
twists and turns, lies and silences,
stigmas and defences, illusions and shadows,
ignorance and fear, frustration and pain
can conspire to hide the truth.

The persistent patient gets the prize
—restorative mental healthcare.

Write and Wrong

When I write,
it is your perfect right
to point out the wrongs.
There is nothing to say
if some things seem OK.

Mood-disordered brains often aren't right
when variable faults and volatile energies
make wrong moods seem right
and right moods seem wrong.

Shifting, changing, surging and creating.

It is hard to feel right
when your brain's working wrong.
Is wiring broken, signalling bad or chemistry missing?
What about genetics, environment, people and experiences?

To repair what is wrong
we can make a good start
by finding some faults
and judging them apart.

As we start to repair
what we know we can't fix,
we can find still more faults
and save later time.

Consistently, persistently, thoroughly
pointing out all that seems wrong
the list gets to long
when so little seems right.
All the wrongs don't seem right
by the start of the night.
In the morning
there is a new light
for another long day.

Things seem rather bright
and I hope things go right.
Until I recall yesterdays and
all that went wrong
as today lingers on.

The lifeline moves up.
Joy sucked away
leaves a shell of a day.

JACQUELINE BOROWICK was born in Montreal and was raised in Val d'Or, a gold-rush mining town in Northwestern Quebec. Recently retired as a Presiding Bilingual Justice of the Peace in Toronto, she can now devote herself entirely to books, languages and writing. She has been published in *Wordscape 6* and *Legacy*.

The Don Jail • Jacqueline Borowick

Like a Victorian battlement
Dickens would decry;
like an architectural artefact
in a city rid of history bowing
only to glass and concrete.

Like a grim warder of intractable men,
captive souls in the toils of the Law,
warehoused in the public interest;
like an ungracious host to loved ones
who shed dignity at the door;
like hope and despair gazing
across grimy glass partitions.

Like a stone and mortar metaphor
for crime and punishment;
like a consumptive organism
whose veins roil in anger,
bitterness, regret,
at misdirected lives.

JOYCE A. PARK was born in England and was a student at Cambridge University on D-Day and at London University on V.E.Day, and in 1946 was the first woman graduate chemist employed by the Shell Petrochemical Company in its London research labs. Marriage to a Canadian clergyman took her to Northern Ontario and then brought her to the Toronto area. Joyce was a scientific editor and writer for many years, and after retirement she decided to try her hand at fiction and memoirs. She has had three short stories published in tne Wordscape series, in the two preceding this one. Last year she received 4th Honorary Mention in the *Winners' Circle 7* Contest for her memoir, "I was a Sally Ann OK."

Search and Rescue • Joyce A. Park

Yesterday morning I hated my sister. I actually heard myself screaming, "Sheila Thomson, I could kill you!" Of course, I didn't really mean it, but you know the feeling! She makes me mad a lot of the time, because she acts so superior. She thinks she knows everything now that she has breasts and menstruates (my mother taught me the proper word—she's like that). Sheila is only three years older than me and sometimes I don't like her attitude. I don't like it one bit! I especially didn't like it after I got my cat Tigger from the pound.

According to Sheila my cat had got "psychological" problems (her word, she even spelled it out for me). I told her she was just jealous because Tigger never went to her to be petted and she was just mad because sometimes he even gave her a little nip. Tigger liked to stay in my room all the time except to eat his food and go outside to do you-know-what. He often came and sat beside me although he never actually settled on my lap like most cats do. That's one thing that Sheila insisted was very peculiar. When anyone but me came into the room Tigger bolted under the bed. That's another thing that Miss Psychologist found was "pathological" (another word she spelled out for me). She didn't seem to understand that Tigger was probably abused before we got him from the animal shelter and was still timid.

"You've heard of scaredy-cats, haven't you?" I tried to explain, "Well, that's what Tigger is, a scaredy-cat. It's his nature. You should just accept it."

But Sheila would always have none of it. "Your cat's a freak. I don't like him. He'll never be a proper member of this family."

When she says hurtful things like that I want to escape from Sheila, and I do. I go to the sand dunes near our house and enjoy being all by myself with the sand and the sea-grass and the ocean and the sky. I don't usually feel afraid to be all alone. Down here it's not like being in the city, where I'm told kids have to watch out for bad people. What a drag that must be! Down here we know everybody by sight and by name, or so I thought.

Yesterday I hated Sheila because she was scoffing at my cat again. She said she was going to let him loose on the dunes because Tigger was a wild cat anyway, and that's where he belonged. She sounded so determined that before I left for school I hid Tiger where Sheila would never think of looking—in Mrs. McIvor's woodshed. I knew Mrs. McIvor wouldn't mind. She's my friend and she has had so many troubles in her life that she's very sympathetic when I have one of my many problems.

She came here from the Ukraine ever such a long time ago and married Dave McIvor and stayed right here. Everybody loves her because she's so generous. Whenever she gives you anything she gives you enough for three. Dad says when she offers you a drink she brings out the largest possible glass and pours the liquid in with great slurps till it reaches the brim. It's as if she was brought up to distribute largesse, Dad says.

Sheila likes to use the word "pathological" about Mrs. McIvor too, because she thinks the old lady is telling us lies when she hints she has some connection with the Tsar of Russia, who was murdered by the Communists way back when. She loves to show you pictures of her son and grandson; she then urges you to compare them with newspaper photos of the guys in the British Royal Family because, "King George V was the Tsar's cousin." She never actually says she is a relative of the Tsar but she gives you a conspiratorial look (at least, that's what Sheila calls it) and says, "Don't you see the likeness? Ah, if you only knew!" In spite of Sheila, I like to think that my friend really is a Russian Grand Duchess. Besides, I enjoy all the lovely cakes and cookies she bakes and shares so lavishly with me. (I love the word "lavishly," and I found it in the dictionary myself; I didn't need Sheila to tell me about it.) Another reason I call Mrs. McIvor my friend is that she adores cats. When I told her where I'd hidden Tigger, she didn't mind at all.

School was a drag yesterday; I was so anxious to get back to my Tigger that I thought it would never end. When finally I was able to check things out, Tigger had vanished from the woodshed, and I couldn't find him anywhere. He wasn't in the Grand Duchess's house. He wasn't in my house, not under my bed, not in my closet, not on, under or behind a chair. He wasn't anywhere in the yard. Mom hadn't seen him. Dad hadn't come in. And, horrors!, Sheila had gone out. So I couldn't ask her, but then I didn't need to, did I? I felt it in my gut that Sheila had carried out her threat! I rushed out to the dunes with the speed of those seven-league boots my Gran used to tell me about.

"Good job it's light till so late this time of the year," I thought. I'll be able to see her and follow her every move. If she still has Tigger, I'll fight her for him, tooth and nail, and if she has already let him loose I'll go over the dunes calling for him until he comes to me. Then when I get home I'll get my revenge." Just what that would be I didn't know, for my parents do have certain rules about fisticuffs for their two tomboy daughters.

I love the dunes. I love the way the sand is grasped by strands of marram grass which seem to struggle so hard to prevent the wind from blowing away their burden. But I love the fact that the sand always escapes and flies off somewhere else to start another little dune. When I was a little kid, my Dad showed me how, on windy days, you can place a big rock on the sand floor and watch a miniature sand dune form. Dad says it reminds us that the dunes are alive.

Our sands even sing. If you walk along the shore just above the water's edge and listen very carefully, you can hear a sort of ringing sound. Dad says it comes from a combination of quartz crystals, moisture, pressure and friction.

And then there are the birds—all kinds of shorebirds—to add their own kind of music. When I come out here I often sing at the top of my voice, "The dunes are alive with the sound of music!" You get the message. I'm at home in the dunes, but a home for my cat it most certainly isn't.

Yesterday afternoon, though, my dunes seemed different. Where I usually found peace, there was none. The soft sand slowed me down; the marram grass tripped me up; the ocean wind took my breath away; the bright sun blinded me; as I frantically ran about in search of my Tigger. I was crying now, short of breath and of hope. I sat down for a bit, as sad as I've ever been in my life. I kept looking in every direction but saw no one for the longest time. Then I saw someone on the dunes making their way towards me, but it wasn't Sheila. In fact, it was someone I didn't know at all. A stranger! And a big burly stranger at that!

I could tell it was a man, and because I didn't know him I felt scared. I wanted to get away. I would start off in one direction and he would follow me. I would go the opposite way and he would do the same. Who was he? Was he trying to get me? What would he do to me if he caught up with me? All those horrid reports I'd seen on TV about kids being abducted or attacked came bubbling up from somewhere inside of me. In a panic I wondered what I should do. It would be no good screaming, no one would hear me; but I did it anyway because I couldn't stop myself from doing it.

I realized I must get out of the dunes. The only way open to me now was to scramble up the largest dune of all and then scramble down the other side to the coastal path. I had never done this before on my own but I didn't hesitate. I guess it was fear that got me to the foot of the dune in record time and started me up the steep slope, but that slope was ever so much steeper than I had imagined, and the sand kept slipping away from under my feet so that I wasn't getting anywhere fast. I was hot and tired and breathless and in danger of slipping right down to the silver beach many feet below, when suddenly above me appeared what I thought was a vision, my sister. But she turned out to be real alright. Sheila had a firm footing and she was able to lean down and hold out her arm to me.

"It's OK, Peggy, I heard you scream and I knew exactly where you were," she said. "Keep calm, I'm here, I'll help you. Put your hand in mine and I'll bring you up level with me and then we'll take it step by step together. Dad's on his way, I left a message that we were out here."

For once I did as Sheila said but as soon as we got to the top and lay down on the crest of the dune and could see Dad climbing up the other side, I had to find out what she had done with Tigger before I would give her my thanks for probably saving me from some horrible fate.

"What do you mean, 'What have I done with Tigger?'" He's here inside my jacket. I saw him chasing something in this direction and he wouldn't come back when I called him, so I came out here to find him and after a mad search, I did." He was purring away in my sister's arms, I couldn't believe it.

I felt myself, like Tigger, warming towards Sheila.

"Didn't you mean it then when you threatened to drop Tigger off out here?"

"Don't be stupid," she said, "I wouldn't do a thing like that to someone you loved."

Someone I loved! SOMEONE! Then she was admitting that Tigger was a person with his own "pussonality." She was willing to accept him as he was. Of course, it didn't hurt that grateful Tigger had accepted her, I thought, but I was pleased with my older sister and I decided not to hate her any more.

Dad was pleased with her too because it might have been a bad man out there who was up to no good, he said. I could see he was worried because a grim look had come over his face, especially round the mouth. Did he know something that I didn't know? Had that man who was following me meant to harm me? Had the evils of the big cities come to my very own dunes? Dad was holding me tight and I was glad to be snuggled against his chest even though his vest buttons were digging into my cheeks.

"I'll take you girls home and then I'll look after this stranger," he said harshly. But the words were no sooner out of his mouth than the expression on his face changed. The man who had been following me was walking along the coastal path directly below us, his face upturned towards us. He waved to us and we could see he was smiling broadly and that Dad was returning his greeting with just as broad a smile.

"Hi, Joe," shouted Dad, "I didn't expect to see you here. You scared the living daylights out of Peggy."

"Sorry, Peggy, I've been trying to catch up with you for the last half hour," the man hollered back," but you kept disappearing, so I gave up."

"Who's this man?" I asked. "I've never seen him before in my life!"

"That's Joe McIvor. He's an old friend of yours, don't you recognize him? He'd never harm you. He used to baby-sit you kids when you were little."

So it turned out that the "bad man" was (to me, and to Sheila) a now unrecognisable Joe McIvor, the Grand Duchess's grandson, the one who was supposed to have a face like Prince Charles. He had joined the army three years ago as a skinny young lad and had come back on leave as a big burly fellow.

On our way home along the coastal path Joe joined me and Sheila and Dad and Tigger. As soon as he'd arrived home, he said, he just couldn't wait to tramp over the dunes so he had just dumped his kitbag in his grandmother's woodshed and taken off.

Before he could say any more Sheila made eyes at me as if to say "So, you know who escaped when Joe opened the door of the shed!" And then she blabbed to him (trust her!) what I was doing halfway up the highest dune, in a state of panic, no less.

"Gosh, I'm sorry, Peggy, but I never for one moment thought you wouldn't recognize me. It's only been three years. I recognised you, with that flaming red hair, and I wanted to catch up with you to get all the news about your family."

All that stuff happened yesterday, and today is a new day. Joe's invited for supper tonight. He said he feels terrible about having scared me. As for me, I feel mortified that I screamed like a baby and had to be rescued by my sister. Right now I think my sister is pretty nice, and she says she thinks I'm pretty nice. There's just one problem. Tigger now spends time in her room as well as mine, so I think I'm going to keep a log of his whereabouts.

At this moment Tigger's purring away on the window seat beside me, his head in my lap, and I'm looking across at the McIvor house. You'll never believe this, but a police car has just pulled up at their front door and two police officers have got out. Oh, I hope Mrs. McIvor's not been taken ill. No, she's standing outside now talking to one of the officers and I think she's crying. The other officer has gone into the house. And now he's coming out with Joe in handcuffs. Whatever could Joe have done?

Dad's here now, his hand on my shoulder. "I was wrong yesterday to think Joe was such a good friend," he said, "The police apparently knew something that I didn't—he's on a list they have. After you'd gone to bed last night they called to ask if I had any young daughters and told me to watch out for him roaming around by himself." I think he and Mom are going to explain it all to me over breakfast.

PHILIP ANTONACCI, M. Ed., currently teaches English and science
for the Peel Board of Education. Over the last twelve years he has
resided in Mississauga. During that time he has written a biography
of the recently canonised German phenomenologist Edith Stein,
along with a two-act play, numerous short stories, several essays, and
a collection of object oriented poetry. Currently he is working on an
uncanny psychological novel set within a surreal suburban world.
The Hyacinth House is his third contribution to *Wordscape*.

The Succubus • Philip Antonacci

Something strange is in this house,
It sleeps above the beams,
I can sense its ragged movements,
Crawling beneath my dreams.

During the stillness of the night,
It descends alone,
A succubus prepared to mount,
What my love will scorn.

Cold arms encircle my aura,
Lips wet with lie's froth,
Breasts tipped by elusive ripples,
Its weight judges my loss.

See it, above us now, my love,
Floating with haste down,
To conceal us both in its wing,
And within it, we drown.

CATHARINE MILLS' first published short story appeared in NeWest Review as the winning entry in their 1996 Late Bloomers Writing Contest for unpublished fiction writers over forty. She has participated in creative writing workshops led by Cynthia Holz, Lawrence Hill and Ann Ireland, and reading groups led by Naomi Diamond. She spent two years as a contributing editor to *Ryewriter*, a newsletter launched in 1997 for current and former students of the writing program at Ryerson University. Recently she's been working on short stories set in places she's visited. She's currently researching a longer piece ("novel" still intimidates her) set in Toronto of the 1880's and 1980's.

Holyrood House • Catharine Mills

Hal awoke with a snort just as the guide's microphone came alive in a burst of static. He looked around, at first not sure of his surroundings. The bus was still rolling through the Scottish countryside, his wife, Miriam, was sitting complacently at his side, and all appeared right with the world. Hal ran beefy hands over his face and rubbed the last vestiges of sleep from his eyes.

Miriam sighed almost imperceptibly and tugged at the cuff of her long-sleeved seersucker shirt. When she sensed her husband's eyes upon her, she hurriedly released the sleeve. Instead, she picked at an imaginary bit of fluff near the hem of her wraparound skirt. Hal's brawny right hand reached out and grasped her slender fingers. Miriam stiffened, then forced herself to relax as her husband's muscular hand enclosed her own. She looked up at him and found him grinning sheepishly down at her. Obligingly, she returned the smile.

" ... along the Royal Mile." The couple gave their attention to Anne, the red-jacketed tour guide, who stood at the front of the bus. "The Royal Mile," she intoned, "connects Edinburgh Castle with Holyrood House."

"Did you say *Hollywood* House?" yelled Hal. There were snickers up and down the aisle. And from somewhere behind them, a man called out, "That Hal, he's such a card."

Anne, the consummate professional, allowed a few moments for the disruption to subside before continuing. "Holyrood means Holy Cross," she said. "It originated as a small chapel built on Castle Rock, then grew into a guest house for royal visitors. The palace has been used as a royal residence since the 1300's. It's the official Scottish residence of the present Royal Family, not the more well-known Balmoral, as you may have thought. Later this afternoon, we'll have the opportunity of visiting the private apartments of Mary, Queen of Scots."

"Hey, Anne. Is Vanessa Redgrave gonna be at *Hollywood* House? Wasn't she the one in the movie?" Hal turned and called over the back of his seat. "Maybe we're gonna see a movie star, guys."

Anne's professional smile never left her face. Inwardly she dwelt on how much she had to rely on tips from boorish tourists to supplement her meagre income. "Not today, I'm afraid, Hal," she said. "But I think you'll enjoy the palace just the same. Its history of murder and betrayal is quite intriguing. I'm sure you'll find it just like a Hollywood movie." Thankfully, once they arrived at Holyrood House she'd be able to turn her charges over to the local guide. Anne resumed her seat and massaged her throbbing temples.

Miriam's hand stirred beneath her husband's. "Hal," she said. "I don't think you should keep interrupting the guide like that. She's just trying to do her job."

A flare of anger crossed Hal's face. "Whaddya mean, interrupt?" he demanded. "She thinks I'm a riot, just like everybody else. Jeez, Miriam, don't be such a bloody tight-ass." He jerked his hand away and glared out the window. An ugly vein stood out on his forehead.

Miriam flinched and felt a flush of heat wash over her face. She sat with downcast eyes, staring at the tattered magazine clamped within the pocket of the seat in front of her.

The north-west tower, where Mary, Queen of Scots had her private apartments, was the original one built by James IV. Miriam listened attentively to the sombre, yet dignified guide. A discreet brass-plated badge pinned to his lapel identified him as Bertram. He stood ramrod straight in his dark suit as he addressed the throng of tourists.

"Many of the original features still remain," he told them. "Included among these are the oak ceiling, decorated with armorial bearings of Mary's relatives, and the mural over the fireplace." Hal yawned and wondered if Bertram—first name or last—was moonlighting from his night job at the funeral parlour.

The canopied bed in the corner, hung in pale pink lace, reminded Miriam of her girlhood fantasies. For a moment she was lost in time, a time when every little girl wanted to be a princess when she grew up. She smiled and hugged her arms to her sides, then winced as she pressed against a tender spot.

"When Mary returned to Scotland following the death of her husband, Francis II, she turned her private apartments at Holyrood into a 'Little France'," Bertram continued. "She hung tapestries on the walls, and brought many musical instruments and an extensive wardrobe from her days at the French court."

Hal had had enough of the history lesson. He yawned again, making no effort to hide his boredom. Dust filled his nostrils and he stifled a sneeze. He'd give just about anything for a pint right now, even one at room temperature. Leave it to the bloody Brits, he thought, to ruin a decent glass of beer. He yawned once more, and wandered into a corner where he stood, apparently fixated on a coat-of-arms.

"Mary's second marriage to her cousin, Lord Darnley, was doomed to failure. It's now believed he married Mary in an effort to secure the throne for himself. But he was a weak man, and the pawn of Protestant lords who wanted to wrest the throne from the Catholic queen. Darnley's rooms were located directly below the queen's, and connected by a spiral staircase."

For the first time since their arrival, Hal appeared interested. Somehow he'd missed the rickety-looking staircase tucked away in the dim corner. "Hey, Bertram," he called. "Question ...." The guide inclined his head and waited. "Did she go down, or did he come up?" The room erupted in laughter. Bertram managed a weak smile, while Miriam blushed to the roots of her tied-back hair.

"I believe we're getting to the episode that will most interest you, sir." Bertram maintained his decorum. "Lord Darnley became jealous of Mary's relationship with a member of her court, an Italian named David Rizzio. Rizzio was a musician who quickly found favour with the young queen; he became her private secretary. Prompted by the Protestant lords, and his suspicions that the child Mary was carrying was Rizzio's, Darnley condoned their plot to murder Rizzio."

Miriam felt slightly ill as she noticed the spark of light that lit Hal's eyes. A sick smile played at the corners of his lips. "So what happened?" he said quietly.

"A *crime passionale*," said Bertram, "that was erroneously believed to have been enacted here, in Mary's bedchamber. In actual fact, the drama occurred in the supper room. Mary, David Rizzio, and several members of her entourage were engaged in an intimate dinner party. Suddenly, her husband, and a band of lords led by Lord Ruthven, burst into the room."

It was oppressively hot; droplets of sweat beaded along Miriam's hairline. The room was swimming before her eyes. She needed to sit down, but dreaded calling attention to herself. Bertram's clipped monotone faded in and out.

"Ruthven accused Rizzio of having an improper relationship, and thus too much influence, with the queen. Rizzio's futile denials—and Mary's—fell on deaf ears. While Darnley physically restrained Mary, the plotters fell upon David Rizzio and stabbed him over fifty times. His mutilated body was dragged from the room as the pregnant queen swooned to her knees."

A strangled cry escaped Miriam's lips.

"When Mary regained consciousness she wept to learn Rizzio was dead. As she regained her composure she declared," Bertram paused dramatically, "'Farewell, tears. We must now think on revenge.' She soon came to realize her husband was a coward and a fool who'd believed the plotters would bestow the crown on him. Now a terrified, desperate woman, Mary became a virtual prisoner in her own castle. Come this way, please."

The group was subdued as they followed Bertram out of the bedroom. Miriam's seersucker shirt was glued to the small of her back; she longed to pull it free and fan out the sodden fabric. Looking at the floor, she almost walked into him when he stopped suddenly. Bertram was silently waiting for the rest of the group to assemble.

"This is the spot," he proclaimed as the company circled around him. They followed his gaze as he stared down, almost reverently, at a discolouration on the floor. "Many believe," he said, "this mark is a result of the lifeblood of David Rizzio seeping into the hardwood flooring. It's said nothing has been able to remove the stain."

"Out, damn spot!" Hal's outstretched index finger pointed at the floor.

"You're a prince, Hal," laughed one the tourists. A stick-on name-tag identified him as Buddy from Red Deer. "A real prince, my friend, but you've got the wrong castle." There was more laughter.

Hal shrugged and spread his upright palms wide. Beside him, Miriam was studying the dark blemish that marred the floorboards like a stigmata. She opened her mouth, but before any words came out she crumpled to the floor.

The cool cloth helped. Miriam opened her eyes beneath the folded face-cloth and stared into the darkness. The room was quiet and she welcomed the stillness. After their return to the hotel, Hal had joined the others for dinner in the dining room. He wouldn't bother making her excuses.

Behind the damp face-cloth she felt disoriented. For a moment she thought she was still in the royal bedchamber, lying in a musty, canopied bed hung in pale pink lace. It was a bed fit for a princess. A bed fit for a queen. A lusty, passionate, but ultimately doomed queen. But Miriam had no tears for the dead queen. It would take more years of murder and failed marriages, more years of betrayal and imprisonment, but her son would become James VI of Scotland, then later James I of England. Her son would be the first to unite the thrones of the two kingdoms. She would have her revenge.

Miriam sat up and swung her legs over the side of the bed. The still damp face-cloth fell to the floor unheeded. She rose on unsteady legs and crossed the room to the vanity table. She sat on its delicate matching chair and stared into the mirror. A hairbrush rested on the table top and Miriam picked it up and slowly began stroking her hair.

She had an abundance of red-gold hair, so like the miniatures she'd seen of the sensuous queen. She continued to gaze, mesmerized, into the mirror until her image blurred with that of Mary's. The brushing quickened and became more vigourous until it popped open the top button of her shirt. Miriam returned the brush to the vanity and slowly loosened the remaining buttons, all the while contemplating her reflection. She lifted the blouse from off her shoulders and let it fall to her waist. One hand caressed the indentation at the base of her throat. A faint pulse throbbed beneath her fingers.

Her hand trailed down leisurely until it rested in the vee between her breasts. Her nipples hardened against the thin fabric of her camisole.

The room was chilly and she shivered. She studied the imprint marring the pale flesh of her upper arm in the mirror. It rose from just above the elbow almost to her shoulder, the purplish stain already turning yellow. Miriam fingered it gingerly. She winced, but shed no tears. She was already thinking on revenge.

Ghosts • Jacqueline Borowick

My ghosts are not mere shades,
shadows lingering too long,
they are not so vulgar
to manifest themselves
in weak ectoplasmic displays,
intrude in strangers' homes
intent on treading ancient boards
re-enacting old tragedies.

My ghosts wear vibrant hues,
fill assorted shapes,
laugh, cry, argue,
joke,
play music, dance the tango,
pop over to reminisce,
eccentricities still intact.

Pauline, forever twenty-one,
Marnie, at seventy-five,
lifted onto the shoulders

of her pallbearer-lovers,
Dad with his soft-shoe routine,
his Chop Suey Piano Fantasy,
the nun, Thais, with her black
enfolding mantle,
Mousa in Buenos Aires, proud
of his presidential connection,
his balcony overlooking Congress.

My ghosts and I inhabit one another;
as long as I live, so shall they,
immortal and fully-fleshed,
lending texture to life,
their presence a bridge to the other side.

JEAN ELIZABETH KEEPING was born in Lansing, Ontario, and enjoys the challenge of writing non-fictional poetry in rhyme. She has been published in newsletters, newspapers, and all *Wordscape* books, also the latest book of poems, *Legacy*. As a Christian spiritualist she writes in poetry uplifting prayers for shut-ins. Her latest achievement has been to finish a book of Christmas stories, and greeting cards in verse. Jean became a C.A.A. member in the early nineties.

CREATIVE NON-FICTION

Mother's Dream Home • Jean Elizabeth Keeping

It was a beautiful old dark red brick commodious home, semi-attached, built in the late eighteen hundred's, on a quiet street in the city of Toronto. At that time Gerrard East was indeed a quiet street, and number 277 at the quiet end.

The windows were large, with stained glass enhancing the upper part of the pane. The solid oak front door was decorated by a brass knocker and latch handle, both of which had to be cleaned and polished weekly. The door leading from the vestibule into the front hall was also of stained and etched glass, exquisitely worked into an intricate pattern. To the right was the sitting room. Then a few steps on, was the magnificent circular mahogany stair case, under which had been built a hall closet. We were all scared of the hall closet as most children are of dark and dusty places.

Heavy oak doors led into the dining room. The hall curved to the left into the kitchen. The house had nine rooms in all: one bathroom; a full basement with a crawl space; and a coal furnace.

Mother fell in love with the house instantly, she said, "This is my dream home." Fortunately Dad was able to buy the house at a very reasonable price. In 1936 houses in the Gerrard area could be picked up quite cheaply. It had been vacant for some time and looked in need of love and care.

We were a big family. Twelve in all. Five sisters and four brothers. With so many of us I was hardly ever alone.

After we moved in, things went well for a while. I don't know if it had anything to do with the house or if they were just of the age to move, but one by one my older sisters and brothers left home. My second to oldest sister, cautioned me before she went, "Beware of the basement, there's something weird about it."   I laughed at her. I was in my late teens, a church going person, brought up to believe there was only one spirit: God. One Saturday Dad had taken my two younger sisters, and brother, out for the day to Niagara Falls. This left my Mother and I alone in the big house. So on this particular Saturday, a day in which we always did the house work, Mother asked me to clean the rooms on the third floor.

I opened the door to the third floor stairs and proceeded up them. On nearing the top three steps, I felt an icy chill (it was summer, and the house was hot). I stopped. I heard whispering and giggling, right in front of me. I froze in terror. I saw no one. I looked up above the stairs and saw Mother's bedroom door a-jar though she always closed it. There was a brightness in the centre of the room. I could see the hall walls, but I couldn't see where the voices were coming from. By this time, I was hysterical, crying out of control. I called out, "Where are you?" but all I got in reply was a manic laugh. I turned around and started to run down the stairs, terrified. I tumbled down a few steps, got myself up and dashed down the remaining steps, all the time feeling hands pushing me and hearing feet behind me. At the bottom of the stairs, laughter turned into shrieks. I reached out for the door knob, it rattled and turned wildly not doing anything. I finally managed to take a hold of it, and turn the knob. The door opened a little, but not enough for me to get out. I pushed harder, but the door still wouldn't open. All the time I felt hands pushing me. It was as if someone was holding it against me. Finally the door was yanked open with such a force it threw me off balance and I fell sideways onto the second floor landing, screaming and yelling.

I ran down the back stairs to the kitchen. Through sobs, and stuttering, I related the happenings to my mother. She stared at me in utter amazement, and said, "I don't know what you're trying to pull off here, young lady, but it just won't work. You're going right back up those stairs and clean, like I've asked you to. I have far too much work to do now to tolerate this. But I will come with you up the stairs, to show you there's nothing to fear."

After Mother had checked all the rooms and was satisfied, she left. I heard her close the door at the bottom of the stairs. I was very scared, I opened the closet door to fetch the broom and dust pan, but the broom flew out and skidded across the floor. I dropped the dust pan, in horror. The radio was switched on and off, then switched on again, then the volume turned up so much it deafened me. There were three lamps in the bedroom, all with pull chains. Some force was pulling the chains continuously on and off. The excitement in the room was wild. Gusts of wind swirled around me. I begged them to stop, but they only laughed and chased me down the stairs.

When my sisters came home, they chaperoned me up stairs and all was quiet and we finished the house-work.

One of my older sisters, confessed to me in later years, that she too had been chased down the third floor stairs by some force.

I tried to make sure I was never alone. If I came home and no one was there, I'd sit on the front steps and wait for one of the family to come home.

The basement was almost worse than the attic. Whenever I had to retrieve something for my mother, I'd pick up the item and hurry back upstairs. I knew that there were souls watching me. Another annoying act they liked doing, was turning off the alarm clock during the night. This would cause quite a lot of confusion in the morning when the clock failed to work. This only happened in the third floor.

Dad eventually had to rent the second floor rooms. An exceptionally large room, with an adjoining smaller one, was rented to a family of three.

Hazel, the daughter, was a nice quiet person when they moved in but her personality changed soon after.

It was her little joke to wait for me to come along the hall. She'd jump out from where she was hiding and chase me, holding a hatchet with both hands, high over her head. As I approached the top of the stains, I'd put my right hand on the wall to steady myself. She then would bring the axe down, as if to strike me, then laugh. One time she sank the axe into the wall. Dad was furious. I never told him about Hazel and her madness with the hatchet. It was too far-fetched and made me the one to sound crazy. The family soon moved away. Thank God.

One evening while I was alone in the kitchen, sitting at the table making lunches, I heard foot-steps coming up the cellar stairs. I trembled in fear. I knew none of the family was down there. I could not move. The door knob turned, the door slowly opened. I looked into a strange man's eyes, hazel brown. He wore a black suit. He walked around the back of me, placed icy fingers around my neck and squeezed. I started grasping for air and trying to scream. My mother must have heard and came into the kitchen at which point he vanished.

Mother didn't believe my explanation, nor did she believe her own eyes when she saw the imprint of fingers round my neck.

My experiences eventually effected me so much I had to leave home.

Some time later my mother wrote me a letter, telling me about an incident that happened one Sunday afternoon. It had been a hot day in August and some of the family, were sitting around the kitchen table. A tea towel, hanging on a rack, burst into flames. Mother said, that they all just sat there flabbergasted. Eventually the city bought the big house together with several other houses. These were all demolished to make way for a library and parkett.

I returned to Toronto several years later to work in Eatons. It turned out that one of my co-workers had lived in our old neighbourhood and knew the house. Everyone but my family seemed to know it was haunted. She also told me something of the history. There had been a murder committed around the turn of the century. A father had strangled his two children on the third floor and killed his wife on the second floor. He had then hung himself in the basement.

I often wondered if every owner had felt something strange about the house and that was why it had been empty for some time when Dad bought it. I thanked God that the ghosts or whatever had finally had been exorcised by the demolition of the house.

MARIA DUNCALF-BARBER is a Counsellor and Educational Trainer and Motivational Speaker. She writes and teaches Empowerment and Creative Groups for women and runs a writer's circle in Muskoka. Maria produced one hundred programmes for Gravenhurst cable TV. She has been published in the *Muskoka TV Review Guide, The Huntsville Herald, The Muskoka Times, The Bracebridge Examiner* and *Hepatica.* During the past few years she has written book and movie reviews of the Sundance Film Festival and the Toronto Film Festival. She has appeared in *Wordscape 4, 5,* and *6* and *Legacy.* She is the originator and chair of Muskoka Film Festival 2000.

Ghostly Tombs • Maria Duncalf-Barber

Standing inside the pyramid
A life long dream recognised
I will never forget
The guide asking me
"Do you want to lie down?
"Me? no thanks
The smell was awful
And the air chilling
My friend laughed
It was eerie
An Egyptian sarcophagus
Waiting for tourists
To partake in the history
Of life and death.
Mysteries

Mysteries

Icy fingers
Linger in the shadows
Noises pierce the air
Campers around the fire
Share stories of horror
Faces shining from burning flames

Suspense hangs like grapes in a vineyard
As the audience wait agog
The storyteller enunciates her words
Glaring at the squeamish
Delivering the mysterious climax
To a never to be forgotten end.

After having four children FRANCES SMOOKLER began night classes at Atkinson College; thereafter she attended Osgoode Hall. Frances practised law for 22 years before retiring. Now, she is president of Ryerson University's Learning in Retirement Institute and spends much of her time writing. She has had two short stories published.

For Better or for Worse • Frances Smookler

His aunt was moving away. George struggled after her as quickly as he could, calling her name. But, as he came near, he felt something pulling at him violently. His body heaved and convulsed. Pain! More pain—and panic. Then, with no warning, an explosion in every cell in his body, and overwhelming relief.

"Are you all right?" An excited voice floated down to him.

Rain tattooed his skin. Flashes of light penetrated his closed lids. Far away thunder rumbled.

He fought to speak, "I—think—so. What happened?"

"You were hit by lightning."

Not even Matthew, who had spent all of his ninety-six years in the remote Northern Ontario mining town of Timmins, could remember a time when his friend, Maya, wasn't a part of the community, looking after sick people. Once long ago she had saved his life. He could still hear his father's voice telling anyone who would listen, "Don't know what she did but that woman gave our boy back to us—only six—but sure as there is a heaven above, he was gone."

Matthew knew it was true. He could still feel the whole experience—becoming hotter and hotter—floating up from his bed—

moving towards light. Then, hearing magical music coming from where he had just been, and being compelled to go towards it as if he were following the Pied Piper. The next thing he knew, he had dropped back into his body. Afterwards, he kept trying to reclaim the sound he had heard, and all his life he could not get enough of a certain kind of music written centuries before—baroque, he thought they called it.

From time to time Maya would vanish, sometimes for weeks. Matthew simply accepted this. He never questioned where she went. Nor did he ever ask her why, though his hair lost its colour and his body became bent, her appearance changed so little. It was only on the final day of his life, as his age-dimmed eyes strained for one last look at her lovely face, that he acknowledged to himself, for the first time, that Maya was not like others, and that it was she who had given him the music.

Bernie Stein lingered in George Pope's office after the meeting ended. It was a fastidiously maintained work space with files, books and papers all resting in their special place. The men, friends since high school, were both thirty-seven, though George, with his receding hairline, a mouth that was often pinched in concentration, and the pale face of someone whose leisure time is spent indoors—he enjoyed reading (mostly non-fiction, but also some science fiction)—looked ten years older.

Bernie, nursing the dregs of his coffee, put his cup down before launching into what was on his mind. "Well, George, old buddy, you sure took me by surprise. Here I am under the delusion that this joint will fall apart if its editor isn't around worrying about every damn detail and now I hear you're leaving tomorrow! How long are you gonna be gone?"

"Not long, Bern, but don't be concerned. While I'm away—I promise you—I'll be worrying full time. OK?"

"Thanks for nothing, boss. Say, it's gotta be at least three years since you last took off. What's goin' on?"

"Not much. I'm going up north to a funeral. That's all."

"A funeral! You're the guy who doesn't go to funerals. You've alibied your way outta all kinds of them, including one of our good friends, if you remember. Whose funeral?"

"My great-grandfather, Matthew Pope. But ..."

George hesitated, then decided to continue, "The truth is, Bernie, the funeral isn't the only reason I'm going all the way up north."

Bernie looked around for a cigarette, and then remembered, as he always did, that George hadn't smoked since high school.

"I know this sounds nuts but, according to my grandfather, who still lives up there, the woman who delivered Great-granddad when he was born was nursing him when he died. Bernie, he was well over ninety. How old must that woman be?"

"Well, I guess she'd have to be way over a hundred but that's not unheard of. What's your point?"

"At first, I just thought it would make a good story. You know—elderly woman, still active in the community at the age of a hundred and something. So I asked Granddad to send me a current photograph of her. Look at what he sent me! Once I saw this picture, I knew I had to meet her."

The camera had caught a tall, honey-skinned woman with thick black hair, tied back from a face that didn't look much more than fifty years old.

"Well, don't get too excited, George, the old boy musta' sent you the wrong picture."

"I phoned him. It's the right picture. Bernie, I have a feeling this woman has some special meaning for me and I need to find out what it is. No matter how good she looks, at her age she could pop off at any time. That's really why I'm going up there. If my hunch is wrong and I don't get something from her on a personal level, at least I'll bring back a good human interest story. I'll be back by the weekend."

But he wasn't.

George stood quite still, squinting at his surroundings. As his eyes became accustomed to the light, they fastened on a seated woman who seemed to be waiting for someone. From where he stood she looked familiar. Moving closer, a shock slashed through him. It was his Aunt Marion who had drowned earlier that year. His flush of shame at not having attended her funeral was immediately submerged by a sense of disorientation.

While he stood rooted to the spot, the woman rose and began moving away from him. Summoning his strength, he hurried after her shouting, "Auntie Marion, it's George! Wait! Wait!" Just as he caught up with her, an assault on his body, coming from deep within him, doubled him over. When he finally looked up, she was gone.

George opened his eyes. Rainwater was running down a concerned face only inches away from him. "Rest easy," she murmured. "You're going to be all right." The face belonged to the woman in the picture.

"I thought I'd died."

"Well, I guess you were wrong."

"I guess I was." He laboured to clear his head, "I know who you are; you looked after my great-granddad. I came up from Toronto especially to meet you. It's important to me that I talk to you."

"Not now. Now, you should sleep." Cool fingers closed his eyelids.

When he woke, this time in his grandfather's house, it was three days later. "Where is she?" George rasped, struggling up, and clutching wildly at the older man.

"Calm down, George. She's been here every day. Won't be back. Says you're fine."

George looked everywhere for her, but Maya Castelli had disappeared.

Maya's sanctuary was a single-room chalet, perched on a mountain two hours north-east of Timmins. The structure overlooked a valley rampant with colour from mineral deposits. The interior space was heated at night by a large stone fireplace, and during the day by the insistent blaze of the sun through a glass wall.

As the dazzling presence progressed across the sky and finally vanished, Maya sat frozen at her desk, her efforts to organize her thoughts challenged by images of George Pope. Beginning to shiver, she rose to light the fire. "Stop daydreaming and focus on your task," an inner voice told her sternly. It was no good; her wilful mental gymnastics defied control.

Maya couldn't understand what was happening to her. Why wasn't she more elated? The George Pope situation was just what she had been waiting for. "Now I can finish my life's work," she told herself for the tenth time. But her thoughts insisted on flitting about, covering the past, the future, then revisiting the scene of George Pope's revival: the sudden storm—running with her coat over her head—lightning—discovering him sheltering under a tree—the lethal bolt striking him just as she screamed her warning—seeing him fall.

She was at his side in an instant, and had got right in, all the way. In the dark labyrinth of his brain, her mind had grasped his deepest secret regret and his final desperate longing. Surprisingly, what he wanted most was to experience the intimacy of coupling. Stimulating a precise spot in his brain she was able to gratify this desire. The procedure, though it started by causing pain, was effective, and revived him.

This successful outcome was pivotal for Maya. At last, after decades of effort, she was about to reach closure on the task she had undertaken. She couldn't help being both happy and sad about this. She had been sent from a far off place with the mandate to use the healing powers they had given her to create and execute a project of benefit to the community. But, on its completion, according to the governing rules of her group, she would be obliged to retire.

Had it really been almost ninety years since that decisive interview with her director, Zandra?

"Soon, you must inform us of the field of endeavour to which you have chosen to dedicate yourself, Maya. The ten years you were given to investigate your options is almost up."

Maya remembered feeling very pleased with herself. She told Zandra, "I'm ready now. My plan is to show that, in all cases of unexpected death, if the right inducement can be found and given, the spirit will return to the body it abandoned. A six-year-old boy I was nursing died of a flash fever last month. When I probed his brain, I learned he had a passion for music. This knowledge allowed me to stimulate the right spot on his cerebral lobe to entice him back from wherever he had gone. My expectation is my investigations will show that this rule applies to unanticipated deaths of all ages."

There had been a problem. The community in Timmins viewed Maya's skills as appropriate for the illnesses of children and old people. She was not often summoned when mid-age adults were at risk. Her powers of resuscitation had worked perfectly for children, as well as for those elderly people who had been taken by something other than old age. But on the very rare occasions when she was summoned to the bedside of a fatally ill middle-aged adult, the final moment had already passed many minutes before her arrival and her revival efforts were unsuccessful. It was many years before she ultimately came to the conclusion that the reason for this failure was timing; once the brain pathways started to close, her mental probe could not reach full depth.

After suffering decades of frustration in her attempts to obtain access to young and mid-age adults at their moment of death, Maya began to think that she would never get the opportunity to offer a general application of her methods to bring back life. Although George Pope's recovery was only one case, the ease with which she had succeeded in resurrecting him plugged a critical gap in the list of near-death incidents she had recorded. Her concentration was evaporating. Standing up, she took ten deep breaths. What was the matter with her? She had better get moving and send her report to Zandra before she became totally distracted. For the next two hours she applied herself to her computer until at last she was ready to push the "send" button.

Good! Now she could think about George Pope without feeling guilty. Discovering his greatest regret had really surprised her. Who would have expected a person, who had apparently chosen to live in celibacy, to have, nonetheless, such painful feelings of longing? The man intrigued her. But what was it he wanted from her? She doubted he knew. Well, revived he was no longer open to her direct explorations. She would have to find out using more conventional methods. And since she didn't have other women's natural instincts for these things, it was probably going to be a matter of trial and error.

The only thing Maya really knew about herself for certain was that she had the ability and a calling to help people who were sick or dying. Original Sister Eva, from whom she and the others had been cloned, had been a highly-focused, prestigious healer. The Sisters' lives—more than double the normal length through genetic engineering—were endowed with Sister Eva's obsession for excellence.

Sisterhood rules dictated that they live in the world, work hard, and apply their knowledge and skills to benefit their communities. Director Zandra had often said, "We all start out the same; it is only through hard work that we become unique. Our noble goal—and our reward—is to make a contribution to others."

Maya enjoyed the way her life had unfolded thus far. But soon her work would be finished. And then Sisterhood rules required that she retire. She secretly wished she could look forward to a reward that went beyond a life of leisure, and the satisfaction of knowing you have done a good job. Before long, she would be facing endless days—perhaps fifty years of them—with nothing specific to do. She could not see herself fussing with a garden, or a paint brush, Those things would never satisfy her. She wanted much more. But was there an option? Maybe it was time to let George Pope find her.

When George, who had been pacing back and forth, smoking one of his grandfather's cigarettes, not noticing that he was dropping ashes on the living room rug, saw Maya through the window, he rushed out without a coat. Afraid she would disappear again he hurried towards her, calling out, "There you are, Ms Castelli. I've been looking everywhere for you. I couldn't leave here without our having a chance to talk."

As George came closer, he stared in confusion. What a beautiful woman! She didn't look much older than he did. He couldn't take his eyes off her, and what he saw was making his pulse race. Was it possible he felt attracted to her?

"Ms Castelli, I ... we ..." he stammered and stopped. Then he managed to get out, "You seem so young. Am I wrong in thinking that you're not what you seem?"

"No, not wrong. I'm not at all what I seem, Mr. Pope."

"Somehow I know you're responsible for my being alive right now. But, even before that, I felt there was some special connection between us. Would you know why? That's really the reason I came up here."

"I think I might. A very long time ago I saved the life of a little boy who grew up to become your great-grandfather."

George was trembling. "But how can that be?"

She paused, as if to consider his question then, taking his arm, she started walking, "George, I am going to tell you some things I have never told anyone before."

When she finished her narrative, he found himself totally unable to speak. As the silence continued, Maya had a thought. "George, I believe I know what you need from me."

He said softly. "How could you, when I'm not sure I know myself?"

She remembered his infinite yearning and how she had used it to bring him back into the world. "Have you really never found anyone you wanted?"

"No," he said sadly. "Never anyone—until now."

He could feel her intense, penetrating gaze burning its way through him. Not knowing what else to do, he took her hands. Turning them over, he examined the lines on her palms. As he touched her, waves of excitement began coursing through him. Out of nowhere an impulse, that he felt helpless to fight, moved him. Slowly, he began pulling her closer, testing for the resistance that would signal him to stop. When their bodies touched he whispered, "I've never known how to relate at that level. But you make me want to learn."

"Then we can learn together," she said simply.

LISA O'LEARY, B.A.Sc., has been seriously pursuing her fiction writing hobby over the last four years. Other publications include previous Wordscape issues. Interests include nature, animals, teaching children, music, and many sports. She is currently working on short stories.

The Apartment • Lisa O'Leary

"Why can't I find the right place?" Jenna lifted her nose into the air. Her neck arched so the back of her head sat on her shoulders. This made reading the paper in the light much easier when one didn't want to adjust her glasses.

"Robert, maybe that little place in Rosedale should be considered?"

"Mother, I've told you before and I'll repeat it again. I don't want to commute. I don't even see why you want to move. We have everything we need right here. What exactly is wrong with this place?"

"There's nothing wrong with this place but it would be so nice to have an address that would impress." Jenna lifted her eyebrows. "People will look much more favourably on us if we live in a more trendy area. Less crime. You see those types in the grocery store every week. I want to be around the kind of people we deserve to be around. Besides if we're with a better crowd maybe you would find a wife and I could find a worthy friend."

"Mother, I don't see anything wrong with the people around here. In fact most are very pleasant and my finding a wife has nothing to do with the neighbourhood we're in."

"I've heard your chances of marrying someone within five miles of your home is higher than any other location. Think Rob, you could meet some nice girl who happens to live in one of those big houses. We would be set for life. I could show her, and my new friend, off to the ladies at the church."

"I can't believe you're talking this way. Even if we did move and I did meet one of those girls, we would be going to a different church and no one there would care who I married."

"Robert, you can be so difficult sometimes."

"Mom, I've already told you if it's important to you to move, and you find a place you feel strongly about, I will move, but I'm just letting you know my opinion."

"Look right here Robert, in this paper. It says, a town house with a view in a prize neighbourhood."

No mention of price. She put the paper down on her lap and watched Robert shaking his head as he left the room. Her brows wrinkled as she pictured herself in this Rosedale home.

I must see it immediately, Jenna thought. She threw her coat over her shoulders and walked down the musty hallway to the elevator. A familiar voice called out to her.

"Hello Mrs. Matthews. How are you today?"

Poor Mrs. Jag. She always looked so tired. It was hard to tell whether the cause was her strains in life or her immense weight.

"Nice to see you, Hannah," Jenna said with a smile, her standard response delivered with the warmth of a grandmother.

Jenna looked around at the people on the subway train. Everyone seemed tired and it was still morning.

I guess I should have asked him what the rent was, Jenna thought. It'll be difficult convincing Robert if it's expensive. Oh well, it could be a nice outing. Look at these sorry sights. Trying to get themselves somewhere, not to be wealthy, but just to get by. Well I shouldn't be so hard on them. I could be in their situation if Leonard hadn't been so tight with our money. I had wonderful ideas but Leonard just looked at me sceptically and tightened his wallet a little more at those times. I should try to remember the good times. I was told many years ago that it is bad luck to speak bad memories of the dead. Was I supposed to cross myself? I can't remember how to reverse it. Oh well, here's my stop.

She walked down the street with a smile and a rigid gait, trying to be elegant. Huge oak trees hung dark and heavy over the sidewalks. Keeping an eye open for numbers, she tried not to become too excited. The house was not far off. A Mercedes drove by.

Imagine if I lived here I might know those people. She lifted her hand to attempt a royal salute. "Hello neighbour." They didn't notice.

She stopped in front of one home and reached into her pocket to collect a wrinkled paper. Straightening it out she verified the address. This was the house. It was beautiful, one of those old mansions that was sneakily divided into apartments. Anyone driving by would never guess it was not one big house. A man outside was doing the gardening.

"Hello, do you live here?" she inquired.

"No, I'm the gardener." He quickly resumed his position.

Suddenly she felt elegant, imagining that she had always lived here. She knocked at the door. A well-dressed man appeared.

"Can I help you, ma'am."

"Yes, I'm here to look at the apartment." She nervously glanced down at the scrunched paper now wet in her palm, expecting that she'd accidentally written the wrong address.

"Yes ma'am, come this way."

"Who are you?" Jenna asked.

"Security, ma'am."

She walked wide-eyed through the spectacular but small apartment. She was going to ask about the neighbours but at this point she didn't care.

"I'll leave you to look around for a few moments ma'am," and he left.

Such an elegant looking man; he could pass for a butler. She pinched herself to make sure she was still alive. A dream? No.

Jenna looked out the window and saw a beautiful English garden with white lawn furniture—wrought-iron, probably painted. She pictured herself sipping tea and allowing the security man to top it up for her. Something made her uneasy. She noticed a neighbour cutting a hedge, rather warmly dressed for a day like today. Jenna thought she could feel him watching her through sunglasses that almost covered his entire face, even though his head was turned to his work. She moved away from the window still feeling his uncomfortable gaze.

"Maybe he's only eccentric," she thought.

"Ma'am this is our rental contract."

She looked over the paper with disbelief.

"Is this price correct?" she inquired. "There must be a mistake."

He glanced at the paper though not seriously.

"Yes ma'am, it is correct. Is there a problem?"

"No, but I thought it might be higher. Are there other costs? Maintenance? Utilities?"

"It's all-inclusive ma'am."

She realized that she should have waited until Robert got home to show him the paper. He always liked to read the small print. But this was just too good to be reality. She had to take it before someone else snatched it. Robert would be so happy—eventually.

Robert wasn't thrilled.

"Mother! What did you do? What if it leaks or something? Maybe they do just want it occupied, but they could occupy it for much more money. This sounds suspicious to me. What was their reason for being so inexpensive?"

"Well I didn't ask, Robert. I didn't want to question people's good intentions. It could be rude."

"It appears you signed the contract so we are going to be there for at least six months. Why would they give you such a deal?"

Jenna only smiled at him eagerly.

The moving day was rather uneventful. Some tears were shed, especially saying goodbye to Hannah, but she would be invited to the house-warming party. Jenna had to have a least one friend there. All of Robert's were coming and he was the one who thought the house-warming was silly. But that day arrived quickly.

"What a beautiful home!"

Everyone complimented them on the house.

Thank goodness we had enough sandwiches, Jenna thought. She wasn't expecting so many people to come. But once a person moves into a desirable area, they become more desirable. At least this is what she told Robert.

She was really shocked when she heard the rumour for the first time. If it had come from someone other than Jason, Robert's best friend, the impact might have been less.

"I never imagined you living in a haunted house, Robert."

Jason, like Robert was also a very accurate and practical lawyer.

"You must be familiar with the house where Georgia Stanton went missing. You remember, Robert, they thought it was the neighbour who lived right in this house, but there never was any evidence. Friends say she was a generous woman. Her family held the opposite view. The investigators said maybe it was her sons. They didn't get along, always arguing. You know the types. Never did find her body. They say it might be hidden in the wall or the floor of this very room. I don't believe much in haunted houses, but if you notice any funny smells, I'd have the police in here in a minute if I were you."

Jenna grabbed Robert's arm yanking him down beside her on the couch. "This can't be so, Robert."

"Mother, I said you were too hasty. This is what we're stuck with. So we'd better make the best of it."

"I have to be here all by myself. Aren't you at all concerned? What if the killer comes for me?"

"What's the saying—if you make your bed ..."

"Robert, you can be so ..."

"I know, difficult. I'll find out more for you. I already knew about this. I briefly looked into it when you took the apartment. Maybe that woman just disappeared, didn't want to be found?

For the first week Jenna was afraid to move. Any movement she did make was to check all the walls and floors for hollow spaces and hidden passages. Unfortunately, she couldn't locate any.

It doesn't mean they're not there, she told herself.

The security man was starting to look at her in a funny manner.

"He probably wondered what all the banging sounds were about. Don't you think, Robert?"

Robert grunted in agreement but continued to read his paper.

"I specifically watched the neighbour on our left. He does seem to be an odd type. Rarely looks at anybody. He wears huge clothing even in the spring heat. Yesterday and today was hot and yet he was so bundled. Robert I'm scared here but you know, I've decided I'm going to find the answer to this crime."

"Mother, I want you to stay out of it. Can't you take up knitting or something? You will get yourself into trouble if you get involved with this."

Jenna thought over Robert's words as she walked to the library. Robert does over react so.

The library was definitely the place to start. The newspapers would tell her what needed to be known. Sure enough, the articles told of the disappearance, but more importantly, gave Jenna a picture of Georgia.

Somehow people don't seem real until one looks at their picture. Then you realize there was a person there. A living, breathing being who suffered this experience.

"Tell me, who did you think did it?" she asked the gardener when she returned home. "Do you think it was a son?"

"I get so angry when people accuse." He threw down his trowel. They always listen to rumours. I can tell you I know the sons did not kill her. At least one didn't for sure."

"How would you know that?" Jenna inquired.

"Didn't anyone tell you? I am her son."

She concentrated on the neighbour on the left side for some considerable time when she got in after the library visit. She decided he had to be the one. He seemed too suspicious not to know something. But she knew more information would be needed. The only answer was to continue spying, but not from afar. She would creep closer after dusk. He never came out in the evening. She would look into his house for clues.

After dinner Jenna made her way to his backyard, feeling a bit jumpy. She exited the front of her building and walked quickly up his side walk, looking around to ensure no one was watching. She lifted the heavy latch on the garden gate and entered; a breeze blew it shut before she had time to close it. She jumped, sure he must have heard. Fearing he would come to the window, she looked for a place to hide but there was none. Not being exactly skinny or flexible, she felt relieved that she didn't get stuck somewhere calling for Robert to save her. Fortunately, no one saw her.

She crept by the vines, past the side door, and stretched forward just enough to look in the window. From there she could clearly see the neighbour. With his back to her, he removed his hat. Then an odd thing happened. He lifted the front of his hair, and all of it came off in his hand. He was wearing a wig.

She cupped her hands and leaned on the window so she could see without glare. He lifted his hand first, to remove his glasses, then, his big sweater.

He spun around and was face to face with Jenna. This was not her neighbour frowning back at her. She was looking into the face of Georgia Stanton. Her heart leap into her throat. She headed for the gate but the side door into the house swung open. Georgia stood between her and freedom, wearing a blank look on her expressionless face as she motioned aggressively for Jenna to enter. She hesitated. The angered face left Jenna feeling she had no choice but to comply.

"As soon as I saw you watching me I knew you wouldn't leave this alone." Georgia spoke with irritation.

Frazzled, and shaken, Jenna managed to quiver a reply. Tears streaming down her face. "I should have listened to Robert. He's my son. I'm just too nosy. He tells me all the time I should leave things alone, mind my own business. I wish I had."

Suddenly Georgia looked softer. A hint of compassion appeared in her eyes. "Please calm down. I'm not going to hurt you. I was scared myself when I saw someone sneaking up my pathway. It wasn't until you banged the side gate and I peeked out the door that I realized it was you. You seem like a kind woman. I always wished I had the kind of relationship with my sons that you have with yours. While you were watching me, I was watching you."

"I was talking to your son the gardener. He seems concerned about you. Why don't you tell him you're here. I'm sure, at least, he is worried terribly," Jenna replied.

"Well, you don't know my relatives. I wouldn't say they don't care but they are a greedy lot. I retired some years ago and I've always wanted to escape my family. They were talking behind my back about putting me in a home. Can you imagine, me? I might be a little shaky and I do need help sometimes, but I'm still as quick as a whip. Yes, I planned my disappearance. But this has given me a chance to see what my sons are like without my influence. They are a little slow. Can you imagine a mother coming under disguise and her own sons not recognising her? So you see, you must not tell anyone. I must conclude for myself what my children are truly like. Maybe I'm the one not so bright as this is the only way I can think to do it. I will let them know in due time.

"Please, dear lady, don't leave. Join me for tea today and again at another time."

She placed the cup in front of Jenna, who didn't have to think. She picked up the cup gently with a friendly nod and smile. After all, it was a friend that I really wanted, she thought contentedly.

Now to find a wife for Robert.

JUNE SALMON attended Lawrence Park Collegiate, Toronto and received a B.A. with double major in French/English from Vic. at U.of T. Since then she has completed 32 years teaching elementary school in North York and Muskoka. She has been married to David for 31 years, has a son Gregory, in 3rd year Queen's and a daughter Jennifer in her OAC year, heading for medicine at McMaster next year. A secret passion for many years, writing is now a daily delight, and recognition in the form of publication is an intense joy.

Moonfleet Remembered • June Salmon

Mystery at night,
dark water, muffled sounds,
the sense of danger in discovery—
shadows cross the moon face
between the trees and on the beach.
What secret search begets these
hurried hidden steps we spy upon?
The answer obvious—smugglers.
Is their cargo smuggled brandy-wine
from coastal France across the sea?
Is it jewels from ancient kings and queens
or slave trade we have stumbled on
this dark and lonely night?

Pull cloaks tight round.
Don't make a sound.
Let's creep back home before we're caught
in grownup revelry.
Wait till clouds cover up yon moon.
Soft at first,
watch for roots,
then run for all your might!

Let midnight sights drift out of mind.
We dare not tell a soul we've seen
the Moonfleet in the bay.

CATHERINE MACDONALD, a Certified General Accountant, is retired after a 25 year career with government and hospitals and now dedicates her talents to charities. She is currently the president of the Manna Food Bank in Bracebridge, a director of the Bracebridge Agricultural Society and an area Co-ordinator for Edgar Cayce Canada. She has published several feature articles with various magazines both in Canada and United States. She recently self-published a novel, historical fiction entitled, *Heaven Knows*.

CREATIVE NON-FICTION

Be Still and Know God • Catherine MacDonald

I was born on Halloween in the middle of a snow storm. The second world war was raging and my father was overseas, and as destiny would have it, he was killed before we ever met. After the war my mother remarried and I never really became part of her new family. I made my life at church and school. My parents were strict fundamentalists so my places for extra-curricular activity were restricted to the public library.

I married very early, eighteen-years-old to be exact, expecting to escape my tethers. But within the first year I gave birth and experienced the pain of losing a child. Now I was caught in a different kind of prison, one of guilt and grief. I gave birth to three more children within the next four years and before the third one was born, my husband decided he had made a mistake and chose to take a separate road through life.

I was a single mother now. Not only did divorce go against my fundamentalist background but I only had a high school education. Jobs that paid enough to support my growing family were scarce. So it became necessary to keep two jobs. This too, became a kind of prison.

I decided that the only way out of my situation was to return to school. So, for the next seven years I studied accounting at night school. At the time my children were graduating high school, I became a certified accountant and could now earn enough money to concentrate on holding down only one job.

Raising three children on a shoestring, working and carrying a heavy school course-load armed me with an unusual stamina and my energy levels soared. To say the least I emerged a highly motivated individual. By this time, I had long ago abandoned the fundamentalist religion, but I still maintained a close personal relationship with God.

By 1985, I was in command of a very large workforce and controlled billions of dollars.

Then my perfect health began to deteriorate. My stress levels flared. I gained unsightly weight, my cholesterol count went through the ceiling. My once-elegant business clothes didn't fit any more. My lustrous curly hair fell limp and dull. I decided to take a long overdue-vacation, and chose Europe as a destination.

The ancient history that I had once found so interesting came to life and I was able to temporarily clear my mind of the daily stresses that I had created in my life.

On the last few days of the vacation, I decided to drive up to northern Holland to see if a historical village that I had been attracted to in a book still existed. I had thought about this village several times in the past year and I had even brought the book with me, with the intent of making time to explore this curiosity.

I found the village on the map and set out on the adventure. As I approached the village I was overcome with the most incredible sensation of returning to a homeland. By the time I got out of the car, I was emotionally distraught. My logical mind was in a panic. Me, who was always in total control of all situations, crying like a baby in the middle of a street in a strange village? I managed to compose myself and spent a few hours exploring the little streets and shops. I knew what was round every corner.

My all-knowing left brain kicked in with, "lucky guesses." "Yes, that was it, lucky guesses," I agreed.

The vacation came to an end, I returned home, back to my stress environment. But I couldn't shake the experience from my mind.

In an attempt to rationalize the situation, my left-brain decided that I should consider the possibility of genetic memory so I spent considerable time exploring this idea and tracing my family tree to determine who had come from this village. I found this a pleasant diversion from my usual no-nonsense life. I had a delightful time tracing my family origins and found that I was Irish through and through.

I returned to the village three more times. Each time feeling more comfortable with the surroundings, particularly the old seventeenth-century stone church, whose unique steeple towered above the little brick houses with their white starched lace curtains.

I had already told several friends about my experience and had kept them abreast of my family tree findings. But now, I was back to square one, with the nagging sensation in my stomach that I was standing on the brink of a great discovery. But what?

Finally a friend questioned, "Did you ever think that you may have lived there in another life time?"

I laughed.

My friend added, "It may not be in the Bible, but do you realize that more than half the population of the world believe that we do live more than one life time?"

I hadn't thought of it that way before nor was I interested in entertaining this theory now and for a short while I put the whole thing completely out of my mind. Well, maybe not completely....

During my fifth visit to the village I was sitting in the little country church, and decided that I was going to look into the reincarnation theory when I got home.

As fate would have it, on returning to work, a friend introduced me to a member of the Association for Research and Enlightenment. Before very many minutes passed I knew the name of Edgar Cayce. So off to my local library I went, keyed in Edgar Cayce, and the only book available was the "Many Happy Returns of Edgar Cayce." By the time I had finished the book, I had firmly decided that the reincarnation theory deserved more than a quick look.

I soon had an appointment with a hypnotherapist and with much trepidation I arrived in her office full of questions and misgivings.

Once my controlling self allowed me to relax and flow with the hypnotic trance, I began seeing a small boy standing in a farmer's field. The surroundings were flat as far as the eye could see and it took me, what seemed like, several minutes to realize that the boy was actually me. The regression took me through my childhood into my adolescence. I was educated in a Protestant seminary in a large city. At the end of an internship in a city church, I was assigned to my own congregation. I boarded a sailing vessel, and after a very unpleasant sea journey I arrived at a port that, at first, I didn't recognize. It wasn't until I climbed a small incline that I suddenly saw the familiar church with its unique steeple, and I realized I was seeing my beloved village some three hundred years ago. Most things had changed, but not the church; there it was gloriously standing guard over the village. The regression gave me the date of mid-eighteenth century. I came out of the trance state into total shock.

I still didn't believe it. I spent many long hours in libraries and art galleries checking for the authenticity of the clothing, architecture, and the development of the protestant church and education system for the time period. The research soon physically took me back to Holland, where I was able to ascertain the name of the pastor that served the church during the time period including his portrait and the original manuscript of an epistle that he wrote on the Apostle Peter. I was stunned. No, I was ecstatically devastated. The concept of touching personal items that may have been mine in another life time was overwhelming.

I was intrigued by the epistle on the Apostle Peter. I kept wondering why a pastor would devote so much time and effort to one single apostle.

Was it possible that I had lived more than two life times? The second regression began with a young man at the university in Athens who had just been invited to join the new Christian movement as a Greek translator for a man called Simon. It didn't take me very long to realize that this young man was myself and I quickly moved along through that life time following Simon-Peter through his ministry.

Of course, this experience started me off on another research frenzy reading everything that I could written about the Apostle Peter, the development of the early Christian movement checking the historical accuracies of dress, architecture and culture. This research lead me right back to Mr. Cayce who had given detailed readings on the early development of the church.

All my beliefs and life philosophies were now under question. Could it really be possible? Could I really have lived more than one life time? And if so, what was life really about? Edgar Cayce believed we live many lives and my respect for the gentleman was growing with every book I read.

Maybe he was right and if so, where had my mind been for the past fifty years? With all my education and knowledge, how could I have been so uninformed about the true meaning of life. Cayce believed that each life on earth is a learning experience, with the purpose of progressing towards spiritual perfection. It certainly made more sense than the fundamentalist's theory that we are born, we live and we die. If we are good, we go to heaven and walk on streets of gold. If not, we burn in hell forever. This had never appealed to me. There was no purpose.

It was when I totally grasped the concept that I am a soul that was created in the beginning of time, currently living in this body, that my life changed. The material things that I had worshipped for so long became unnecessary. My life took new meaning. In meditation, I questioned God. "Why did you send me across the ocean all those times, you could have just pointed me to a book or something?"

The reply was loud and clear, "You wouldn't have believed it unless you had your own personal experience." He was right, I wouldn't have.

Family Superstitions • Maria Duncalf-Barber

Shhhhhh
She heard the noise behind her
It sounded like a banshee
Her head was full

With the stories she'd been told
From her grandmother in Ireland.
Yarns about people that had passed over
And where not happy
Tales of apparitions and spirits

Legend has it
That their souls would roam around at night
screaming from rooftop to rooftop.
Wailing into the wee small hours

In her safe little home at night.
She closes the curtains
Clasping her hands together
To pray for the souls
Wandering aimlessly in the cold

JENNIE T.S. CHOBAN was born in Ukraine, lived in Germany during the Second World War, and emigrated with her family to Lachine, Quebec, Canada in 1949. She and her daughter April Qureshi co-wrote *Kapusta or Cabbage*, a mother and daughter historical and culinary journey. Anecdotes and recipes from *Kapusta or Cabbage* were reprinted in the *Mariposa Cook Book*, published by Vehicule Press and sponsored by the Stephen Leacock Museum in Orillia. Jennie loves to travel and is writing a romance novel and a self-help book. She lives in Toronto.

Maybe you can go Home Again • Jennie Choban

Mike was his name and I was his game. But never on a Friday. Friday was Mike's night out with the boys. Or, so he said.

I was twenty at the time, lived in Lachine, Quebec, and worked for the Canadian National Railways in downtown Montreal.

Mike was two years older and lived in LaSalle. He wanted to study agriculture, but his father insisted no son of his would live a life in manure, so Mike opted for the respectable trade of tool and die making. All the time I knew Mike, I never understood what tool and die meant, and still don't.

Mike stood five ten, slim, athletic built and a brush-cut that made him irresistible to women, especially me. We dated regularly during the week and on Saturday night. But I never knew what his definition of "out with the boys" on Friday meant. Especially since the guys in Montreal had a favourite saying, "Friday night is poultry night—every girl present gets a free goose." Funny as the joke was, it didn't console me that Mike spent the evening shooting pool with his buddies, in an all-male tavern where no women were allowed. A man's world. But I didn't believe him, and six months into our relationship, mistrust took over and I gave him an ultimatum.

But my jealous demands backfired and Mike turned every day of the week into Friday night. *Sans moi.*

Weeks later, I realized his need for freedom, and pleaded for a reconciliation. But Mike was a stubborn Taurus and the damage was done.

Back then, in the early 1960s, when I fell in love with Mike, the latest issue ran off the press around midnight and the street vendors stopped pedestrians and cars in downtown Montreal to peddle the morning's paper. "Montreal Gazette! Read all about it! Get your morning Gazette!"

"Went home with the Gazette, eh?" male friends often teased each other after an unsuccessful night of "chercher les femmes."

Saturday nights bars and dance-halls reverberated with party-goers. At the beginning of the evening, the dateless guys were too selective and by midnight all the good looking girls were taken, leaving the guys crying in their beer. By closing time, some guys were too drunk to know the difference between a good-looker from a bad hooker and would have settled for anyone. But, alas, even the lowly wallflowers had standards and sent the poor slobs on their way.

Those rejected young men seldom learned from experience and many nights they were seen trudging on home with a newspaper tucked under an armpit. Anything to hold onto for comfort and warmth.

The next day, right after confession at the church, they gathered at the local corner bar and bragged about their conquests.

"Did you see that one beg me? I told her to cool it, man. Maybe we'll run into each other some other time, eh?"

"Yeah, like when she's finished developing, right?"

"Right on, man."

"Women, eh? Just can't live without us, eh?"

"Me? Come home with the Gazette? Never! Unless I just choose to."

"Yeah, me neither. Could have had any one of those chicks last night. Just needed to catch on my reading. You know me, eh?"

Sure, we knew them. Well, at least they didn't go home empty handed. Those type of guys were labelled as "Sunday Morning—Dimanche Matin—Gazet-tears."

Yet, while we dated, Mike always went home with me on Saturday night. At least until I pushed him too far and then Mike was back on the streets.

For a while I shunned all friends, stayed home and cried. And prayed that Mike's misery contributed to the Montreal Gazette's circulation.

Months flew by. Once or twice we bumped into each other in public, but each time, I was either with a date or ignored him for spite. When Mike finally did call, three years had gone by and I was wearing an engagement ring.

"Why are you marrying that guy?" Mike asked.

"Because you never asked me."

Was I flattered? Of course. But too much time had passed and I was in love with someone else.

By the time I was twenty-six, my husband and I moved to Toronto and we were expecting our first child. After thirteen years of marriage that shouldn't have happened, we separated. So much for 'till death do us part.

Shortly before we married, my husband-to-be insisted I tear up every picture I had of Mike. But, I couldn't bring myself to destroy the negatives and kept them hidden among my most cherished possessions, greeting cards and cocktail napkins Mike and I ever shared. Why did I save them? Why else if not for those uncertain times in my life. Or maybe that's why my marriage didn't last.

In 1990, after my divorce became final, I reverted to my maiden name, stashed away all the wedding pictures and had the old back and white negatives developed. And to celebrate my independence and a fiftieth birthday, I opened a bottle of President's Champagne and settled comfortably on the couch. With a box of tissues beside me, and using Mike's picture as a bookmark, I proceeded to read the latest tearjerker. And as my heart did a flip, I couldn't help but wonder what would have happened had I given Mike his Fridays off.

When I finally managed to talk about my obsession with the past to a friend at work, she suggested I try to locate Mike.

"Nah, I wouldn't know where to begin," I said, half dismissing the idea.

"Check out the phone books," Lois said with great optimism.

"Well, actually I've done that," I admitted my foolish actions.

I heard through the grapevine from friends in Montreal that Mike had moved out of Quebec. So I spent one boring Saturday afternoon at the local library going through city telephone books, but never had the nerve to call any of the Mike K's listed.

"I'll do the calling," Lois got excited. All of a sudden she was my own personal private investigator.

"What if he doesn't remember me?"

"What if he does?"

"But I'm not as young as I used to be."

"And you think he is?" she assured me and then laughed. "He's probably bald and pot-bellied. You sure you want to do this?"

I wasn't sure of anything. Not anymore.

When Mike and I were an item, I was five feet two and weighed just over a hundred pounds. Thirty years later, I'm almost the weight same as I was when I gave birth to my first son and an inch shorter.

"He probably prefers women half his age," I said, ruling out more possibilities.

"What if he doesn't?"

"What if he's married?"

"What if he's not?" Lois was such an optimist.

"What if he's gay?" I offered my last option.

"Then stop wasting your time," Lois lost all patience. I was sure she meant her time. "Stop dreaming about the impossible and go on with your life. You don't really have that much to feel sorry about, you know."

She was right. My son and daughter were grown and on their own. I had not yet been blessed with grandchildren, but life was pretty good.

So, I decided to let bygones be bygones and devote my life to my job as systems analyst. Since there were no men in my life to give me a lifestyle I rightfully deserved, I would concentrate on RRSP's so not to spend my old age as a bag-lady living out of a no-name shopping cart.

But Lady Luck was on my side. A couple of weeks later, I was at a hotel in Ottawa for my school reunion. The ballroom was crowded and people hugged one another—as if they hadn't seen each other in years. A banner suspended from the ceiling read WELCOME FRIENDS FROM THE 60'S.

There was Tony, who married my best friend Natalie. I laughed as his arms held me tight and his potbelly almost knocked me over.

"For an old broad, you look good," Tony snickered.

I caught my reflection in a wall of mirrors. The knee-length royal blue cocktail dress hugged my waist and the matching heels gave me height. My short brown curly hair, streaked with highlights, reflected a much younger me. Tony was right, I didn't look half bad.

Then there was Terry, a friend who went to teachers college. My mother warned me that one day I'd regret not marrying him.

"A nice respectable professor," mother said many times. "You could do worse."

Unfortunately, Terry never once asked me out on a date, so the choice was not mine to be had. Terry was better looking than I remembered him and so was his wife.

As I hugged and laughed and mingled with the crowd, I couldn't believe the changes in the friends and acquaintances I hadn't seen since high school.

"Did you see him?" Natalie nudged me.

"Who?" I said.

"Him. You know," she bubbled with excitement.

"No kidding? Brian's here?" I said. "Is Mila with him?" After all, it was their town and Prime Minister Malroney escorting his wife to a high school reunion was a great political step, with the elections not far off.

"No," Natalie shook her head. "Mike ... Mike is here."

I was in shock. It couldn't be. I panicked and like Cinderella at the stroke of midnight, I ran out of the ballroom and into the gardens. I had to get away. All the years of looking, thinking of him and being so close to him now ... I just couldn't do it. I couldn't bring myself to look at him. Cowardly, I ran across the lawn until I came to a country road and as I got further away I realized that I didn't even get a chance to see what he looked like. I turned to go back, but then stopped . I was mesmerized by a group of people standing on a hill.

As one of the men turned to face me, I froze when I recognised him. Ever so slowly, as he walked way from the crowd, he removed his grey trench coat and casually let it fall to the ground. With his right hand, he removed a hat off his head and flung it through the air—like a kid tossing a Frisbee.

My eyes were fixed on him. As slim as ever, ageing had been very kind to him. Handsomely dressed in a light grey summer suit, he had an air of class about him as he nonchalantly strolled down the hill. His short, pure white, wavy hair shone as the sun
behind him rested on the horizon. He was just a tinge shorter than I remembered and as he came closer, my heart beat so fast I thought any second now it would pop out and he'd bend down to scoop it up off the grass and hug it to himself.

"Mike," I heard his name come out in a whisper. "It's really you."

He said nothing, yet his piercing blue eyes danced, forming little crows feet on his tanned face. He shook his head slightly as if saying, "I don't believe it." His cheeks showed deep dimples as his mouth turned into a wide smile—the same smile that made me fall in live with him. So many, many years ago.

He stopped a few feet in front of me, turned away for a split second and then looked back straight into my eyes. For a moment I thought how much his actions reminded me of Paul Newman—cocky and yet shy, in a cute way. The way Paul's face squints as if saying "Ah, shucks! Joanne ..."

I gulped in air. I couldn't believe it. After thirty years, he was still the same man I once knew and loved, and lost. Now, I had been given another chance to right the wrong of my past.

Mike spread his arms open and I walked into them. My arms circled his waist and as he held me close, I buried my face into his chest. His presence was overwhelming, a faint aroma of Old Spice filled my nostrils. I closed my eyes. My body tingled as his heart beat fast against mine.

To enable me to catch a breath, I drew slightly away from him and as I raised my head, I slowly opened my eyes. But instead of Mike's smiling face, I saw darkness. My eyes searched around, but the only image I saw was a shaft of light beaming through a window. As my eyes became accustomed to the surroundings, I realized I was in bed. Alone.

I tried to understand what had happened and then through a daze, it dawned on me that I had been dreaming. Mike came back to me— but only in my dream. A dream so real that I had to get back to sleep again. I wanted the dream to continue. Mike was about to say something just before I awoke. I needed to know what he had to say.

Resting my head on my pillow, I tossed and turned for what seemed like hours and at last I slept. But the dream did not continue.

That day at work, I asked Lois to interpret my dream. She's no help, just shakes her head in mockery and shrugs her shoulders.

"Your dreams are a prediction of future events," Lois said when she realized how desperate I was in my quest.

"That's impossible. There's no way I can predict the future," I said.

"Maybe your desire to see Mike was so strong, you willed it to happen."

"If I can will those things to happen, why can't I will a win at the lottery?"

Lois grinned.

"I have to know what the dream meant," I said. "I just have to know."

"Fine," she pacified me. ""Let's go look it up in one of those dream books."

After lunch, Lois and I walked down Yonge Street to Lichtman Books and I made a beeline for the occult section. Finally, I waited impatiently my turn at the cash register. It didn't matter that the book cost thirty dollars. The book jacket said the author was a world renowned expert. If he couldn't tell me what my dread meant—no one could.

"Don't buy the book!" Lois grabbed my arm and pulling me out of the line, she dragged me to stacks of out-of-town newspapers lining a bottom shelf along the floor.

"Read that!" Lois points to an article. "There's your answer."

I scanned the article quickly ... something about a high school reunion at the Chateau Laurier Hotel. The headline read WELCOME FRIENDS FROM THE 60'S. The reunion was to be on the 24th.

"That's next week. Where's the Chateau Laurier, anyway?"

"Same place as in your dream," Lois said. "Ottawa."

"Can't be," I dismissed the connection. No way could this be happening as my dream had happened.

"Take a good look where the newspaper's from."

My heart beat rapidly, and as I tried to control my shaking knees, I grabbed hold of Lois' arm as we both stared at the newspaper banner—which read: The Ottawa Citizen.

OLGA DEY-BERGMOSER THOMPSON was born in Holland and grew up in Germany. Trained as a multilingual translator, she has done a lot of travelling and came to Canada in 1963, settling in Toronto. She worked for twenty-five years as a full-time multilingual translator for the Government of Ontario. In 1976, she served as VIP hostess at the Montreal Olympics. She has written travelogues, contributed to a major European linguistic journal, conducted numerous interviews with authors and artists, authored *"Under the Spell of India"* and *"People."* She co-authored many books on art and travel.

I Shall Keep Your Image Intact
• Olga Dey-Bergmoser Thompson

Swaying with the rhythm, his eyes slightly closed, he sings:

Nous n'avons qu'une vie pour nous amuser
nous avons toute la mort pour nous reposer

telling us not to waste the so precious hours of our lives, not to waste time that waits for absolutely nobody.

I feel his piercing glances but ignore him. He has black curly hair, pitch-black eyes, a handlebar moustache and a voice of gold.

He puts down his mike, steps off the stage and leads me to the dance floor. The dance is sheer ecstasy, for he is an excellent dancer. None of those smothering contact manoeuvres. And while dancing he continuously sings to me in his mellifluous provoking voice.

He's a great leader and brilliant conversationalist, switching easily from English to French, to Spanish, and Arabic.

He politely excuses himself to return to the stage but asks me to wait for him till the end of the show when he wants to take me bar-hopping.

We leave by about midnight and meet several friends of his; we drink, dance, and laugh—the most carefree laughter I remember for quite some time.

Ismail is his name. And although only twenty-five, he already had one marriage behind him.

"Glamour, that's what screwed up our heads until there was nothing left but ashes. But what I regret most, is the loss of Nedja, my daughter.

"How about you?" he asks me brusquely.

"Also one broken marriage behind me—and nobody but myself to blame."

We are totally frank about ourselves. Secrets neither of us would normally talk about, pour forth. We enjoy the unreserved confidence total strangers so often spontaneously share.

Like children we walk hand in hand through the balmy night and end up in his suite. At four in the morning he gives me a karate demonstration and then takes me back to the hotel two hours before the wake-up call.

The group I travel with is extremely friendly and well organised but nobody associates too intimately with the local people. Many of the tour participants are married couples and those who are not, guard the aloof, cool, academic approach and consider the local inhabitants colourful elements of their studies—nothing more, nothing less.

Walking home in the wee hours of the morning Ismail says as if he could read my thoughts, "Don't worry. I shan't single you out. Anything to please you. But I promise you one thing: tonight the moment my programme is finished, I shall follow you. Please don't go dancing with anyone else. Wait for me there. Fès is the intellectual centre of our country. Let me show it to you. Good night, Silvia."

"Good night, Ismail. Thanks for a truly lovely time."

"See you in Fès, Silvia."

By the time our bus leaves, Ismail just happens to be walking around but doesn't give me a single glance as if we had never laid eyes on each other. Nobody suspects anything about our outing. Everything is *comme il faut*.

Our tour starts at 6 a.m. sharp as we head for Moulay Idriss, a holy city of pilgrimage, built on a rocky slope, dominated by the mausoleum of Moulay Idriss the First, a most venerated saint.

I am not really listening to the guide as my thoughts start drifting to Ismail. By the time I open my eyes, we are in Volubilis, an ancient, yet well preserved Roman city, a historical site, which has been deserted apparently since the third century AD. It abounds in mosaics of breathtaking detail and gently flowing lines, crowned by a triumphal arch overlooking the plains of Volubilis.

Our guide for the day is an elderly man who considers women the greatest boon that can be bestowed upon mankind. In glowing colours he praises Moulay Ismail who is said to have had four official wives and as many as 496 women offered to him as presents which he magnanimously condescended to accept.

Old, but still full of life, the guide presents a love song about meeting his beloved at the bewitching hour of 6:15. It has so many wailing refrains that we start feeling uneasy and when he finally seems to have come to the end we are so relieved that we give him tremendous applause which he seems to mistake for encouragement. Oh, what miscalculation on our part: He is still wailing away when we drive into Fès.

We visit a medersa, a Koran school, where a little boy of about eight, approaches my friend Carmen and asks her to go for coffee with him. It will be his treat he insists. When Carmen smilingly refuses, he tells her that it's OK for her to go out with him since he's only small. It's safe—small boys only want friendship, but watch out for the big boys when they invite you, they are after something quite different.

That day Carmen has her first coffee-shop outing with an eight-year old.

At the hotel, Ismail's message is waiting for me. He hopes to complete his programme by nine.

when Ismail arrives, we have a few drinks with Carmen then he takes me to the night-club at Les Mérinides. This is the first time I see men dancing by themselves. Most of them so good-looking and extremely suggestive in their movements. What a waste, especially with those looks and bodies. We watch for a moment but decide to go to the Volubilis DiSco instead, where we dance to our heart's content. Although the place is overcrowded, it has, nevertheless a cosy atmosphere created by a cave-like set-up with soft lights.

We stay till the early morning hours and then drive back to the hotel together. I throw off my clothes and have a fast dip in the pool. Still wet, I join Ismail in his suite where he wants to show me his photos.

Back home in Canada we would say 'etchings'.

"Oui, étampes Japonaises."

But Ismail does mean photos. He has brought a whole attaché case full of them and wants me to pick the nicest one as a souvenir. I end up with quite a few.

Again he sings. This time, he sings an all-time favourite of mine: Muñequeita Linda. And that does it. I adore his boyish body and immerse myself in his strong body language. A language so warm and generous, his manly pride engulfs my body. Suddenly he releases a long pent-up sigh and shudders.

"*Oh, comme ce'st beau de t'aimer.* Silvia, will you
see me again tomorrow? Promise, you won't take another. I will follow you all over the country up to Agadir, your point of departure. Let me take you all over Morocco. Let me show you the beauty of this land of ours? And what a better way is there than seeing Morocco by the side of a Moroccan!"

I am flattered but terribly scared for I do not want
to hurt him and yet I cannot quite picture him following me
all over. Besides, it just wouldn't be fair.

"Ismail, it's wonderful, but let's not worry about tomorrow."

"I knew it. You've already made other plans. I knew it."

"Ismail, not at all. I am afraid our encounters might interfere with the tour programme."

"Silvia, I'll make up for it. I'll give you a royal
private tour."

"And your work?"

"I'll have someone else take care of it."

Closely entwined we fall asleep.

During the night I make up my mind not to see Ismail again and we both dress in oppressive silence the next morning. For the last time I feast my eyes on his velvet-like brown body.

"I shall go first, Silvia. Nobody will know: I will try not even to look at you. I shall join the tour manager and guide for breakfast. That will keep your image intact."

I don't reply but his words hit home. I remember my father, "If you can fall by the side of a man, you can also rise together with him."

Back in my room, I put on my most elegant dress and elaborate jewellery. Very calmly I walk into the dining room where separate tables are laid for the tour participants and the native tour manager and guides.

The group I usually dine with are already there. I look them straight in the eye, slightly nod and politely smile, then turn round to join Ismail. His eyes show surprise and then his face lights up in a big smile.

"*Ismail, si je peux pastager ta couche,*

je peux aussi partager ta table."

The poor waiters are totally confused and one of them ceremoniously carries over my place-setting from the group table.

Let the other people think what they choose. Ismail stood up for my dignity, the very least I can do is to reciprocate.

LILLI MECH, born in Toronto, Married psychiatrist Z. Ronald Mech and lives in Brampton, Ont. with three great grown up kids. Has studied extensively, A.R.T.C. music (piano); B.A. McMaster (religion); two years Masters degree, York (teaching the gifted); T.T.C. (primary). Many positive life experiences including a month long canoe trip (honeymoon) in Temagami, a single person art show of giant tapestries. She is published in *Companion* annually, *Medical Post*, quarterly, yearly in *Wordscape*.

Charlie is My Darlin' • Lilli Mech

It was a good day. The one flyers used to call a great flyin' day. High in the very blue sky were wisps of trailing cirrus clouds. The kind that gave your airplane a push. A good day.

As to why Ted was sitting here, in front of all the brass, listening to the drone of fine words, only God knew. His eyes roamed around the whole parade square to the periphery of the field where assorted flags blew lazily in the breeze. Everywhere was a sea of blue. As it should be.

He rose after the clapping was finished and was led to inspect the gathered personnel. God, he could do this in his sleep, in total darkness, following the escorting officer with bare sword upraised to the tune of the band now playing various WW2 songs. It was here, in mid step, that Ted lost his mind.

The band was playing some kind of swing tune. Teddie could barely hear it and certainly hadn't heard it before. It drifted to him ... something patriotic about Jonny going to sleep. Hot damn, but there she was again. With Charlie, the lucky bugger. He swung his date around to get a closer look at her face, make eye contact with her, say something memorable. But the two of them were clinging tightly together and didn't notice him.

Hot shaped she was. A perfect English beauty, with long bouncy chestnut coloured hair. Why was it that Charlie always wound up with the best girls? Yes, they were hugging, eyes only for each other.

A sound came to him, alerting him to the fact that his own date was trying to catch his attention. She was a looker as well. He was very keenly aware that his men envied him his date, but she was nothing, nothing, compared to Charlie's wonderful handful.

Someone during mess had mentioned that Charlie's girl was Lady something and the cabbage field the airplanes had been shifted to when their aerodrome was destroyed, belonged to her old man.

Looking around the cavernous dining hall, now decked out for Saturday night all-ranks dance, he reflected on how much the mass of very young men all looked like his high school class back home. It could be another graduation class dance. Same kids, same slicked back hair, goofy bursts of nervous laughter, bumping along, having the time of their life.

Making sure they had the time of their life. Right now, it seemed damned short. No guarantees.

"Yes," Teddie thought, "same kids, different music, new girls and odd clothes."

All the guys and a few of the women were in uniform. Neat, well-pressed, sky blue tidy double-pocketed tunics over slim same-coloured pants or short skirts. Their rank was on their sleeves, shoulder flashes read Canada.

These hundreds, no thousands of young people on the wrong side of the pond were Canadian Air Force, overseas, fighting what now seemed, a lost war.

Ted shrugged and twirled his date around, enjoying the way her skirt fluttered up. He took her hand and twisted her around again. Great. Just great.

Here, against the side of the flimsy building, away from the blare of the music, he could hear the thin sound of a repaired plane engine as a technician fired it up to test. He ignored the noise.

He laughed out loud at a comment his girl had made. Hell, she was the funniest woman he had ever heard. He couldn't stop laughing.

People started to clap and he realized the music had stopped. With his girl's hand in his, he dragged her to the bar and got some watered-down pink gins. Before he had arrived in England, groggy and sick on a troop carrier, he had barely tasted strong liquor, and now, he loved, really loved pink gin, any gin, any booze.

They stood in a group, full of camaraderie and Charlie told a joke. God, Teddie thought he would split his pants laughing at it. Never had he heard anything so funny. Not Buster Keaton, nor Charlie Chaplin, no one could tell a joke, wow, another one. He excused himself and went to the lavatory.

Charlie came with him and they stood side by side.

"Great band."

"Conkers, really conkers."

"How's your girl? Lady something?"

"She's nice. Very, very proper." Charlie rolled his eyes. "Know what I mean?"

"You going to marry her?"

"Marry? Hell. I'm only nineteen. I've got lots of time, and a lot of women lined up before me. Hell no. I don't want to marry young. Screw young, shit that's different. Yeah."

Doing up his buttons he staggered back to the dim-lit entrance of the mess and the siren's call of the huge dance band.

Ted's eyes focused on the pencilled sign Charlie had scrawled above the urinal a few days ago. He followed the letters. "September 9, 1940. Still here."

He walked back to the dance. They were most of them, still here. Reaching out a hand he found another girl and whirled her around. Her dress twirled even more than the first. Wow. She was a keeper. For the night anyway.

He blinked. He could smell faint perfume—something light, floral, enticing. His eyes closed. It was Charlie's girl, he knew.

Sunday's sorties sobered him up. "Eleven o'clock. Eleven o'clock, overhead. Cover me."

He could smell the perfume. It was everywhere. The enemy bounded away and he lost him in the early light of dawn. "Shit. Fuck. Behind you. Behind you, Charlie. Behind you." He tore in a breath as his Hurricane hurled down, missing fire, and darted away.

The blast lost him control and he fell down several thousand feet, finally regaining command by fighting with all his might, just above the hungry waters of the English Channel.

Here he found a lonely predator, confused, and fired short efficient bursts from his guns. The plane cart-wheeled and dropped into the water like a stone. No time for a parachute.

Someone else went down. By ducking his head for an instant he made out the RCAF roundel. He couldn't tell who it was. "Shit." One of his men. "Fuck fuck."

Debriefing was brutal. "Heaviest losses today. You men should know this. Today was severe for our side. The enemy suffered considerably more, but that is the way the tides of war are turned. We must strive to have more kills. Sell yourselves dearly. This is a fight to the death. Remember. That is all. Thank you. Edward Grey stay."

Ted was pale and trembling after the endless sorties their squadron had flown all day. He couldn't seem to focus. He dragged on his cigarette fiercely. He needed a drink. He needed a woman. He needed a sleep. "God damn."

The senior officer consulted a piece of paper. "Lieutenant Edward Grey."

"Yes Sir." Teddie was too tired to stand up. Who needed this kind of shit anyway? Why didn't the big brass let him go, or get up and fly a God-damned plane himself.

"Some of the Hurricanes carry cameras that are activated by the firing of the guns, or even at random. Did you know that?"

"I suppose so. Yeah. I mean, Yes Sir. I did know that."

"During a rough mêlée, your film shows you turning from a good shot at the enemy, and by not taking your man out, you allowed a fellow officer to take his fire, unawares, and go down."

"Sir?" Ted sat on the edge of his chair stunned. His mind raced back to the pencilled notation. "September 9 1940. Still here."

"Along with others, we lost Lieutenant Charles Neville. Too many. Often in sheer negligence. carelessness, or loss of concentration. Who knows? Nevertheless, when the squadron regroups, goes on, you will remain and become a flight training officer. That is all.

"Too many. Often in sheer negligence, carelessness or loss of concentration. Who knows? Nevertheless, when the squadron regroups, goes on, you will remain and become a flight training officer. That is all."

Ted sat. "September 15—1940. Not here."

Oh Teddie knew it was not great punishment to stay well behind the lines, training kids to be fighter pilots. No great disgrace, but, no great honour either. As for Charlie boy being down, he didn't want to think about it. He couldn't think about it. What about his girlfriend?

What if his girl was pregnant? What if? They were very much in love. Seemed to be together every spare minute Charlie had. Even if he made that great folderol statement about lots of women? What if? What would the great Lord of high Muckety Muck think of his darling Kathleen being banged up by a fighter pilot from the colonies? Now very much dead.

Would he disown her? What would she do? How did people in love survive things like this? Being in love with a flesh and blood person one minute, and bam, he's gone, away out of this world, the next?

Ted called on her. "I was given the duty of packing his stuff to send back home when I came across his bathrobe. It's not army issue so it occurred to me you might want something of Charlie's to keep, sort of—remind you of him."

Kathleen, looking smaller than he recalled, her eyes shocked, stunned, vacant, looked up at him. "Thank you very much. It was really thoughtful of you." She buried her face in the cloth bundle for a moment then quivered.

"Are you moving up with your squadron? A rumour says they're going to the Norfolk area since Jerry's moved on to bombing London"

"No. I'm being posted north. Going to train pilots." His tongue ran around his suddenly dry lips. "Up there." He glanced down at her. Her eyes were focussed somewhere in middle distance.

"Come with me. We'll find a pub somewhere. Grab a pint or two. Have a break?" He leaned down to her and looked into her face.

"All right." She put the bundle down on the hall table and walked out of the big house, not even saying a word to anyone, just trailed out.

To find a licensed house that was open, they drove miles away to the nearest town. Both got silly on cellar-temperature English beer and ended up together, shacked up in a shabby upstairs room, with the loo down the hall. Ted was too far gone to realize that Kathleen hadn't been Charlie's girl. Not at all. Until he drunkenly had her, she had been nobody's girl.

At dawn next day, she was still hiccuping, red-eyed and barely under control. He was dry-eyed, smoked-out, hollow with concern, new knowledge and self-disgust.

Ted left for Scotland, a young angry twenty-year-old with more emotional baggage than gear.

Sorties flew out of northern Scotland now. New men poured in and poured out. Action was as fast as you could manage it. War was real. Everyday fresh casualties were posted but the one that had ever made any impact on Ted was Charles Neville, Flying Officer aged nineteen. Who didn't want to marry for a long time yet, and now, would never get married nor do anything else.

Late November, a tired, haggard voiced Lord high M-M broke through the telephone censorship. Somehow he had found Ted. "Look here, young man. You must do something. The girl is pregnant and still in much of a state. You must marry her or something." Since Ted knew very well the child was his, in a bleak December morning, in the coldest church in Christendom, no flowers, no candles, no kindness, under the disapproving gaze of a know-it-all Scottish minister, he married Kathleen. She turned to him and called him Charlie. From then on, whenever Kathleen was under the weather she would call him Charlie. It only made him kinder. When he found her clutching the old dressing-gown with the name Charles Neville on the inside back collar, crying into it and moaning, he would see that she was warm, comfortable, take their two sons out and go for long walks.

Finally, at war's end he brought her home to Canada. She loved the country. Was a good wife to him. Endured the military base life, could cook banger's and mash like nobody's business. Still, every now and then, she would collapse, hide her face in the old bathrobe that likely still smelled of Charlie faintly, and cry. After discretely consulting with a friend who was an Air Force psychiatrist, Ted simply left her alone. As time went by he rose in rank. As time went by, she clutched her robe a few less times.

Now today he was retiring out of the service with a much higher rank than he privately felt he deserved. At his final parade, his eldest son, all smiles, proudly dressed in blues, kept his eye on young Charles, a name his mother suggested for the eldest grand-child.

Ted Grey's sudden pause during the inspection signalled the escort to end the ceremonial march and return him to the dais. The changeover parade didn't seem as long as usual to Ted. In no time his official car was waiting for him at the foot of the reviewing stand.

He helped Kathleen inside. Stood for a second. Turned and looked at the group assembled to honour him. Silence reined everywhere. The commanding officer was about to leave. The only sound he could hear was the snapping of the flags on the tall posts. Momentarily he swayed. His eyes were drawn to the red maple leaf in the centre of the flag. For the Charlies, really, he saluted it, standing stiffly to attention, then bent, and ducked into the car.

GERRY PENROSE was born in London England in 1917. He spent seven years in the Royal Air Force, achieving the rank of Sergeant Air Gunner Wireless Op Mechanic. He emigrated to Winnipeg in 1954. After ten years in Winnipeg as a TV technician, salesman, bill collector and owner of a TV repair business, he settled with his family in Oakville, Ontario. He has had four stories published in previous *Wordscapes*, and an Hon. Mention in an early *Winners' Circle*. He has had articles in *British* and *American Model Engineering* magazines, and computer articles with programs in *Amiga Magazine*.

Hell Hath No Fury • Gerry Penrose

The chimes ring out across the roof tops; echoing through the dreaming spires, and out over the meadows beyond, to meet with other chimes; dancing along the river, and bouncing under bridges, the chimes are tolling a requiem for a dying day; little do they know that they are also sounding a death knell; for in a lonely room one side of the college quadrangle, there sits a figure. It occupies an armchair set companionably by a cold fireside. Sticking out from the figure's chest, like an obscene hat peg, is the handle of a knife, gold in colour, and carved with intricate figures.

The chimes strike the note of ten, and fall silent, leaving the town to its own subdued noises; hurrying footsteps, and the more measured tread of returning fellows and collegiates. Among these is the purposeful tread of James Petherick the Master of this college. He enters the porter's lodge and greets the lone occupant.

"Good evening, Beasley, quiet night."

"Ah, good evening, Master, yes it has been quiet. At least it was before the chimes began, and is quiet again."

"So, Beasley. Have you seen Dr. Armitage this evening. He wasn't at table this evening, and nobody seems to have seen him for a while.

"Yes, Master. He came in about four this afternoon to pick up his mail, and then went on through to the staircase. I've not seen him since."

"I had better go up and see if he is alright. He may have fallen sick or something. It is most unusual to not see him at table."

"Very well, Master, I won't be closing up until curfew, so if there is anything you need, please call."

"Thank you, Beasley, I will."

The Master passes through to the staircase, and mounts to the first floor. He taps gently on the door. No answer. The door swings slightly open under the light rap, rap. The Master pushes it wide, and steps into the room. What he sees, brings him up short. He stands there as if unable to believe his eyes. Then, without touching anything, he backs out of the room, gently closing the door on that shocking sight.

Back at the porter's lodge, he says, "Beasley, I am afraid Dr. Armitage is dead. Phone the police, and ask them to send a plain clothes man in an unmarked car. Tell them it is murder, and there should be no publicity until more is known about this unfortunate event. If you ask to speak with Chief Inspector Thomas, he will understand. Tell him that the Master is standing-by awaiting his arrival."

In fifteen minutes there is a slight swish, and a very quiet squeal as the unmarked car draws up at the porters lodge. Out steps three men. They walk into the lodge, and stop before the Master. Ah! There you are, Thomas, and your good companion Detective Sergeant Wendell. Your other companion I have not had the pleasure." He pauses and Thomas says, "This is the pathologist. This is Dr. Sam Pender."

"My pleasure, Doctor," says the Master.

Thomas says, "Since the call indicated murder, and in view of the time, it will be as well if we began. Will you show the way, Master?"

The three men follow the Master. He halts at the door, and indicates they are to enter, and says: "If you need me, I shall be in the lodge." He turns and walks back downstairs, to await their findings. He has hardly settled himself in at the porter's lodge, when the three men return. "Well, Master, you are right about murder. He was strangled manually, though the autopsy will confirm or deny that. Then he was stabbed with that rather fancy knife. There is no external blood, indicating he was dead before the knife entered his body. But again the autopsy will tell."

"Thank you, Thomas. The knife belonged to me. It used to hang over my mantelpiece. Come, I'll show you where. My room is on the ground floor." In the Master's room, he shows them the empty scabbard that had once held the knife.

CI Thomas looks carefully around the room, paying some attention to the fender before the fireplace. He then looks at the two small dining chairs, carefully glancing sideways across the seats. "Whoever took that knife, stood upon the fender, and reached up for it. This indicates a rather tall man, or woman, though I doubt a woman could have strangled the victim, much less have driven that knife so deep into the body. No. We are looking for a man of something over six feet tall, and with a long reach. Which lets you out, Master. You would have had to stand on a chair to reach it. This begs the question, why the knife, when the man was dead? There is only one answer to that, to incriminate you. Supposing they had been successful, and you were charged with murder, what would be the outcome?"

"I should be stripped of the Master's robes, and the next in line would have been installed, pending a new election. The next in line would have been the victim, next to him would have been … "

"Yes?"

"The next in line would have been Dr. Weston. He is over six feet tall. But there was never any rancour from him when my name was chosen, unlike Dr. Armitage who has gathered a reputation … but I mustn't speak ill of the dead, suffice it to say, he did not take kindly to my appointment, and would argue that he was the best man for the post. I cannot see Dr. Weston as a murderer, there must be some other explanation."

"As I remember Master, there were four candidates. There was yourself, Dr. Armitage, Dr. Weston, who was the fourth?"

"The fourth was Dr. Fielding. He was highly regarded in his field: physics. It was I who put his name forward. I have no idea who put my name into the hat. I had been quite content in my chosen field, ancient literature, and considered having my name removed from the list of candidates. However, I was persuade to let it stand, by none other than Dr. Weston."

"Well Master, we shall see. In the meantime, we'll have the body removed. Quite quietly. In the morning, you can alert the college to tonight's happenings, and ask them to hold themselves in readiness for our visit. We shall be on the premises before you have a chance to alert everybody. Nobody will be allowed to leave the premises until we have been able to interview them. I tell you this, for your ears only, there is one clue we have, which shows an error of judgement in behalf of the murderer. I will say no more. Good night."

"Good night, Thomas."

The Master turns to Beasley and says; "When they have removed Dr. Armitage, you can lock up and go to bed. Please say nothing to anybody."

"Yes, Master. Good night."

"Good night, Beasley."

Next morning, as the chimes of eight o'clock ring out across the town, a convoy of vehicles drives up to the porter's lodge. Chief Inspector Thomas, and Detective Sergeant Wendell in the first car. Three constables, three WPC's, and a police Doctor make the rest of the convoy.

The Master greets them all, and then asks what he can do to help.

"Thank you Master, if we could have a room in which to interview the staff and students, we can get this job done."

"You can use the dining hall. I take it that you will wish to see the staff first."

"Not necessarily. We shall interview each one as he or she arrives for this mornings classes, which start, I believe, at nine o'clock."

"That is correct. If you wish anything further from me, you will find me in my room."

"Thank you." and turning to Detective Sergeant Wendell, he says; "Right, Wendell, lets get this thing on the road. You know what we are looking for, a six footer with a badly scratched hand. I have asked for Doc Pender to be in attendance. I want things to go smoothly if we need a blood or skin sample for a DNA test."

"Right, sir, I think we can overcome that problem, but we'll see, if and when the time comes. Here come the first batch of students sir. Constable James will direct them to the dining hall, there will be enough tables and chairs to enable the crew to sit down with each one as they come in. James has orders to direct, anyone tall and damaged to my attention. Doc Pender will be with me, and we'll take it from there."

"Right, Wendell, I'll leave you to it. If you need me, I'll be with the Master."

At that moment, Dr Weston arrives. He looks rather startled to find the quadrangle full of police. He is directed to the dining hall, and as he passes Wendell, Wendell looks closely at his hands. They are both free of any blemish.

There is a sudden flurry of students as the bells started to toll for nine o'clock. Among them is one well over six feet tall. Constable James directs all of them but the six footer, to the dining hall. Wendell steps forward and says, "Will you come this way sir?"

The tall one follows Wendell into the porter's lodge. The porter had been asked to go for a walk, and in his place is the police doctor.

"I say, what is all this about? Why are all the police here."

Wendell looks at the tall one and says, "One of the Dons has met with a nasty accident, in fact, he is dead."

"Dead, you say? How?"

"Never mind that for the moment, your hand seems to be swollen up, what did you do to it?"

"I was out for a walk last evening. I scratched it on some brambles."

"Oh, very nasty. But it looks as if it has poisoned. We'll forget the interview for now, let the Doc have a look at that hand. What do you think, Doc?"

The doctor takes hold of the hand, and unwinds the bandages. He looks closely at the wound, nods his head and says, "We'd better get you to the hospital. That looks gangrenous."

"I say, is that really necessary?"

"If you don't get that seen to young man, you'll be dead in two days."

An ambulance is called, and the tall young man is whisked away.

"Well Doc, is there enough on that bandage for a DNA test?'

"Oh, yes, quite enough. I'll have the results by this afternoon."

The tall young man, whose name was Jeremy Bucket, sits at one side of a table. Next to him is his lawyer, James Banister. Opposite sits CI Thomas, flanked by DS Wendell.

"Now Bucket, these are the facts as we have them at the moment. The person who first strangled Dr. Armitage, and then plunged a knife into him, was scratched rather badly. So badly in fact that enough material was recovered from his finger nails for a DNA test. The bandage we took from you yesterday has also been tested for DNA. The result is a perfect match. Now, do you have anything to say to that?"

Bucket looked hard at his lawyer, who nodded his head slightly, then said, "Armitage and I were lovers. He had told me that our affair was over, and mentioned another person whom he was interested in. I lost my cool then, and strangled him, and yes he did scratch me. Then to hide the motive, I went to the Master's room, and took that knife he was so proud of. I rammed it into Armitage. I thought the Master would be charged. I knew that Armitage had been pretty forthright in his claim that he should have been Master."

"Jeremy Bucket, I charge you with first degree murder. Take him down."

SHERRY BAGNATO works as a career counsellor, and writes in her spare time. In the next year she hopes to be writing full time on her first novel, as well as writing freelance magazine articles.

Starving People • Sherry Bognato

There are people starving in Africa. No kidding! Don't you hate it when you hear that? There are people starving here for God's sake. I pass them every morning when I open the grocery store. One fellow in particular I like because he calls me missus and he doesn't feel important knowing me. He threw up on my shoe once. That was proof enough. I bring him a coffee every morning as thanks for keeping me in my place.

My customers think I'm great.

"You're always so happy and helpful."

That's what they say to me when I take their order for deliveries and help them find the radicchio lettuce. They think they are so sophisticated. Yea, right. They love me and they feel important because they know the manager by name. Just imagine how self-important they would feel if I were the owner. Small people, what can I say.

I'm not jealous or anything. I have an education. Sure I do. I went to university for a year. I quit after one year because it wasn't going to get me a job, you know. My mother paid for it so it didn't really matter cause I wasn't out anything, and I could always get a job. That's the easy part. You just have to know the emotional angle, everyone has one, and just give them what they need. You get hired on the spot. I got top grades too. I'm not dumb.

I could be a lot of things. Right now, I'm just sitting back despising people who are nice to me. I know it's not the nicest thing to do. My mother says it to me all the time. "Carol. You don't appreciate kindness, nor what you have in this world. You have a good job and all you do is look down on people, and look up to people who get you into trouble."

"Yea, Mom."

I say that a lot to her. Since I'm living at home again I have to say that a lot. I got tired of basement apartments so I moved back home to save some money. I need a new car too. Mine died and if I take my mom's, I would have to drive her everywhere, which I don't want to do. Too many doctor's appointments. And it's because I'm a girl, you know. All these responsibilities fall on my shoulders. If I ask my brother for help he says the same thing over and over again.

"Get a steady job and stick with it, then I'll help you out."

Right! I was always the favourite and he has been so obviously jealous of me that his comments don't count.

I do whine a lot. My family says that to me. Maybe that's why they took my kid away. It certainly wasn't because I didn't have enough money or a place to live. Come on, I'm not a homeless person or white trash. I was living at Mom's house again, because I quit my job as a night manager for a restaurant. I can always get a management job. But I was pregnant. Why shouldn't I be home again where my mom can help look after the kid. She really wanted to. Honestly, I didn't want the kid, but sometimes you

have to take a political stand in life. You can't go around killing babies now can you? If you were my brother he would have said, "You can't go around ignoring infants either."

But he was always jealous, so just ignore what he says. What I say is that you are born to love kids or your not. Personally, I'm just not that interested in them. It broke my mother's heart when they took the baby away. At least she still has me keeping her company.

"Your so dissatisfied with your lot in life," she tells me. "You don't appreciate how worse off things could be. You could still be in jail."

She has a point. I guess the truth of it is my heart is broken. Not because of the baby. No, she's got a good home with people who think they are doing me a huge favour by taking the kid. See what I mean about people being born stupid. My heart is broken. It's embarrassing to admit it but it's true.

My boyfriend's in jail.

"The drug addict" is what my brother calls him. What did he know? My mother knew nothing.

"Everything's fine, Ma." That's what I told her when she called one night and Jim was stabbing that guy because he made a pass at me in our apartment. "Were just having a party, Ma. It's real noisy here. What did you say. I can't hear you. I'll call you back."

Our apartment! Some people have a lot of nerve. He was trying to make me do things in our own home. Big time drug dealer thought he was so important, but Jim got him.

"Self defence. It's self defence." I kept screaming and screaming it at the police when they finally found the body. It took them one month to find it. We cut it up and rolled it in a sheet and buried him under the deck. We had barbecues on that deck, and would clink are glasses at our own private joke. We even made out there under the stars. It was a weird time for Jim and me, but it was proof of our love for each other. It sounds corny, I know.

A neighbour's dog dug up a piece of the guy, and my life fell apart. Jim got nine years for that. They didn't allow the attempted burglary charges to be brought up, else he would have got longer. Me? I was given three years. Just because I lied and helped him hide the body. What else could I do? You don't rat on your boyfriend, do you?

"You would rob your brother though, wouldn't you."

He loves to rub that in my face, my brother. That was different, I kept telling him. I needed money and he had lots of it and wouldn't give me any. Mom said she had just bought me a new car and gave my brother twenty thousand for a down payment on his first house so she was broke. I just forged his name on a cheque for one thousand bucks; just to keep things equitable. Its not much when you think of it, but he never lets me forget about it.

"You won't ever learn." My brother says that to me, and shakes his head in a superior way. My family wants me to go out with the neighbour who is a computer programmer, to try and get my life back together. He's not my type, too boring, but maybe he could help me start an internet business. I should talk to him, even though he's not that cute.

"Don't tell him you've been in jail." They both said, my mother and brother.

"I'm not ashamed of it. I did it for love." Jim dumped me and squealed on me. That's how I was caught. But people do funny things when they're scared. They are like wild animals. "It doesn't mean that he didn't love me. I still have his ring." I screamed at them.

My brother just shakes his head. He's got such an attitude.

It's hard to get over your first true love. I've gone out with a few guys. Last night I went out with a few people from work. Mostly the guys who stock the shelves; who don't have a lot of responsibility like me. We drank some beer and danced till we were asked to leave Lido's. Boy did we make a scene. We called the owner some choice names because he said we were too loud and cut us off.

"Were paying customers. Who do you think you are anyway?"

See what I mean? A little power and these guys are scary. Anyway we left and everyone except John and me went home. We went to his car. It wasn't the first time either. Management and staff aren't suppose to do that. We are not suppose to fraternize with the employees. But whose it hurting. John's not going to tell the owner if he knows what's good for him. It's not hurting me, that's for sure. Just a bit of fun. Not true love. Nope.

That's reserved for Jim. I write him letters to let him know I'll wait for him. I am waiting to receive a reply. He killed someone and he did it for me. If that isn't love, what is?

Sometimes I wish I had a better job that was going somewhere. I would like some real respect. Maybe a regional sales manager cause I'm good with people, or like I said, start my own internet business. I don't want to be a grocery store manager all my life. They tell me I'm lucky, my family. That I only got three years, and have a chance to start my life all over again.

"It depends on how you look at it." I say to my brother. "Store manager isn't what I would say is moving up in the world, is it?"

"You idiot." my brother says. "Think of the fellow who died. Who you killed."

"But I didn't do it." The routine with this guy is tiring. I don't need to feel guilty. He's just trying to make me feel guilty because I was the special one.

I had a premonition that this was going to be a bad day. I don't know why. I was edgy at work, and almost quit at lunch when a customer wanted me to carry her bags to the car on my lunch break. People can be so rude. I was meeting my brother and the lawyer downtown to go over my mother's will. She died two weeks ago which is just as well because old people are a responsibility on you. I rushed to the lawyers, looking forward to finally moving up in the world. Maybe I should have quit today. I can definitely pack it in tomorrow.

They tell me I wasn't left anything. I'm stunned.

"What about the house. Sell the bloody house."

"It all goes to your brother."

"She got tired of holding your hand." My brother says. He's hiding behind the lawyer.

"It's not fair. The economy is going downhill. It's fine for you Mr. Sixty-thousand-dollar-a-year man. What about me? What about me?"

"It's time you stood up by yourself. You never do anything for yourself or take responsibility for your life. Wake up."

I was shaken. You think you know someone. Here I was living in the same house with this woman and eating the same food, and she cuts me out of the will. God, he must hate me to have turned mother against me.

"I should get something. It's only fair." I hated myself for having to beg from my brother.

"Five thousand is what you get to get you started in a place of your own."

"But how can I buy a house with that?"

He didn't say anything. I got him there. I should have known about my brother. The kind of person he is. One Christmas, I wanted a dog, and my brother wanted a cat. Well of course I got the dog, which was supposed to be for both of us.

"You can both play with him." Mom said.

At first, he loved my brother. Followed him everywhere and wouldn't come near me. He loved that dog so much it was funny. The dog was suppose to be mine though. Even though we were suppose to share it, I asked for the dog, and got it; not a cat, which made the dog mine. So, I started putting treats in my pocket so he could smell it and follow me around. It worked great and my brother was mad. He couldn't figure out why the dog

turned on him, and you can bet I never told him. He's got the dog now. He waited till I was in jail and brought it to the house. Sometimes you just can't trust your own family.

Sometimes you have to do something about it.

Mistaken Identity • June Salmon

He lay cold, immaculate on marble slab,
attended by white-coated men reluctant to start.
"Careful moving him; this one must be clean."

Who was he, body washed on North Shore beach
far from the business world of Armani suit and matching tie?
They assumed the power role, sniffing remnants of expensive
    scent.
He could be poster boy, so perfect the chiselled cheek.
Easy speculations came to mind—drug dealer, Mafioso son,
too masculine for designer crowd, too posh for common CEO.

"On with it; identify cause of death."
The tape recorder runs; "Head clean, no bump or contusion
    here."
Pomaded hair, now drooping over ears, hid naught.
"Time of death—midday," the voice droned, impersonal,
unmindful of the man whose heart had pulsed
perhaps for someone else, well-loved and loving back.

"Pin-drop of blood, cranial cavity; needle prick?"
Two heads bent close, agreed; "Poison:
brain function paralysed, death instantaneous."

But why? The white coats shrugged.
"Parker's domain. Endless possibilities there."

Meanwhile, on one side of town, a small crowd waits,
uncertain where the son could be;
devoted all these years, he'd not miss burying her now.
They'd stay one hour more, then complete the funeral rites.
Harbourside, dark warehouse phone clangs off the wall.
One partner's pallor shows the worst is yet to come.
"It couldn't be! We saw him dead, I swear!"
No one alive to tell the tale of brothers, like as twins,
raised apart in separate worlds—
one good, one opposite, ignorant of the other.
Both to die by violent means within hours of one day.

Perhaps in death, where souls drift and float,
purged of rights and wrongs,
one will find the other and combine proud family ties,
as never allowed on earth—one mortal mystery solved.

IAN DONALD KEELING is an odd, loud little man who acts a little, writes a little, and suffers from delusions of grandeur whenever he can. He has been published in *Queen's Quarterly*, *TG Magazine*, and *The Canadian Writer's Journal* and has recently self-published his first book of short stories. He lives in a subterranean cave near the beaches in Toronto and is convinced there are icebergs in Lake Ontario.

The Cyclist • Ian Donald Keeling

Danny Masino pulled up beside the condemned apartment complex, his head steaming from exertion in the frigid air, and leaned his bicycle against the rusting chain-link fence. Pulling off his gloves, he squirted some lock de-icer into his Krypton lock to prevent it from seizing up, as it had the night before, and locked the bike. His hands were already stinging from those few seconds in the frost-bitten air as he put his gloves back on, pulled the briefcase containing a hundred thousand dollars from his knapsack, and walked up to the third floor for his meeting with Frank.

The first thing Danny noticed when he walked into the room was the dead body lying in the centre of the icy floor.

Frank Marangello, heir to the largest 'family' in south-western Ontario, looked up from his chair in the corner and waved Danny into the room. "Come on in, Danny, it's cold outside."

It was supposed to be a private meeting, one guard dog at most. But there were five other people in the room, not including the body. The briefcase in Danny's hand suddenly felt very heavy; when one of the men took it from him, Danny could actually feel the cool empty weight of the air press against his palm.

"How was the ride?" Frank asked conversationally.

"Cold," Danny replied, staring at the body.

"And the race on Saturday, did you win?"

Danny looked up, blinking at Frank in confusion.

"Your bicycle race," Frank offered warmly. "You were *very* excited."

Danny blinked again, off-guard, then remembered—the Winterfest Off-Road Downhill—he had told Frank about it last week. "I came in second," he mumbled.

"*Second*? That's not bad. Perhaps riding to work every day is paying off. Did you get to stand on a podium?"

"Yes."

Frank grinned impishly, an odd expression on a two-hundred and fifty pound man. "Did they give you a silver medal?"

"No," Danny shook his head, dazed—Frank was acting very odd, there was a dead man ... "it was a trophy."

"A *trophy*? Very nice." Frank pursed his lips, impressed. "Something to put on the mantelpiece."

Danny didn't say anything, just looked back at the body.

Frank lit a cigarette, stood and walked over to the centre of the room. Looking down at the body he shook his head and made a tisking sound with his tongue.

"Poor guy," Frank said, bending down and lifting the man's head. It was a black man in his forties, wearing a tattered woollen toque, a mouldy brown overcoat and fingerless gloves nicked with cigarette stains and blood. There was a large hole in the left side of his head.

Frank looked over at Danny. "He must have been freezing out there. What is it, eleven below? And that wind ..." Frank paused so they could all hear the rattle of the wind through the window. "Poor guy leaning up against cold concrete, praying so that some goof might come along to give him enough money for a hot coffee, knowing that they won't 'cause no idiot would be out on a night like this. Hard bein' a bum." Frank fingered the man's hand, inspecting the gloves as if in sympathy.

"Of course," Frank continued, dropping the hand but still holding the head, "this guy wasn't a bum, *was he*? Oh, sure he acted like a bum, he looks like a bum, smells ..." Frank leaned down and took a deep sniff, "... like a bum, but he isn't a bum. In *fact*, this gentleman ..." Frank held the head up higher, so Danny could take a good look at the face he had seen several times before. "... is a police officer. His name ..." Frank blinked a couple of times thoughtfully, then turned to one of the men lining the walls. "What was his name, Michael?"

"Lieutenant Edward Griggs."

"Lieutenant Edward Griggs," Frank repeated, mulling over the name. He nodded once, as if to affirm the identity correct, then let the head thud onto the floor, and stood.

"Frank ..." Danny began.

"Danny," Frank held up a hand. "*Daniel* ..." For a brief second, a heart-beat, a deep pain cut across Frank's eyes, tore through his tough-mobster act and rested on that one word like a concrete block. Danny fell silent.

Then the pain slashed away like the wind outside and Frank's menacing nonchalance reasserted itself. "Danny, it doesn't matter how you came to know this man, or what you told him, so don't waste my time by explaining. Nor does it matter how this man came to be lying here in the centre of this room, dead, so I will not waste your time by explaining. What does matter is how *this* situation, that *you* have created, has made me feel. Do you know how it has made me feel, Danny?"

Danny shook his head silently, his heart slamming in his chest like a door caught in an icy draft.

"It has made me feel betrayed, Danny. It has made me feel alone in the world. It has made me feel ..." Frank seemed to reach for the correct words, "... as though I were naked. Do you know what it is like to be naked, Danny?" He paused, staring across the room at Danny. A silence.

Frank sniffed and flicked his cigarette to the floor. "Perhaps you don't. Boys."

Moving like sudden cracks in the ice, five men rushed at Danny from the sides of the room and began forcibly removing his clothes. He started to struggle but Frank surged across the room, slapped Danny once, hard, then, grabbing Danny's hair and pulling his head up sharply, the older man froze the younger with a gaze cold and hard like an ice-pick. "*It is very important that you don't make me kill you now.*" Frank slapped Danny again, hard. "Hmm?"

Danny stopped struggling and Frank walked back to the centre of the room, as his men stripped Danny down.

The last item was his boxers and as they grabbed them Frank held up a hand and said, "Leave those." He smiled at Danny benevolently. "After all, it *is* cold."

Danny felt goose-bumps begin to prickle his flesh as he watched Frank, in his thick woollen trench-coat, begin to pace, stepping over the body of the dead police officer once, then again, before stopping to light another cigarette.

As he placed his lighter in his pocket, Frank looked up abruptly, as if suddenly recalling something. "How is Melinda?" he asked casually.

Without thinking Danny took a step forward and felt a blunt, icy pressure on his temple. There was a loud click as the man beside Danny cocked the semi-automatic in his hand. Danny froze and through clenched teeth said, "She's fine."

"Good," Frank nodded. "Such a pretty girl. Any little Danny's on the way yet?"

"No." Frank knew this.

"Ahh." The older man sounded disappointed. "Well, there's time. I imagine she's home now, yes?"

Danny nodded, slowly, the barrel grinding against his skull.

"I thought so." Frank grinned. "Probably waiting for ER to come on in, oh ..." he looked at his watch, "fourteen minutes. I like that show ER. So fraught with tension and drama, it's very exciting. And that George Cloony, ho-ho ... better not let Melinda ever get any closer to him than the TV screen, if you know what I mean. "He smiled, then lifted his hand and waved it several times. " I'm sorry, Danny, that was a bad joke. Still, it is a good show and I imagine she is waiting breathlessly. Probably sitting on your couch—that's a nice couch, Danny, it goes very well with your decor—waiting anxiously for the show, completely unaware of the four pounds of explosive attached to the underside of that lovely couch, set to go off during the opening credits."

It was all Danny could do not to take another step.

Frank watched him for a moment, then nodded again, once, in approval. "Good. Danny, I'll tell you that tonight you have hurt me *very* deeply in a *very* personal way." Danny remembered the pain in Frank's eyes—*Daniel* ... that one word—but the pain was gone from the older man's expression now. Only Frank's play of tension and drama remained. "Despite my personal injury, however, you and this police officer," Frank nudged the body with his foot, "have not hurt the business. And, as all good business men know, you should not mix personal injury with business dealings. *And* you have comported yourself with honour tonight by not whining or begging or offering trivial explanations for things that do not matter which might have otherwise wasted our time. So I'll tell you what I'm going to do, Danny ..." He flicked his cigarette onto the floor.

"I'm going to let you ride home to your wife. You are always telling me how much you enjoy riding your bicycle; how it saves you money and is environmentally sound. Your home is not far and I know you are a very fast cyclist—you have a *trophy*—so I am sure that you will make it in time. I am going to place a small pair of scissors on your key-chain ..."

Danny heard the sound of keys jingling; something cold, loose and hard was tied around his naked wrist.

"The wire you should cut is the green one, Danny. This is *true*." Frank gave him an intent look, then continued. "After you have cut this wire and watched ER with your lovely wife, you will then have twenty-four hours to leave town and get far enough away so that I never see your traitor's face again. As a parting gift, you can have my watch." He handed his watch to one of the men, who came over and wrapped it around Danny's other wrist. "So you might know exactly how much time you have left.

"You can even," and Frank spread his hands benevolently, "keep the boxers on so you don't freeze your pecker off."

Danny felt the pressure against his temple pull away as the men surrounding him stepped back to the edges of the room. He watched Frank reach into the pocket of his trench-coat, pull out another watch, and put it on.

Lighting another cigarette, Frank checked his new watch and looked up at Danny, as if in surprise. "You have ten minutes, Danny. You had best be getting home."

It's easy, a quiet, confident part of Danny's mind whispered to him as the door to the complex closed behind him and the cold wrapped itself around him like a blanket eaten by moths.

Ten minutes, it whispered as he crossed to the rusty chain-link fence and fumbled with the lock, the ice sharp and raw on his naked feet, his breath already coming in short painful rasps. Ten minutes to ride a distance he had covered before in seven. Of course that had been in the summer, when the sun was shining and the roads were clear and wearing nothing but a pair of shorts was a good thing. Not when it was eleven below and the wind was coming long and hard all the way from the Arctic Circle and the roads were corrugated with drifting snow and black ice; when already he couldn't feel his feet on the pedals as he began to churn furiously down unlit streets.

Still ... came the whisper, there had been no motivation in the summer. Now there was plenty of motivation: a driving need to get home. Home, where his skin wouldn't shrink taut and tight, where his teeth wouldn't chatter like ice-cubes in a glass, where his eyes wouldn't bleed tears that ground to a halt halfway down his cheeks like thwarted glaciers. Home, where his wife sat on a couch and four pounds of explosives. So many motivations ...

Of course, there were other things to consider as he came to lit streets and the centre of town. Like the fact that the faster he rode the harder the air cut through his lungs, the faster the capillaries in his extremities snapped shut—*You can keep the boxers*—the quicker the heat generated from exertion—heat that normally allowed him to wear only a windbreaker when he rode—built up and vanished into the night without anything to break the wind.

So many things, as he ran through a red light; tires screaming in anger, cars slamming into each other in his wake. Like the probability that his hands could no longer uncurl themselves to reach his brakes to stop. Like the fact a cop might pull him over at the next red light he ran; pull him over with one of those nice *warm* cars they drove. Except, of course, he couldn't stop for a cop, any more than he could for the lights, because five minutes had passed and he was only just now coming to the coffee shop that he knew stood halfway between his house and a room on the third floor of a condemned apartment complex where a man lay dead on the floor.

Things in the cold, like the fact that even if somehow he made it home without dying of exposure—short, painful rasps—he still wouldn't be warm right away; he couldn't simply run a hot bath and jump in, because the shock would probably kill him. He would have to slowly suck the heat back into his body, perhaps turning nothing but the cold tap in the shower, because the water would still be warmer than a man stupid enough to ride naked for ten minutes through a hell frozen over.

Ten minutes, his mind whispered. *It's easy,* it whispered; which wasn't so bad because it kept him from thinking about the dying strength in his thighs, the ache in his calves, the fact that even as he turned the corner to his street as fast as muscles and bone and sinew could strain he was still *slowing down*. The fact that the hands that couldn't unlock to reach the brakes might not unlock to let the bike go when he got to the porch light now burning only the distance of frozen eyesight away.

Perhaps it was cold enough that he might just break away from his hands, that they might just cleave off at the wrist, solid and brittle like iron ingots that had been dropped to absolute zero too quickly.

No, he needed his hands. Needed them to throw the bike to one side, to turn the doorknob to his house, to drag his battered body into the living room of his home.

To cut a green wire beneath his couch.

The porch light was close now, and it was burning; cold burning like his eyes, like his chest, like his genitals. Cold burning, but perhaps lending enough heat to make his legs move just a little faster.

And suddenly ... abruptly ... there is no more road.

There is no more road and Danny is throwing the bike onto his icy lawn and his hands do uncurl just enough to come away clean. And though he stumbles twice up the porch stairs, his hands are somehow steady enough to drag him up to the light, to fumble the keys into the lock, to open the door. He steps through into the furnace on the other side, past the searing heat of his front hall, the desert of his dining room, and into his living room, where Melinda is turning to greet him, smiling, as the credits roll on ER.

Well, the quiet part of his mind has time to whisper as there is a roar like a molten avalanche and Melinda's face erupts into the inferno ... at least we're warm.

SPYROS MOSHONAS is a part-time freelance writer. He writes a column for the Toronto Free Press and his other interests include mystery and children's fiction. This is his second publication in *Wordscape*.

The Store that Disappeared • Spyros Moshonas

He's barely visible from the cracks in the picture. John Klippert in tweeds and bowler hat poses in front of a railway station. Scribbled on the back of the photograph is the date: "May 15, 1891."

Four days before this picture was taken, Klippert had arrived in Colinridge on a cool, sunny morning. His instructions had led him to a white, frame building just outside the village.

He took off his bowler hat and clawed through his silky, brown hair. He wore bowlers only to make himself look more authoritative. Sometimes, his youth and smiling eyes made him too personable and amiable to be taken seriously as a lawman. He put on his bowler and glanced at the absurd telegram note. 'Go to Colinridge. Store disappeared.'

He stepped inside and smiled for indeed that ludicrous telegram had said it best. The store was all empty.

"We're still closed!" The storekeeper said irritably.

"Closed? I thought you had disappeared! John Klippert, Ontario Department of Justice!" he replied congenially and reached for a handshake.

"I'm very sorry! My name is George Pinnock," the red-faced storekeeper rushed to shake his hand. "As you can see for yourself, everything we brought from Toronto for our new store is gone. We didn't even unpack a single bundle. Our chairs, tables, baskets ... all gone!"

"Your store was robbed before it opened," Klippert noted as he glanced appraisingly at the storekeeper. He was a clean-shaven, burly fellow in his early forties. His scared face, square jaw, darting eyes were strangely familiar, but he was certain that he hadn't met him before this occassion.

Klippert's gaze shifted toward the back door's broken panes. "Do you still have the broken glass," he asked, and Pinnock pointed to a tin bucket. Squatting down, he emptied it on the floor under the disapproving scowl of the storekeeper. He lined all the pieces side by side. It puzzled him that no piece was smaller than an inch. He made a note of it and put them back in the bucket.

An hour later, Klippert and Pinnock rode on a dog-cart to meet the other partner, John Wilson, who lived in a distant farm. The detective was impressed with Pinnock's driving. He drove fast, avoiding the most treacherous potholes on the dark, forest track. It was obvious that he had been in these parts more than a few times.

The farm was a serene but also bleak place where a wall of trees hid the horizon. Klippert's attention was drawn to a young boy who had climbed up the only tree left in the clearing. The boy called to his parents who came out of the log house.

"I drove my family to Fisherville to stay with relatives," Wilson started. "Not safe to leave a woman and child alone out here. I came back and left with my partner for Toronto."

Wilson's account matched his partner's to the letter. They had returned from Toronto late in the evening and had left the supplies unpacked in the store. He had spent the night in a room at the back of a barber shop that belonged to James Farley, a good friend of Pinnock's. The next morning he had set off for Fisherville to pick up his family while Pinnock went to the store, and everything was gone.

While they were talking, Wilson's seven-year-old boy fell off the tree. Luckily, he landed on his feet, and the soft grass cushioned his fall. He only suffered a large cut on his arm. The child pulled a plain wrinkled handkerchief out of his pocket. Pinnock was the first to attend to boy's cut with a fatherly devotion. He put the boy's dirty handkerchief on the ground beside him and took out his own and wrapped it round the arm. Still kneeling beside him, Pinnock helped the boy up to his feet. As they walked toward the house, Pinnock turned round as if looking for something.

"Detective! Have you seen the boy's handkerchief," he asked.

"Must still be under the tree," Klippert replied and walked back to the tree. When he found it, he pocketed it.

Inside the log house, Klippert looked at some discarded pieces of lace littering the floor beside the sewing machine near which Pinnock took a seat. The detective walked over to him and plucked a few scraps of lace off the floor to wipe a smudge on his shoe before they left the farm.

Back in town, he strolled leisurely into the barber shop. Farley was the typical barber, garrulous and pleasant. Klippert frowned as the barber rambled about the break-in and how it would ruin his friend Pinnock financially. "At least Wilson has his farm. George put all his life savings in that store, and now is left with nothing," he kept saying.

"But, Mr. Wilson has put in over two thirds of the money while your friend has committed his time to run the store," Klippert interrupted him. Farley turned frosty, and his face darkened. Still silence filled the shop.

"May I see the room where Wilson spent the night?" Klippert amiably asked as if he had not noticed the coldness. Farley hesitated but agreed and led him into a big room separated only by a curtain from the shop. With a raised eyebrow, Klippert eyed a row of 10 lamps that were lined against the wall.

"Late town meetings," said Farley reading the detective's thoughts. Klippert nodded and headed for the door.

Once outside, he sat down on the plank sidewalk like a kid. Doffing the oppressive bowler, he bathed in the afternoon sun as he pored over his notes. He still had to see the Toronto suppliers. He paused and looked up, sprang to his feet and fished out a folded piece of paper. It was a wanted bill, which bore a drawing of a highwayman named *James Melvin*.

"It still makes no sense!" he mumbled to himself.

Two days later, he was back in Colinridge with another detective. They first went to see Pinnock at his home. "We have some good news and some bad news," Klippert begun, and the storekeeper inched closer to the edge of his seat. "The good news is that we know who did it. The bad news is ... that you know them too."

Pinnock glared at the two detectives and his fists clenched.

Klippert said quietly, "Your partner and your friend, the barber."

Pinnock jerked back in his seat holding his breath. "There ... there must be a mistake!" He stammered.

Klippert fished the handkerchief and lace out of his pocket. "These were found in Wilson's farm, and your Toronto suppliers confirm that they sold them to you.

"They entered your store through your back door by breaking the glass. But, if they broke through that back door, they would have walked over all the broken glass and crushed it into small pieces. So they must have entered with a key and smashed the windows later to make it look like a break-in. Wilson could not single-handedly do this; he needed a partner, Farley. This was the same individual who offered him lodging for the night after you had come back from Toronto. Later that evening, they came here and scooped up everything and so much for good friends!"

"Do you know where the supplies are?" A shaken Pinnock asked.

"A day or two in the gaol makes people talk. Before we arrest Farley, we would stop briefly at the tavern to book rooms as the next train comes tomorrow. You may come with us if you wish!" Klippert said as Pinnock saw them to the door.

"I rather go for a long walk," he said and humbly extended his hand for a handshake. "I don't know how to thank you," he said before they parted their ways.

Less than half an hour later, the two detectives were across the main street from the barber shop. Barely visible in the street reflections of his shop's windows, Farley locked up his door and put up a "Closed" sign.

"Stay here! I'll cover the back!" Klippert dashed to the back of the building pulling out his revolver. As he rounded the corner, Farley swung a spade at him. Klippert raised his hands in defence, and the spade knocked the revolver out of his hand. He lost his balance and fell to the ground. Then, the spade came hard on his head, and he was knocked out. His dented bowler rolled away.

A couple of minutes later, he regained his senses with an throbbing headache. He was surrounded by several people. The other detective broke through the crowd with a glass of water, which he held it to his lips. Klippert took a sip and groaned as he sat up.

"You're lucky to be alive! We can't say the same for him," the other detective said, taking a glance at a body nearby. It was Farley. He was dead. The smell of gun-powder drew his attention to his side. A thin wisp of smoke drifted out of the barrel of his revolver. He turned red with anger and cursed while reaching for his colleague's arm to get up. "We don't have much time. We have to go now!" he yelled.

They moved fast to arrest Wilson before news of Farley's death had spread.

It was a very unpleasant scene. A despondent Wilson did not resist, but his distressed wife and son made quite a heartrending scene. They had prudently brought Pinnock with them, and in spite of what Wilson had done to him, he volunteered to drive them to their Fisherville relatives.

When they had gone, Klippert took a walk around the farm. He had searched the entire farm house and found no stolen goods. Where could they possibly be, he wondered until he looked down to the ground, and an idea was hatched in his mind.

Bathed in grey moon light, a two-horse cart entered the abandoned farm. The driver carefully steered the horses along the side near the forest. Four men sluggishly alighted from the cart and lit up ten lamps before digging for an hour. They must have dug a ten square-foot hole that was two feet deep, and their spades repeatedly knocked on something hard.

"Good evening, Mr. Pinnock, or I should say Mr. James Melvin, Ontario's most wanted highwayman," a voice shot out of the dark. Three men walked closer to a lamp that lit their faces. Klippert was ahead with a revolver in one hand and the wanted poster on the other. Behind him stood the other constable and Wilson.

"You … you?" Pinnock stammered upon sight of his former partner.

"Ah, that's what we wanted you to think, Mr. Pinnock," Klippert begun. "You tried to frame Wilson by planting the handkerchief and the lace in his farm. But, I remembered that the boy's handkerchief was plain. The one you asked me to pick up was striped. And the lace was found near you. I searched every nook and cranny, and I found no garment with that lace sewn onto it. What I did find was this part of the farm where the ground was broken.

"Still, it was not enough to clear Wilson from my suspicions. Your face was familiar," Klippert continued and tossed him the *Wanted* bill, which he caught. "Also, the way you drove me the first time here proved that you've been on these rural roads as often as a highwayman. And what need did your friend Farley have for all those lamps? Maybe digging a hole at night in someone else's farm?

"We followed you to Farley's shop. We made you think that we were going first to the tavern. But, you must have seen us from inside the store because Farley was waiting for me in the back. After he knocked me out, you shot him with my revolver to make it look as if it went off during the struggle. With Farley gone, and Wilson arrested, the case was over!

"It was a brilliant plan and quite a ways from the simple steal-and-run life of the highwayman. Wilson puts up two thirds of the money for the store. You rob him of his share. Hide it in his own place. Frame him. And you own the store. Then, whatever your gang steals is sold quickly and legitimately in your own store."

Klippert jumped in to arrest them. Suddenly, one of the other gang members swung his spade at him. He ducked. Pinnock took his spade and hit the other detective in the leg. He then pulled him down in the pit.

With one hand, Klippert warded off a punch, and with the other he slammed the butt of his revolver into his attacker's forehead. The man fell heavily on the creaking boards. Wilson joined in, taking a few punches from a bigger adversary until Klippert knocked the attacker on the back of his head with his revolver. The third man jumped on Klippert from behind, and tried to force him down to the ground. Klippert held his balance but dropped his gun.

Pinnock had wrestled a pistol out of the hands of the other detective and held everyone at gunpoint. With a crazed look of satisfaction, he shuffled backwards. "How convenient, I have a grave ready for all of you ..." He continued to shuffle backwards until he tripped over one his men lying unconscious on the wooden boards. He fell over backwards, and the boards cracked under his weight and snapped. Both men plunged inside the dark pit and landed with a loud crash. When Klippert shone a lamp over the enormous hole, Pinnock's, broken-necked, lifeless body lay on top of a pile of crashed chairs. The other was writhing in pain but alive. It seemed that everything from the store was there too.

The next day, Wilson and his family escorted Klippert to the Colinridge station. Behind them stood the other detective with their three handcuffed prisoners. They had to cut their way through the curious crowd. Upon news of James Melvin's death, people had gathered from nearby villages to cheer at the man who brought him down. It was a noisy but happy crowd, and there was even a photographer on hand to capture the occasion.

Klippert agreed to have his picture taken and posed in front of the station. The photographer dashed behind his tripod camera and buried his head under the dark curtain. The flash went off with a loud phut, and everyone started to cheer again.

BILL MACDONALD sells his scenic photography at the Fireweed Gallery in Thunder Bay. His stories and poems have appeared in *Wordscape 6, Geist Magazine, Prairie Fire* and *Winners' Circle 4*. His book of short fiction, *HOME BEFORE DARK,* a sequel to *WINDOWS ON THE STREET,* will be published later this year.

The Undertaker • Bill MacDonald

"As for Cassio, let me be his undertaker."

~ *Shakespeare: Othello*

Maybe we were doomed from the start. Maybe I should never have listened to my mother's ghost. It's not the first time she's led me astray. Come to think of it, she's given me bad advice ever since she died. I'm the one who had the nightmares, who heard voices in the dark. I'll admit to being the instigator, the malcontent. It was my idea to get the hell out of Toronto and head for wide open spaces.

I'd had it with the rat race. I'd had it with dragging myself to work every morning at Moss Park Collegiate. Most of all, I'd had it with my stinking classroom, with trying to maintain civility in a hostile, chaotic environment. I'm not saying that my colleagues at Moss Park had as much trouble as I did. But I was definitely losing the daily battle with insolence. I'll admit I didn't handle disinterest or stupidity very well either. Instead of teaching Keats and Shelley to quiet, receptive teenagers, I was wasting my energy shouting for silence in the midst of bedlam. What enraged me was that while these sneering adolescents could vent their hostility, I could not. I had to keep mine bottled up. When I came home at night, after riding the jam-packed Yonge Street subway, or after slogging my way against the flow on foot, I would need a joint and three martinis to stop shaking. I mean, how could I go on like that? The answer is, I couldn't. Not and stay outwardly sane. Not and refrain from suicide.

Mindy now, she was perfectly happy where she was. She liked her new job at Chapters on Bloor Street, where she managed the travel and language sections and took care of Internet orders. She said she actually enjoyed the high volume of work, the pressure, the crush of customers. Though she came home tired at the end of her shift, she also came home fulfilled, satisfied. She liked dealing with people and solving problems. She liked making decisions. She liked the staff she supervised and went to lunch with. Above all, she liked selling books and was good at it. That's what started her up the corporate ladder. It's also what infuriated me, made me jealous and resentful. Why should she have been so lucky with her career choice while I was dying a slow death?

The night Mindy and I moved into our new apartment, I had a vivid dream. The idea for this western sojourn came from that dream. In it, I saw my deceased mother, as imperious as ever, beckoning to me from the back porch of my grandparents' house in Lethbridge. I'd only ever been there once, when we went by train the summer I turned eight, but I remember being impressed by the empty prairie, the endless blue sky, the herds of beef cattle out on the range. It all suggested freedom and tranquillity, the very things now lacking in my adult life. In the dream, I somehow knew my mother couldn't still be alive, yet it didn't matter— she was calling to me, telling me to flee the horror of my classroom at Moss Park Collegiate and escape to Lethbridge, where she would be waiting. "But you must hurry, son," she warned. "Before it's too late."

That's where the dream ended. I sat bolt upright in bed and shouted, "Too late for what, mother?"

Which of course woke Mindy. It wasn't the first time I'd wakened her by yelling in my sleep. Usually I'd be in verbal combat with a spectre, or a rebellious student. Or with principal Spottiswoode, standing at my classroom door, demanding to know why I couldn't control my angelic pupils.

In the dark, Mindy put her arms around me, asked me if I was all right, even though she must have known I wasn't.

"Yes," I said, "I'm fine. Although I may not be too much longer. I may soon have to accede to Mommy's wishes and take arms against a sea of troubles."

Over the next few weeks, things got steadily worse. It became increasingly difficult for me to go to school every day, just as it became increasingly difficult for me to tolerate Mindy's burgeoning self-esteem. We began to have tiffs and arguments, where before we hadn't. We even disagreed as to what movies to see on the weekend. If I wanted to go to the Cumberland, she invariably preferred something at the Carlton. One Friday night we ended up going our separate ways and both came home miserable.

On our second wedding anniversary, we went to a taping of the Mike Bullard show at the old Masonic Temple, then rode the subway down to King Street and walked to Ciccone's for dinner. Over a bottle of Bardolino I asked Mindy if she'd go west with me by car, say for a month or two.

"But we don't have a car," she pointed out.

"Blair Castlefield, assistant math head, is selling his ten-year-old Taurus. I could get it for a song, pay it off in instalments."

"But we can't just up and leave. We wouldn't last a week on our savings. Besides, I have no desire to go west. I'm happy where I am. I like Toronto. I like our life here. I like my job. If we vamoosed, I'd lose all my benefits, all my seniority. I couldn't do that."

So as not to spoil the evening, I left it there. I didn't push it. But at least the seed had been planted. During dessert, Mindy said how lucky we were to have such a nice apartment above the Britnell book shop. Despite the occasional mouse, the traffic noise, the faulty plumbing and heating, we had a comfortable bed and windows overlooking Yonge Street. We had a microwave and a rack of decent wine. We had a computer, a VCR, a CD player. What else could anyone want? And best of all, we had each other. I asked her if she'd like a Galliano to top off our anniversary meal, but she said no, what she really wanted was to walk all the way home, twenty blocks up Yonge Street. It was something we used to do before we were married—hike the length of Yonge Street from King to Bloor, looking in shop windows, bumping into people on the sidewalk, rubbing shoulders with humanity.

That night, for some reason, the idea filled me with dread. There was no way I could have done it. Over Mindy's protest, I splurged on a cab and we rode home in silence.

By the end of October, I knew I was close to the breaking point. My days were bad enough, full of uncontrolled anger, but my nights, plagued by dreams and spooky visitations, were even worse. Most troubling were the dreams in which I saw Mindy laughing at me, belittling me, calling me a hopeless failure. On occasion, I heard her planning my funeral. I began to fear that if I didn't get away soon, I'd do something regrettable

One Sunday afternoon, after I'd made my lesson plans for the week and we'd done our usual stroll through Rosedale, during which we'd been showered with falling leaves and cawed at by crows, I mentioned the western trip again, asked Mindy if she'd had a change of heart.

"No," she said. "I haven't. I don't think it's a good idea. As a matter of fact, I think it's a terrible idea. So if you're bent on going, my love, I'm afraid you'll have to go alone."

In my state of agitation, on the verge of a breakdown, it wasn't what I wished to hear. "I couldn't do that, Mindy. I couldn't go off to Alberta and leave you here by yourself. You know I couldn't."

Walking back along Bloor Street, neither of us spoke. The wind had sprung up and a cold drizzle began to fall. In the apartment, we turned on Beethoven's Pastoral Symphony and brewed mugs of hot buttered Bacardi. Outside, the traffic noises on Yonge Street were nicely muffled. It was a good afternoon for being indoors, safe from bugaboos, for enjoying the company of your wife and counting your blessings. Along with the Bacardi, we shared a reasonably satisfying joint, rolled from our dwindling supply of high potency Montreal weed. We lit candles and ran a hot bath. Then we crawled into bed and stayed there till after dark, when all you could hear was rain on the roof and the faint rumble of the subway, far underground.

That Monday, I bought Blair Castlefield's old Taurus for five hundred dollars down, giving him a cheque I feared would bounce when he tried to cash it. Magnanimously, he threw in a tattered road map of Alberta. I also had a truly ugly encounter with a student in my eleven o'clock class, a notorious troublemaker named Abruzzi, who, when I ordered him out of the room, refused to go. He sat slouched at his desk, legs in the aisle, openly defying me.

"Get out!" I shouted.

"Up yours," he said, giving me the finger.

It wasn't the first run-in I'd had with him, or with his classmates, who were enjoying this altercation immensely. For once, I had their undivided attention. They sat there making crude suggestions.

"I take it you refuse to go," I said, mouth dry, heart pounding.

Abruzzi guffawed, gestured at his crotch. Then he raised a clenched fist. "Take this, dickhead!"

For the briefest moment, I considered rushing at him, punching his sneering, insolent face. But I didn't. Had I, he might very well have done me physical harm. I also knew I'd be in serious trouble with Spottiswoode, who took a dim view of teachers punching students. And so I did the only thing possible—I picked up my books, locked my desk, and departed. I didn't bother to close my classroom door. I said not a word to anyone. I walked down that long, dim corridor, hearing other teachers' voices, smelling the old familiar smells of gymnasia and chalk dust. I went straight out to the parking lot, climbed into Blair Castlefield's blue Taurus, and drove to my apartment.

There, I mixed a large vodka martini and rolled myself a fat joint of Montreal weed. When I was halfway through these two relaxants and could feel my pulse slowing to normal, I telephoned Moss Park Collegiate and informed Spottiswoode's secretary that I was much too indisposed to teach my afternoon classes.

"Well," she said, "what do you expect us to do on such short notice?"

"That's your problem," I said. "Call in a substitute. Pump my room full of mustard gas. I really don't care."

"I'll have Mr. Spottiswoode call you the moment he comes back from lunch."

"Don't bother," I said, prior to hanging up. "It won't do either of us any good."

I mixed a second, stronger martini, re-lit my luscious joint, and with the phone off the hook, sat at the front window, watching a monumental noonday traffic jam at the intersection of Bloor and Yonge. Cars were honking, people screaming, because the stoplights had malfunctioned again.

I think I had four more martinis and two more joints before Mindy came home from work at six o'clock, by which time I was pretty well zonked. Not violent, or antagonistic, just inert. Mistakenly thinking she was working late, I'd planned to take a nap, but don't remember doing so. I might have, though. Come to think of it, I probably did, because I seem to recall having a nightmare, in which Spottiswoode, Abruzzi and Mindy rode off in the blue Taurus without me, laughing hysterically at my impotent protests.

Mindy was furious at finding me so wasted. "What the hell's wrong with you?" she asked, as though I were some sort of imbecile. "And whose blue car is that parked at the front door?"

"That's our car," I said. "Yours and mine. The one we're going to Lethbridge in. And there's nothing wrong with me."

"Then why are you blitzed and why is the phone off the hook?"

"I have no idea. But may I say, Mindy, I don't like your lofty, accusatory attitude. I've survived a horrendous morning and requested a few days off to regain my equilibrium."

She sat down then, staring at me as though I'd lost my mind. It made me uncomfortable. I didn't like it a bit. I could visualize her sitting in the car with Abruzzi and Spottiswoode, the same bemused expression on her face, laughing at me.

"Regain your equilibrium?" she scoffed. "Give me a break. By the look of you, I'd say you need to regain more than your equilibrium. I'd say you need to regain your sanity. Get a grip, for God's sake."

Which I felt was rather harsh. It showed a lack of compassion, of empathy. I wondered if she talked that way to her subordinates. It occurred to me that she perhaps didn't quite comprehend the urgency of my situation. She didn't know about the bridges I'd burned earlier in the day. I said, "If you'll just listen, Mindy, I'll try to explain."

"You can explain all you want, my dear. I'm not going west with you in that blue car. Or in any other car. Not now. Not in the foreseeable future."

I've often wondered what made Mindy change her mind. All I can think of is her instinctual generosity, her innate sense of fair play. That and a commendable urge to please me, her husband of two years. I didn't have to use threats or remind her it was her duty. I mean, though at first she was adamant, in the end she relented. She could have said, "If you love me, dear, you won't force me to do this." But she didn't.

She put me first, herself second. She said later, "I've nothing to wear. No winter clothes."

"We'll shop on the way. In Winnipeg. In Regina."

"I need to have my eyes tested."

"It's not as though we're going for ten years."

"I'll lose my job."

"They know how good you are, how indispensable. They'll rehire you. There might even be a Chapters in Lethbridge."

"But I don't like car travel. I don't like mountains. I don't like prairies. I've told you that."

"And I've told you I'm not going without you. Nor am I leaving you here alone. My mind's made up."

We fled Toronto while it was still pitch dark, heading north on Yonge Street. I must admit, at that moment, Lethbridge seemed as far off as Neptune. After an hour, I eased my way west on Highway 11, and by mid-morning we were in Orillia. At the city limits, we ran over someone's yellow Labrador retriever. Judging by the thumps, I assumed we'd killed it. As I told Mindy, it had no business being on a busy highway. Though she would have stopped, I saw no reason to, and pressed on toward Gravenhurst. Secretly, I pictured Spottiswoode standing at my classroom door, crimson with rage, demanding to know where I was. I could also picture Mindy's boss at Chapters wondering the same thing about her. And though it was foolish to suspect that either man would bother following us, the only stop I made between Toronto and Sudbury was at Parry Sound, where we bought gas for the car and a dozen jelly donuts.

We slept that night at a motel in Espanola, and early next morning set off for Sault Ste. Marie. Skies were grey, the trees bare, and by noon there were snowflakes. All day we drove through a bleak, forbidding landscape, and when we finally saw Lake Superior, stretching away flat and empty toward the horizon, Mindy said it was like approaching the edge of the universe. We ate hamburgers at a truck stop outside Thunder Bay, where I scanned the Globe & Mail for headlines of our defection. Of course there weren't any. We slept that night in a town called Upsala, and next morning broke our rule about hitchhikers. An elderly man standing beside his disabled pickup flagged us down. I let him sit up front with me and gave him a lift as far as Dryden. "My damn cell phone's kaput," he said. "Or I'd have called for help. Where you headed, young fella?"

"Alberta," I told him. "Lethbridge, to be exact. Maybe Calgary. Maybe Banff."

"You gotta watch them mountains this time of year. Big snowstorm comes along, you're shit outa luck. I'd steer clear of them damn mountains if I was you."

We talked about Toronto and life in big cities. He said he had two daughters, one a nurse in Kenora, the other a social worker in Sioux Lookout. "They got their hands full, them two. What line of work you in, young fella?"

By now, I was tired of him, sorry I'd stopped. "I sell burial plots. In my spare time, I'm a mortician. My wife owns a funeral parlour in Scarborough."

Although I'd said we might shop for warm clothes in Winnipeg, we didn't. Instead we bypassed the city and spent the night in Brandon. Next day, under a thick overcast and more snow-flurries, buffeted by a cruel north wind sweeping across frozen wheat fields, we drove through Regina and Moose Jaw. Darkness overtook us at Swift Current, which surprised me, because I'd forgotten to turn my watch back. At noon next day, feeling pursued and paranoid, we crossed safely into Alberta. We stopped for gas and donuts at Medicine Hat, where I checked the newspapers again for mention of our great escape. Finding none, I still felt apprehensive.

Two hours later, on the outskirts of Lethbridge, we were pulled over by a police car with flashing lights. For a brief moment, I considered putting the accelerator to the floor and heading for Montana. But I didn't.

The young police officer who approached my window sported a military moustache and a sombre face which reminded me somewhat of the hateful Abruzzi but I wasn't the least bit afraid of him. He wore a belted tunic with silver buttons, and was brusque, but not impolite. "Your car, sir?" he inquired.

"Yes," I said. "I bought it the other day from a colleague in Hogtown, though I haven't paid him for it yet. I hope that's not what this is about. Or the golden Lab I clobbered."

"Could I see your driver's licence, sir?"

Handing it to him, I was embarrassed to note that my entire arm was trembling. He looked at my picture on the licence, and at me, and asked that I get out of the Taurus and put my hands on the roof. When I did, he patted my pockets for God knows what, slapped cuffs on me, and asked that I accompany him to his patrol car. He put me in the back seat, punched some numbers into his dashboard computer, spoke into the microphone pinned to his shoulder. I heard him say he'd stopped the blue Taurus they'd been looking for, the one with Ontario plates, and that its driver was indeed a man named MacDonald. Looking at me in his rear-view mirror, he said, "Are you by any chance a school teacher, sir?"

"I was until recently. By now, I imagine I've been defrocked. I'm what you might call a pedagogical fugitive."

"Do you know where your wife is, sir?"

"Truthfully, officer, I don't. Not exactly. I've been pretending she's here with me, but as you can see for yourself, she isn't. Which makes her a fine travelling companion, by the way. Doesn't talk too much, thrives on jelly donuts. The last time I saw her, she was in our apartment above the Albert Britnell book shop on Yonge Street. To the best of my knowledge, she's still there. She was supposed to accompany me on this trip. I asked her to. I begged her to. But she's a stubborn girl. She said no. At least I think she said no. I'd had a few drinks, a whiff of smoke. I hope that's not against the law."

"You have the right to remain silent, sir. It might be wise to consider hiring an attorney."

"I'm afraid I don't know any attorneys. But may I ask you something? Why were you searching for Mindy and me? I didn't see anything in the papers, and I looked."

"In case you're not aware, sir, though I suspect you are, your wife is dead. The fax we got said someone killed her with a hammer or blunt instrument. Seems her employer phoned the police when she didn't show up for work. So they went in and found her. The party you bought the car from said you asked him for an Alberta road map."

"That's all very interesting, officer, but a bit over my head. Perhaps, as you say, it's time I thought about retaining a lawyer."

I watched as he went and opened the trunk of the Taurus. I could see him rooting through my luggage. I saw him put on a pair of white gloves and pick up a claw hammer. It looked much like the hammer Mindy and I use for hanging pictures in the apartment and pounding lids back on paint tins. We keep it in a kitchen cupboard. I've used it to kill cockroaches and straighten warped doorjambs. I once joked that if an intruder ever broke in, I'd smack him on the noggin. But how the hammer ended up in the trunk of Blair Castlefield's car, I have no earthly idea.

SHIRLEY HUTCHINSON was born in Toronto and started writing in her teens, but gave it up for directing festival plays, which won awards, as well as acting. She had leading roles in "You Can't Take It With You," "Arsenic and Old Lace," and "Father of the Bride." Later, she obtained her private pilot's license. Shirley has written a number of short stories. She has also written three novels. One, *SADANDRA*, is set in the mythical kingdom of Atlantis. *THE GREAT HOUSE OF PHARAOH* and *THE CONCUBINE'S SON* are set in Ancient Egypt. She is currently working on another novel, *LADY OF THE TWO LANDS*, which also has a background of Ancient Egypt.

The Totem • Shirley Hutchinson

"Did I have the right to take another person's life?" I asked myself as my paddle rapidly cut in and out of the water.

When I began my journey, the early morning fog hovering over the lake had resembled evil spirits, but the sun had quickly vanquished the demons to the nether-world. Now its golden beams sparkled on the green water with only faint ripples to mar the surface of the lake. Deer, on the tree-lined shore, raised their heads as my canoe passed. Sensing that I presented no danger, these shy creatures put their heads down and continued to drink.

Today, the weather was different from the last few days of rain. The dampness had made my bones ache. Surely, after a man has two daughters, and years of sharing a woman's tepee, it is only natural there should be signs of ageing.

I had left camp before a new day had dawned. My father had been the only one to see me leave as the birds announced the coming morning with their songs. I always felt their melodies were filled with joy, but today their noise felt like arrows piercing my soul.

"I know you are troubled," my father said. "You must talk to the Great Spirit."

"Will the Shining One speak to me?"

Pressing my shoulder, he replied, "Listen to the spirits of the wind, the trees, and the water, then retreat into the silence and talk to your totem."

"Black Bear no longer comes to me," I cried.

"You are troubled. Your totem will appear after you have sought the stillness of nature."

Perhaps my father was right. My paddle no longer jabbed the lake's surface. I had become one with my slender birch bark canoe.

As the sun rose higher in the sky, and the distance from the camp lengthened, pangs of hunger gripped me. Spotting a landing site between the trees, I paddled to the shore, and pulled my craft onto the rocky beach. Then, because I was thirsty, I went back and kneeling down cupped my hands and drank of the clear liquid.

After choosing a large tree trunk on which to rest my back, I took some dried meat from a pouch at my waist. Above me the branches formed a high canopy allowing only a few shards of light to find its way to the ground. The only sounds were the whisper of the leaves, and the gentle lapping of the water. Soon the peace, the midday heat, and the food made me sleepy, and my eyes closed.

A noise awakened me. A chipmunk stood on its hind legs peering at me, then fled to the safety of the trees. He need not have worried. I had not brought my bow and quiver of arrows. Today I would not kill any living creature.

I had been asleep for sometime judging by the distance the sun had travelled across the sky. I wanted to reach the burial ground of my ancestors before evening, so I left my sanctuary, and pushed my canoe into the water.

I was bone weary when I reached the island of the Shining One. After pulling my craft onto the bank, and taking a refreshing drink of water, I greedily ate more of the dried meat. Then I stared at the lake for a long time. I could see the distant shore of the mainland and the hill thick with trees, which soon would be awash with splashes of brilliant colour. I watched white and grey birds with touches of black on their wings swim and then dive into the water as they hunted for food. While in the almost cloudless sky above me, a flock of big birds with long necks headed for their evening campsite.

Realizing the light would soon fade, I picked up my buffalo robe.

During the day my leggings and moccasins had been all the warmth I needed, but the nights were cool. I had to search for the way to the sacred rock. The path had become overgrown and was difficult to see. My band no longer used this island as a burial ground for their dead. It had been a long time since anyone had been here. When I finally found the way, I had to fight my way through the thick shrubbery.

My arms and legs were scratched from the bushes when I arrived at the place of the spirits. Trees refused to grow in the circle of ground surrounding the sacred rock. Perhaps it was kept open as a pathway to the great hunting ground in the sky.

Smoothing out the earth, I rolled myself in my buffalo robe and gazed up at the sky that was lit by stars. Some of them were so large, I felt I could reach up and touch them. While no sound broke the silence, the place was alive and pulsing with life. I sensed a great company of spirits and the beat of unseen drums in the darkness.

When I finally slept I was abruptly awakened by someone speaking to me. I opened my eyes to see a young man sitting on the rock. There was a single red feather in a band around his head. His muscular body was covered with the signs of animals, and he wore only a breechcloth to cover his loins. All was darkness beyond the mysterious circle of light that illuminated him. While he was dressed as a warrior, a feeling of peace emanated from him.

"You are troubled, and you shouldn't be," he said.

"Does the Shining One approve of murder?"

"Murder isn't the right word."

Drawing my knees up to my chest, I gazed up at him. "Since I have killed the girl, my totem no longer speaks to me."

"He will, when your spirit is quiet. Black Bear hasn't left you. It's more than the death of this person that is making you uneasy."

"Yes. Never before have I felt such an uncontrollable urge to share a woman's tepee."

"She tempted you."

"True, but she assured me she could give me a son. I will take my father's place when he goes to the Great Hunting Ground in the sky, and when it's my turn to join him, the feathers of a Chief will pass to a man of another family."

"You have a wife," he pointed out.

"She has only given me daughters."

"Do you love her?"

"No. I no longer feel that way."

"That's because thoughts of this girl have filled your mind. You should be proud that you did not share her tepee."

"I could not bring myself to reject my wife. If I had shared this girl's tepee without publicly turning away from my woman before the entire band, I would have been shamed before my father's people. I wouldn't have the honour of being their leader when he dies. Besides, my father is very fond of my wife. His heart would have been torn asunder if I had rejected her."

"You must go back to your woman. She loves you. You have been cold to her, and she is unhappy. If you rekindle the love you once had, I predict that before three new moons appear in the sky, you will find your wife has conceived, and the child will be a son." He smiled. "Your eyes are shining so bright they are like fires glowing in the moonlight."

"You have given me hope."

"Now you must put the thought of this girl's death out of your mind."

I protested, "I will never forget standing on that high hill, and smelling her fear before I pushed her. When I looked down, I could see her body lying on the rocks. It was broken, but I knew she wasn't dead."

"You are forgetting that she thought her friend was more attractive, so she poisoned her. She was afraid you wanted to share the girl's tepee."

"I was only kind to her friend because she had lost her mother several years ago and her father had been recently killed during a buffalo hunt. She was all alone."

"The woman who died had no sensitivity for others," the brave said. "She didn't care about her friend's loss, she was only concerned with herself."

"Why did my father force me to be her executioner? I was haunted by her. I kept going back to see if she was still alive. It was three days before her spirit left her body." At the thought of her slow agonizing death. I put my head down on my knees trying to blot out the dreadful image."

The voice above me persisted, "You only carried out the wishes of your band. It was your father and the elders who sentenced her to death." Then in a gentler tone, he continued, "Your father is a wise man.

He knew what was in your heart. He felt you needed this experience to give you the strength you will require when your turn comes to lead his people. Yours is a peaceful band, and you have never had to kill in battle. When you are a chief, you will have to make decisions your father never had to face."

He stopped talking as the early morning light outlined an enormous large black bear emerging from the trees.

"How," I cried, "did you swim across the lake? It's very deep."

"I came because you called."

The young man had disappeared. Only shadows from the surrounding trees covered the rock. When I looked for the bear he, too, had gone.

For a long time I listened to the chatter of the birds, and the leaves that whispered in the breeze. After one last look at the sacred rock, I picked up my buffalo robe and followed the path to my canoe. After finding my peace, it was time to go home.

RUTH BARRETT studied English Literature at Trent and the University of Leeds. She also trained as an actor at the London Academy of Music and Dramatic Art (LAMDA), U.K. Her first published short story "Family Secrets" appeared in *WORDSCAPE 6*. She won first prize in the 1999 Cambridge Writers Collective Short Story contest. In 2000, Ruth was enrolled at the Humber School for Writers under the mentorship of Peter Carey. At present, she resides in Toronto busily completing a first novel *BASE SPIRITS*.

Transformation • Ruth Barrett

Gasping aloud, Paula jerked awake. Blood pounded violently in her temples and she found herself bathed in cold sweat.

"Oh God, not again," she groaned. Another nightmare about her ex-lover Michael. Getting back to sleep was out of the question. Kicking off her covers, she dragged herself downstairs to the kitchen. She banged the kettle onto the stove and slammed cupboard doors in search of tea bags and a clean mug. No need to be quiet, despite the early hour. Her flatmate Jacquie was away in Bath for a romantic weekend with her latest boyfriend. All the more room for Paula to brood in peace. There's nothing more sick-making than watching someone else happy in the throes of a new affair while you're still mourning the passing of your own last relationship.

She slumped into a chair and stared blankly into space as she waited for the water to boil. A familiar ennui settled over her like a shroud. Outside the window, a foggy drizzle obscured the hilltop view from the deserted North London street. On a clear day, you could see the dome of St. Paul's from the back of the house. No chance today. Paula felt like it had been raining ever since Michael had dumped her six weeks ago.

It was hopeless. He had been just another loser in a long string of disappointments. Nothing good or exciting ever seemed to happen to Paula. Her clerical job was dull, she was getting too old to go out clubbing, and most of her friends had either married and drifted away to lead idyllic lives in the countryside, or moved to the continent in pursuit of sexy careers and even sexier European men. It seemed unlikely to Paula that her life would change course. Her's was a colourless destiny.

There was a sudden rustle and snap at the front door. The Saturday morning post was early. Paula shuffled in slippered feet to the front hall, praying for something other than a guilt-inducing letter from her well-meaning mother. Her heart sank another notch as she rounded the corner. It looked to be nothing more than a heap of fliers and junk mail. She stooped to gather it up, hoping vaguely for a halfway interesting catalogue to read over her cup of tea. Underneath the pile lay an embossed linen envelope. Another love-note for Jacquie, she expected; but Paula's amazed eyes read her own name inscribed in unusually spidery calligraphy. She tossed the fliers unheeded into the bin and hurried to the desk to open this unsolicited mystery.

Face flushed, she examined it eagerly. No postmark. No stamp. No return address. Someone must have hand-delivered this piece of elegance before the postman's arrival. She flipped it over and saw it was sealed with crimson wax, an indecipherable scroll-mark imprinted in the centre.

Paula's breath quickened at the romance of the offering. She opened it carefully so as not to tear it in any way. Inside was an embossed invitation card with a message written in the same spidery hand:

My Dearest Paula,
Your delightful company is requested
on Saturday, 27th April at 9:00 p.m.
Location? To be revealed.
Dress? To be arranged in the afternoon.
Occasion? Your transformation.
Car to collect you promptly at 8:40 p.m.

It bore no signature, merely a series of looping flourishes underlining the brief communication. Paula stood reading and re-reading the card. She was utterly mystified as to who it could be from. And whatever did they mean by "transformation"?

She met her own eye in the mirror over the desk and smiled. Yes. Why not?

The shriek of the kettle brought her back down to earth. Still clutching the precious invitation to her heart, she padded back to the kitchen. As she waited for the brew, she let the cat in from the back garden. He coiled against her legs and mewled for breakfast.

"Transformation ..." mused Paula out loud. She liked the sound of that. She gave a delighted laugh and whirled about dancing on the tiles, causing Hotspur, who was a skittish feline, to dart upstairs and hide under the bed.

Paula did nothing. She simply waited to see how the day would unfold. At 2 p.m., flowers were delivered along with a note in the same script. It read: "So glad that you'll be able to join me this evening." It was as though her thoughts were being read, her willingness to go along taken as granted. Paula arranged the oversized bouquet of roses in Jacquie's best vase. The blooms were of an unusual depth of red and had an intoxicating scent. The whole flat was soon filled with their perfume.

At 4 p.m., the front bell rang. Paula opened the door to see a charming older woman, all smiles, holding a garment bag.

"Is now a good time for your fitting, Lovey?" she asked in a smooth, warm voice. Her manner and tone inspired instant trust, and soon they were upstairs in Paula's bedroom, bustling her into a lovely gown. It was perfectly tailored to fit, and showed off her curves to advantage without being vulgar and exposing too much skin.

"I do hope that black is all right for you," said the kind woman. "I find it best suits these occasions to go with an elegant simplicity."

Paula nodded knowingly, not wishing to reveal her ignorance regarding the exact nature of the "occasion." The woman chatted amiably as she smoothed and fussed over the dress. She seemed to know all about Paula; where she worked, her schooling, her taste in theatre and music. Unobserved, Hotspur glowered down at them from the top of the wardrobe.

Paula tried to steer the conversation in order to discover who the mystery person who sent the invitation might be. Despite her gentle probes, she could not get so much as a hint. Every question was deftly parried by a change of topic.

Once shoes were fitted and Paula's approval willingly given, the gentlewoman embraced her and slipped out of the room, down the stairs and out of the door. Paula heard a motor start and a car pulling away, but was unable to follow quickly enough to see either the car or the direction it had taken. The stranger had left while Paula was in a state of semi-undress, ensuring a clean escape.

She was too excited to eat supper. She drew a deep, fragrant bath. Hotspur perched on the bathroom counter indifferently grooming himself. As Paula slid into the water, her skin tingled with an erotic anticipation. She leaned back and closed her eyes with a sigh. *Please God, let tonight be wonderful.*

A cynical voice in the back of her skull nagged at her, whispering of impending disappointment. *Surely this is some elaborate joke. Maybe even some new cruelty of Michael's doing? Do you really think your life is going to transform? Fool.* Paula twisted in her bath trying to block out her inner pessimism. She ached with a need to believe.

A gentle evening breeze drifted into the room carrying with it the heady scent of her roses. Paula breathed in deeply, finding the confidence to stifle her doubts.

At precisely 8:40 p.m., a black sedan drew up and the uniformed driver called at the door. He made a small bow to Paula, and handed her formally into the back seat. Waiting for her inside was a corsage of the same lush red roses. Beside the flowers sat a black velvet jewellery case which she fondled, considered, and finally slipped unopened into her evening bag.

Flushed and nervous, she peered out to see if any of the neighbours were watching as their dear, mousy Paula was chauffeured away in an expensive European car. She found that the windows were also tinted from within.

At 9:00 p.m., Paula was ushered through platinum double doors into an exclusive nightclub. She was too disoriented by the journey to know what part of the city she was in. The place exuded an air of wealth and prestige, which both intimidated and excited her. She was seated in a cavernous dining room at a round table covered with fine white linen. The room was very dimly lit—almost black—and Paula could just make out shadowy figures moving between tables. There was a continual flow of human traffic: waiters and busboys with trays, and patrons being escorted to and from their seats. Each table was cleverly and discreetly spotlit from an unseen source, and glowed like moons in the darkness.

She felt self-conscious. Her central table was large—too large to be properly intimate—and she'd noticed that all of the other tables had gatherings of four or more at each of them. She was the only solitary figure in the room. Her tightly clasped hands felt damp on the tablecloth.

A handsome young man with slicked-back hair and a long apron, whisked up to her table and poured her a glass of golden wine. He picked up her invitation (she had thought it wise to bring it along), gave it a quick glance and broke into a wide grin. He leaned in towards Paula.

"I'll bet you just can't wait to finally see him," he enthused. "May I say you look wonderful? Absolutely stunning. He'll be ever so pleased."

She gazed up at him mutely, a mix of blurred emotions tugging at the corners of her painted mouth. The waiter's brow furrowed with concern at her apparent discomfort. His voice dropped a level and became more soothing.

"Don't fret, Love. I know it seems a bit on the odd side, but it's just his way. He'll be along any moment to explain. Relax. Enjoy your wine."

He moved off, gently giving her bare shoulder a reassuring touch as he vanished between the circles of light. Paula felt a renewed surge of panic. She felt stranded sitting alone in such a place. Maybe it was some weird hoax after all. It would be foolish to stay, but she couldn't find the courage to stand and walk out. To bolster herself, she took a sip of wine. It was beautiful stuff, heady and flowery with a glowing aftertaste. Paula had never before tasted anything so perfect, and was a little surprised to find that she'd drained the glass.

A voice from the darkness to her left spoke her name. A man's voice; mahogany rich, with a cultured and slightly clipped edge. She shivered at the sound.

He stepped into her pool of light and sat beside her, pulling his chair in close beside her own. "May I?" he asked, as he lifted her hand to his lips and kissed it. She gazed at him, instantly captivated. He was older by a good ten years, but still youthful with a smooth, finely formed face and thick dark hair. His moustache was trim and neat and he wore a goatee, slightly elongated along the line of his jaw, framing his lovely full mouth. His eyes were dark and deep, set off to perfection by long lashes, which gave an almost feminine beauty to his face.

The young sommelier reappeared to fill their crystal glasses with more of the miraculous wine. He grinned approvingly at the couple. The man smiled back.

"I'll wager the poor girl thought I was never coming. But I always keep my promises, don't I, Thomas?"

"Oh yes, sir. If you say you'll be there, then your word is as good as gold." Thomas winked at Paula as the two men chuckled together like old friends. She felt compelled to laugh haltingly along with them.

"A toast," offered her admirer, as Thomas discretely withdrew. "To you, my dear, for your terribly kind patience."

Paula felt a sensation of relief wash through her like a drug. He seemed sincere in his attentions to her, and she was electrified by her attraction to him. But she was still as much in the dark as she had been that morning. She saw that he read the confusion in her face. His features softened in compassion.

"I'm sorry, but I must ..." he whispered as he leaned over and kissed her full on the lips. Paula reeled with intense desire.

"Forgive me," he said, drawing back. "That was too forward."

"No!" she blurted, lunging after him to catch his arm. After a stunned silence, she smothered a giggle with her hand, amused by her own audacity. His eyes twinkled as he laughed gently with her. Paula pulled him back to taste his mouth again.

Thomas returned, smiling apologetically for his intrusion. He spoke in a low voice to her lover, who heaved a sigh and nodded in reply, waving the sommelier away. He turned back to Paula and caressed her cheek with gentle fingertips.

"I'm sorry to have to leave you before I've explained myself, but I've been called to another table. It's a special night for them, and I've been asked to say a few words. I'll be back in no time." He brushed a feathery kiss on her neck as he stood. "You smell wonderful," he breathed into her ear. "I could eat you. Perhaps I shall before the evening's out ..."

Paula, head buzzing with wine and inflamed lust, strained to hear and see as he emerged from the darkness at a nearby table. There were several tall waiters clustered about in a semi-circle, almost identical with their lean young bodies and long white aprons. They obscured her view of the people who were seated. She could hear muted laughter, a short speech given, a toast proposed; but all individual words were swallowed up by the constant hum of chatter and soft jazz music. A deep voice, that of her lover, was raised loudly in question. There was a lull in the music and a profound silence as all those present waited for an answer. After a moment's pause, a small murmur was made in reply. As if by signal, the waiters quickly and neatly dispersed back into the dusk of the room. A strange scent of freshly snuffed candles hung in the air.

The other table and its occupants had vanished.

Paula felt a chill like fingers of ice race down the back of her neck. All else in the room seemed just as it had before. The band had resumed their song and dining conversation continued where it had left off. There was a gaping black hole like a missing tooth where the table had just been. Paula cast her eyes around in search of a way out when she met the gaze of her lover.

He stood motionless at the edge of a pool of light, his face lit from beneath with sinister shadows playing across his angular face. The look he gave her seemed brutal and cold, silently warning her to stay put.

As she blinked at the apparition, he stepped fully into the light at her table. All traces of the fleeting malevolence were gone. He once again looked irresistibly charming and, in one fluidly elegant move, he seated himself and pressed up against her. At the touch of his body to hers, all fear melted away. Paula was drunk with need and wanted only to fuse herself with him and leave all her loneliness behind forever.

"Forgive me," he purred, trailing kisses down her face. He took her hands in his own. "Now. I'm sure you know there's a small matter of a jewellery case in your evening bag. I think it's time you opened it up, don't you agree?"

Paula nodded, eyes nearly closed, breathing in the beauty of him through her narrowed field of vision, giving in to this dream that she so wanted to believe. She slid her hand into her bag and grasped the half-forgotten velvet box. He tightened his fingers over hers.

"But first, a question ..."

She was only dimly aware of the cluster of waiters gathering around their table.

Hotspur heard the sound of footsteps on the walk and stalked out to the front entrance hall. He had been driven past all patience by his owner's negligence. He'd been stuck in the flat alone for two days without fresh food, haplessly watching birds in the back garden through the window. This was a double-indignity he did not intend to endure without complaint. He sat in a rigid pose of contempt and fixed an expectant, stony gaze on the doorway.

The steps ascended the front stoop at the door. Hotspur uttered a loud and peevish miaow. His petulant greeting was answered by a shower of junk mail and bills shoved through the mail slot. Humiliated and shaken, Hotspur bolted into the living room and leapt onto the coffee table with his tail twitching in anger. He brushed hard against the vase of roses and toppled it over, spilling the contents across the oak surface. Hotspur stepped a clumsy paw into the liquid from the bouquet and yowled in pain. The pad of his foot felt on fire. There was a powerful scent of burning wood and seared flesh.

The Hyacinth House • Philip Antonacci

Mother, for love of grace
Lay not that flattering unction to your soul,
That not your trespass but my madness speaks:

William Shakespeare
Hamlet Act III Scene 4

Î

The story of my mother's abandonment of her only son has been told over the passing years to many attentive and enthraled listeners. Since its occurrence five years ago, police officers, detectives, lawyers and judges have meticulously documented the sordid details surrounding her body's disappearance. At the same time, social workers, psychologists and psychoanalysts have probed into the effect that her desertion has had upon my torn psyche. Accommodating my desperate requests, mediums, clairvoyants and psychics have searched for the disclosure of her concealment in various spiritual realms. Yet all who have listened to the details of her departure have presented a somewhat different explanation pertaining to her presumed non-existence. And now that I finally have an unlimited amount of time in solitary confinement, I have decided to record my mother's tale for posterity so that you too, dear reader, may also have the privilege of providing your own determination with regards to her present whereabouts.

Allow me to begin by stating that my mother's impending departure began with an expected arrival.

"Last night, while I slept," I recall her saying on that gloomy Sunday morning over breakfast at the kitchen table, "someone moved into the hyacinth house."

I, somewhat astonished by her statement, immediately inquired how she could have acquired this information if she was in fact asleep during the occupation of the house.

"I don't know how," she conceded, while staring at the tablecloth. "Perhaps," she whispered, so that only I could hear her, "it was through a dream."

She then rose silently from her chair and walked out of the kitchen. During our brief conversation my stepfather's eyes never stopped staring at the newspaper.

For the rest of that rainy Sunday my mother sat solemnly on her worn chair within the front room shelter of our home. Alternating between reading her paperback novel and staring out the room's bay window and through the drizzle to the house across the street, she only left her chair to prepare our evening meal.

At dinner she merely said, "I hope our new neighbours improve the exterior appearance of their house—but keep the hyacinths."

"If they did that, then ours would be the only unkempt house on the street," I whispered to her snidely.

Upon hearing my comment Branscom, my stepfather, lifted his eyes from the book that he was reading and stared directly at me with an air of solemn hatred.

That evening my mother retired prematurely to her upstairs bedroom, locked its door and, I presume, fell asleep early. This manner of withdrawing for the night was somewhat unusual for her. My stepfather never noticed the change in my mother's evening routine since, by now, he slept alone in a room in our basement.

When I left for school the following morning my mother's bedroom door was still closed. Branscom had previously emerged from the basement and, thank goodness, left for work. As I walked down the driveway of our suburban home I noticed through the morning fog nothing different about the house across the street, except the absence of its 'sold' sign. I quickly surmised that my mother's intuition had been correct. And she would be pleased to know that the garden hyacinths surrounding the house, although unopened in the constant drizzle, remained intact. But I also noticed, to her future chagrin, that the lawn still remained uncut.

Not before too long of a walk I entered the doors of St. George's High to partake in yet another dreadfully boring day of classroom confinement to the new standardised curriculum. Taking my seat in the same Monday morning first period desk I resumed feigning attention as Mrs. Rosenbach continued to drone on about the Prince of Denmark and his constant indecision. And as I stared at the rolling rain droplets on the classroom windows, as usual, my thoughts began to wander back to a happier place and time.

Slowly within my mind's eye I recalled how my mother and I had lived contentedly alone together since the disappearance of my father. He had deserted us when I was only two and I wondered about the type of man he had been. I was also baffled as to why my mother had ruined our carefree life together by marrying Branscom. And I pondered why, as a threesome, we had moved to the oppressive bedroom community of Port Whitby to live at number four Crescent Terrace in a large, mainly empty, two story suburban home. The reasons why my mother and I had arrived here unaware of her second husband's true character still bewildered me. I thought also about my mother's mistake and how our lives had deteriorated, living forever paranoid within our rooms, until Branscom had finally decided to move into the basement. My stepfather to then become mainly out of our sight but not entirely out of our minds, since his presence still emerged daily when he partook of his meals and a shower.

During that final thought I suddenly felt a cold shiver descend down my spine, caused perhaps by a draft from the rear of the classroom. Turning around to see if a window had been opened, I noticed that a new student had silently slipped into the back of the class at some point during Mrs. Rosenbach's long-winded dissertation. Another Goth, I quickly surmised, by the all black colouring of his clothes and the shades of paleness of his face. Just what St. George's needed, I concluded, yet another member to find their place within the holy high school trinity—Jocks for the school's withering body; Nerds for its deteriorating mind; and one more Goth for its dying soul.

Over the lunch hour, while strolling in the parking lot, I noticed the new arrival standing as expected in the Goth's territory. He was tall and thin and wore a long black trench coat above high black laced boots—the standard gothic fare. But there was something different about this recruit's manner. For while the new member stood tall, surrounded by the regular assortment of strange dark figures, he neither spoke nor seemed to acknowledge the existence of the others. Instead, he just stared off towards the dull, rain soaked horizon, cigarette smoke trailing behind his coal black hair as the wind blew upon the lean paleness of his blank face. And yet why should I care about this new creature, I finally thought, as I butted my own cigarette on the wet pavement and reluctantly returned to the building for another afternoon round of constantly graded compliance.

During my walk home I decided, upon my return, to converse with my mother concerning the correctness of her supposed dream. While still lost in contemplation I turned the corner onto Crescent Terrace and noticed a dark figure standing directly across from our house. As I approached, the tall thin form gradually revealed itself to be the new Goth from the back of the class. Not being one to generally initiate conversation, as I passed before his body's pale visage, I hesitantly nodded my head in its direction without making direct eye contact.

"I saw you at school today," he soundly answered. "My name is Louis Troublant. What's yours?"

Reluctantly I stopped walking and responded to his question.

"That's a rather standard English name," he said with a manner of strained elegance. "My name was given to me by my grandfather, Imago Troublant, the Marquis d' Imprevu. He owns a Basque castle in Bonney, France. But he had to move Clairmonte, Quebec when my parents died. He adopted me at the age of two. Both my parents were illegitimate and so am I. My grandfather says that makes me a vampire. What do you think?"

During his brief speech my eyes stared only at the dull wet pavement, but upon hearing his final statement I dubiously raised my point of view to peek at his face. It was thinner than I had even expected, with its green gleaming eyes set in deep hollow sockets. I quickly turned my gaze from his and told him I didn't believe in that horror nonsense.

"Neither do I," he agreed. "But my grandfather does. So I just go along with him. He has become very wealthy speculating on suburban properties in this province. Buys low, renovates, then sells high. We don't stay in one place too long. Have you been here long?"

I responded negatively, contrived an excuse for leaving and, turning my back on him, proceeded to walk towards my driveway.

"I suppose I'll see you again," were his final words. But until I reached the door of my house I could feel the glare of his green eyes roaming along my spine.

After entering my home and removing my coat and boots I felt a cold shudder cringe through my body. Turning towards its suspected source I saw my mother sitting in her shabby chair, staring out the front room window. I stood motionless, noticing the changed pallor of her skin, the oncoming greyness of her once dark hair, and the exquisite loneliness of her languid fingers. At first glance, due to the stillness of her body, I presumed that she was asleep. But then I noticed that her eyelids were open. And yet her eyes, as if in a trance, remained transfixed upon the hyacinth house.

With concern I spoke to her, about her correct intuition, and our new neighbours, and the continued presence of the hyacinths. But she only nodded her head in response, exuding the faint interest of someone who was already aware of the facts that one presents. With reserve I asked if she had seen the new neighbour while I had been talking to him.

"No," is all she whispered. She then continued in a wheezing voice, "I felt too tired to make dinner today. Would you mind making your own tonight son?"

I assured her that I didn't mind preparing my own dinner.

"Thank you," she said, as she slowly lifted herself from the worn bare cloth of her chair. "I must go to my room now before he arrives home."

With care I moved to her side, to take her arm and escort her to the stairway. As we ascended the stairs together I noticed that the smooth skin of forearm felt unusually cold and clammy. Upon reaching the doorway to her bedroom I asked if she could possibly be ill. She assured me that she felt fine, and may be only tired. She then stood on the threshold of her boudoir, bid me farewell for the night and closed the door before me.

With concern and regret I descended the staircase and entered the kitchen where I proceeded to prepare a dinner. After I ate Branscom arrived home from work. He neither asked me about the whereabouts of his wife nor did he thank me for the preparation of the meal. Instead, he simply loosened his tie, turned on the kitchen faucet, splashed water onto his face, to only dry it off with a hand towel. He then piled the cold food upon his plate and disappeared into the basement without uttering a word.

After cleaning the dishes I once again ascended the stairs to retire to my own bedroom. As I passed my mother's room I noticed a sliver of light beneath its closed door. I decided to check on her state later and entered my room quietly.

At first I stared for sometime at my computer screen thinking about the day. I then began to indiscriminately browse the Internet. Later I played a video game but I soon lost all interest in it. Bored, I turned to look out my bedroom window in the direction of the hyacinth house. Its exterior remained dark, unlit by its porch light. There were also no lights on in its windows. Suspiciously the house appeared unoccupied, still waiting for its new owners to take possession of the premises. And yet another 'for sale' sign had not miraculously re-appeared on its lawn.

Begrudgingly recollecting my English assignment for Mrs. Rosenbach's class, I lay upon my bed and opened the confusing play. After reading a page I was within the Queen's closet listening to Hamlet argue with his mother. Not before long I suddenly became tired and put the book down. Gazing at the ceiling I thought of our new neighbour, Louis Troublant, and what he had said about his grandfather.

As far as I recall I must have fallen asleep with my clothes on since I dreamed I saw: a row boat without oars gliding along a calm, blood red sea toward darkening storm clouds on the horizon; the backs of two hooded black figures, one standing, one seated in the boat; my feet and legs sinking deeper into the sand on the shore; the figures turning towards me as the boat sailed into the impending storm; the hideous face of the vampire inside the standing figures hood; my mother's face beneath the cloak of the seated figure; my body unable to move, submerged up to its neck under the shore's sand.

After the dream I must have awakened, for in the morning I found myself beneath the sheets naked, shaking with dread.

Weeks past since I met Louis Troublant in English class, which had remained the constant repetition of the same thing—Mrs. Rosenbach stressing the Prince's internal turmoil, while I daydreamed recurring fantasies, as the new Goth sat silently in the back row.

But the grounds around the hyacinth house had changed. Workmen had installed an interlocking stone driveway, poured a walk and porch, landscaped the lawn with fresh sod, tress and shrubs, and erected a backyard fence and deck. Yet there had never been a sighting of Louis' grandfather or a vehicle, which, I presumed, was tucked away within the garage. Perhaps he only drove away at night, using the automatic garage door opener to exit and enter the premises. Surely though he must exist, I concluded, since someone had to be paying the workmen.

Mother's condition had worsened, as she became weaker, thinner and more pale, to finally reside bedridden in her room. The doctor was called. He took blood for further analysis, and diagnosed her present symptoms as similar to anemia. Or perhaps, he whispered to me in private just before leaving, her condition was a recurrence of her manic depression. To be safe, he wrote a prescription for lithium, which I was to fill and administer three times daily. Throughout this ordeal Branscom became accustom to taking care of himself, seldom to be seen coming and going to work from his basement room.

Then one day upon my return home from school I found my mother, after being on medication for a week, sitting in her living room chair. She appeared more alert, less pale and somewhat excited. She said an envelope had been slipped under the door and handed its contents to me. Taking a card in my hand I read:

The Marquis d'Imprevu
Imago Troublant
invites Catherine Lamia
to attend dinner
at 9 p.m.
in the Hyacinth House
66 Carfax Rd.
RRSP by 3 p.m.
on the chosen day

"How does he know the name?" I immediately asked.

"It's in the phone book," she snidely responded.

"No!" I barked, "I mean for his house?"

My mother smiled for the first time in weeks and merely replied, "Neighbours will gossip."

"And are you going to attend?" I frowned.

"Perhaps," is all that she responded.

"When?"

"When I am struck by the urge."

"Into a complete stranger's house!" I gasped.

"Time will tell," she whispered, as if talking now only to herself.

"Well let me know when and I will at least accompany you," I assured her.

"Only to the front door of his home," she sharply replied. And on that statement she rose from her chair, climbed the stairs on her own, and retired for the night into her bedroom.

Only three days later, at 9 p.m. my mother descended our staircase dressed in a flowing white silk gown, her bare shoulders covered merely by a matching shawl. I reluctantly took her arm and accompanied her across the street. As I stood back from the door of the hyacinth house she rang the doorbell. The heavy wooden door somehow seemed to instantly open without any personal aid. Casually, she stepped alone into the house and the door quickly closed behind her.

I returned home to my room, lay upon my bed and tried to read the final scene of the play. Suddenly I was in a hall in King Hamlet's castle but I found the dialogue all too confusing. Rising, I peered out the window at the hyacinth house. A light in its downstairs window was now visible. Dark shadows of its surrounding hyacinths swayed in an invisible breeze. I lay back upon the bed and must have fallen asleep. In the morning I awoke from another nightmare, shaking again naked beneath the sheets. When I left for school mother's bedroom door was open but she was not there.

Later that day, after I embarrassed myself in Mrs. Rosenbach's class by not knowing the cause of Prince Hamlet's death, I spoke with Louis during lunch. I asked him if he had been with my mother while she was in his house. He said he did not even know that she had been there. His Grandfather, he continued, was definitely a vampire and if I was smart, Louis warned, I should keep my mother away from him.

Upon obtaining this information I skipped my afternoon classes and rushed home to check on mother. I found her sitting in the living room still dressed in her silk gown without the shawl. After I revealed Louis' account she said:

"How preposterous of you to believe the demented ravings of an unstable teenage boy who dresses as he does. Imago Troublant is a wonderful man who served me a delicious dinner, took sympathy upon my recent illness and did not bite me on the neck. He is tall, dark and elegant, of Basque origin yes, and is fluent in French, Spanish, Italian, Hungarian, as well as English. The interior of his home is immaculate and clean, with wall to wall Berber rugs and antique furniture mixed with a dash of modern Bauhaus designs. His china is entirely Royal Doulton, glassware strictly Waterford, and his silverware solid Guy Degrenne. He behaved as a perfect gentleman, we talked the entire night away and as you can see I returned home quite safely. So whom do you believe now, the eyes of your own mother or the delusions of your disturbed teenage friend?"

Hearing the sincerity in her voice made me stop to ponder the question.

"And anyway," she continued, "they will be moving soon since Imago is a real-estate speculator who has now put the hyacinth house back up for sale." She then rose from her chair with a renewed air of sophistication and glided up the stairs, closing her bedroom door behind the trail of her gown.

I felt relived, not because I now knew which version of Imago Troublant's character was correct, but because he would be soon gone with the sale of his house.

îîî

The hyacinth house was sold quickly. Nightly, from my bedroom window, I witnessed my mother's white ghostly figure crossing the street. Two days before the real estate deal closed she informed me that she would be moving away with Imago. Once re-settled she promised to divulge her new location so that I could join her. Branscom knew nothing of her adultery.

On the night of her departure mother packed only a few clothes and left our house. The following day Branscom emerged from the basement and moved into her room. He was pleased that she was gone and that I would also be leaving soon.

I waited weeks but received no notification of my mother's whereabouts. In my dreams she came to me often, dressed in white to only fade back into the shadows. The hyacinth house remained unoccupied, silently waiting for its new owners.

And yet I still felt the presence of something within that house— some alluring force drawing me into its interior. This attraction grew nightly as I continued to stare into its vacant windows while visualising the disembodied image of a white gown floating across the street.

Then, after weeks of allurement, I felt a definitive compulsion to enter that house. To satisfy my recurring impulse I took a flashlight and crept unnoticed into its backyard. A translucent blue flame seemed to flicker before its basement window. Using the end of the flashlight I smashed the window, clearing the glass from its frame. Entering the house feet first I squeezed through the opening cutting my wrist on an unseen piece of glass. Falling to the concrete floor I peered into the darkness along the flashlight's beam. Dust rose like dry fog from my footsteps as I noticed only a torn mattress lying in a corner. Then I discovered a wooden staircase above the furnace. Upon climbing the stairs I opened a door to emerge onto the main floor.

Walking from room to room I saw old paint peeling from walls, ripped and stained carpets, filth piled against baseboards, cobwebs in corners. The kitchen was filled with bags of rotting garbage, the washroom appeared to be encrusted with excrement and grime. Could this be, I thought, the same house that my mother had described?

Finding a staircase I ascended to the second floor. In an open bedroom doorway my light beam seemed to catch the Gothic figure of Louis sitting in a swivel chair. His eyes gleamed green in the light's beam while his lips seemed to be paralysed into a hideous smile. Turning away in fear I noticed two tables on either side of the master bedroom's doors. Upon the tables withered hyacinths hung limp from vases filled with a dark red liquid.

With trembling hands I opened the bedroom doors. Upon entering I was immediately aware of the putrid rank smell of rotting flowers. Many red vases filled with more dead hyacinths sat on tables and dressers throughout the room.

And then I noticed a four-poster bed protruding from the far wall.

Upon its foul dusty sheets there appeared to lay two prone figures. As I approached the bed slowly, what appeared to be the bodies of a woman and a man reflected the flashlight's beam back into my eyes. She wore a white silk gown, he a tuxedo. Holding hands they both stared towards the darkness of the ceiling. I bent towards the female's head, looking into eyes that did not seem to see. No breath emerged from her nostrils. No warmth flowed through her cheeks. Her mouth remained motionless and sealed. And yet here lay the lips that I had kissed a thousand times. In anguish I ran from the room.

Entering my home I screamed to Branscom that my mother's body was inside the hyacinth house. He calmed me down somewhat and said he would phone the police. I waited shaking in shock within my room for their arrival. Soon two ambulance attendants arrived. They sedated me with an injection causing my body to lose all consciousness.

Now, after being confined to my room for the last five years under Branscoms' care, I still sit awake at night, staring at the hyacinth house. All I can do to occupy my time is re-read the Barb's play. Revenge seems to haunt me as it once haunted the Prince of Denmark. The rest is silence. But my mother always seems to come, to soothe me, if only in my dreams.

ELLEN MARGRETHE Edmonds was born in Denmark and came to Canada in 1966 on a visit to her brother. Wishing to stay for a while, she got a job at the extension division of the University of Toronto. In 1968 she married and enrolled at Atkinson College of York University as a mature student attending most of her courses at Glendon College. After a B.A. from York and an M.A. from U of T, both in English Literature, she began teaching English and continued doing so until 1995, when she took early retirement. Since then she has done some tutoring and taken university courses purely for interest.

Stygian Cycle • Ellen Margrethe Edmonds

Slowly, slowly the room grows darker and quieter, and the heavy smell of chrysanthemums disappears.

My wife and sons have remained here with me. Their silhouettes become less sharp. I can still hear their soft voices and feel their touch on my skin. She holds my hand and they come forward to kiss my brow, one by one. I only sense their presence as I slip away quietly.

Later, when I turn to wave a last farewell, I see them standing on the other side of the murky river. They are not looking in my direction and they seem preoccupied and distraught. Reluctantly turning away from them, I glimpse a path in front of me and I start walking. There are no other roads and there are no road signs, so it must be the way for me to go. I see no evidence of life anywhere. The road is steep, but the walking gets easier the closer I get to the top of the hill.

I see the house. It is right there sparkling in the sunshine. I look around but can see no other houses, so it must be the place I am looking for. The house is very tall and it has no windows. White clouds cover the roof. I can hear birds chirping somewhere. The wide double doors in the centre of the wall are locked. My hand is shaking, but I make it ring the bell. After a little while a very old man with young, sad eyes and a long beard opens one of the double doors.

I hear sounds of confusion from inside. The old man looks at me and says, "Sorry, my friend. You cannot come in. We are full up."

I clear my voice and whisper, "But I thought that you accept everyone here."

The old man turns his head and brushes a little dust off his tattered robe. "We used to," he says haltingly, "but a lot of things have changed lately in our profession. You see, a higher authority has forced us to close off several departments, which means that some of our best people have felt it necessary to leave. Today has been a particularly busy day, and we have already reached our quota. I have been instructed to send away all newcomers, and I am not empowered to make any exceptions."

I grab his arm, "But where will I go?"

Looking down at his sandals, the old man says in a shaky, barely audible voice, "That is up to you." As he turns to go inside, his beard is caught on one of the heavy door hinges and I see his name-tag pinned to his robe. 'Peter' it reads. I think I see a tear rolling down his furrowed face. The door swings softly shut.

On my way back to the river I meet a teenager gasping for air as he holds on to a tree by the side of the road. Farther down, a group of old men and women scantily dressed and supporting each other walk slowly towards the top of the hill. Their faces all wear the same mask of no-expression. Next to a rosebush covered with white buds slightly opened I see a young child lying very still. In its arms is a love-worn teddy-bear. I am aware that the sun has gone down, and I feel a sharp wind blowing through my thin clothing. I understand that the ferryman has left for the other side of the river and I sit down in the middle of the road. I am too tired to go on. The air fills up with the smell of chrysanthemums.

Slowly, slowly every sound and shape fade away and I lie down to become one with the darkness and the quiet.